D1098054

THE RELATION OF FUNGI

TO HUMAN AFFAIRS

THE RELATION OF FUNGI

TO HUMAN AFFAIRS

William D. Gray

THE OHIO STATE UNIVERSITY

A Holt-Dryden Book

HENRY HOLT AND COMPANY, INC.   NEW YORK

Preface

Recent studies of fungi have led to two important conclusions regarding these organisms: their role—potential and actual—in human affairs is even greater than has been assumed by mycologists, and this role is predominantly beneficial. Perhaps because of the apparent simplicity and primitive nature of fungi—as well as their generally small size—they have never received, from laymen or from workers in allied fields, the attention that their numbers and potential usefulness have merited. Part of this is the fault of the mycologists themselves for, as Alexopoulos has said, "Mycologists are poor propagandists."

This inadequate recognition of the practical importance of the fungi has created the need for a text that can play a dual role. On the one hand, the rapid advances in practical mycology—particularly in its industrial aspects—deserve an up-to-date summary of the achievements and experimental frontiers of that field; on the other hand it is becoming increasingly important for the student taking an introductory course in mycology—or even general botany—to have access to current information regarding the relations of the fungi with the animal and vegetable kingdoms.

The present work brings together under one cover a discussion of many ways in which fungi affect man's affairs. Primarily it is designed as a textbook for industrial mycology courses, but it may also be used as a reference by the biologist who wishes to present some facts concerning fungi to his general classes. In a few instances I have used data from my own unpublished research, but most of the material is not new—as, indeed, textbook information rarely is.

Following the introductory chapter I have divided the discussion into

v

two rather unequal parts, concerned with the beneficial and harmful activities of fungi respectively. The larger amount of space devoted to the first is not, I believe, a manifestation of prejudice but an opinion based on the evidence insofar as I have been able to read it.

In spite of the importance of the Actinomycetes in antibiotic production and as part of the soil microflora I have not included them in this discussion. In my opinion their right to be placed with the fungi must, at this stage of research, still be regarded as questionable.

The arrangements of topics has presented a difficult problem. For example, the position of the chapter on Mycorhizae may seem somewhat unusual, but since these fungus-root complexes develop in the soil I have considered them to be appropriate neighbors to the fungi in the chapter on the destruction of organic waste, an activity also occurring to a great extent in or on the soil. The comparatively short chapter on plant pathology may appear inadequate to the plant pathologist, but any discussion of such a large and expanding field of plant science must of necessity be abbreviated in a textbook of this nature.

I have taken the liberty of making certain speculations but have confined these largely to the biosynthetic potentialities of fungi. I believe such speculations to be justified for three reasons: (1) there are tremendous numbers of species of fungi, most of them with many different varieties and strains; (2) thorough biochemical study of a single species usually reveals that the organism is capable of synthesizing a wide variety of organic compounds; and (3) a relatively small number of fungi have been subjected to exhaustive biochemical study. A realistic conclusion from these facts would seem to be that we have explored only the fringes of the biosynthetic capabilities of fungi, and that the future may well make our present body of information seem woefully small.

I am indebted to many individuals for the aid they have extended to me during the course of this work. Colleagues in academic, industrial, and government positions have allowed me to use their illustrations and data quite freely, and in some instances have exerted considerable effort to provide me with the materials I wanted. In each instance where I have used the work of others I have included a credit line but wish also to express my gratitude here. I wish to thank Drs. C. C. Allison and C. W. Ellett, who read and criticized the chapter on fungi and plant disease; Dr. Samuel Saslaw, who read the chapter on medical mycology; and Dr. G. W. Martin, who read the introductory chapter; this does not imply that they necessarily concur in all I have said, and certainly if there are errors they are mine not theirs. I am especially grateful to Dr. Norman D. Davis, who as a graduate student read the manuscript and provided invaluable criticisms from the student's point of view. Last but not least the members of my family are due my thanks for their tolerance and patient understanding during the long hours spent in handling the many details that went into the making of this book.

W. D. G.

The Ohio State University
January 1959

Contents

Part II

HARMFUL ACTIVITIES OF FUNGI

THE RELATION OF FUNGI

TO HUMAN AFFAIRS

1 · *Introduction*

To A PERSON not trained in plant science, the term "plant kingdom" ordinarily calls to mind the larger and more obvious green plants. However, to the botanist the term has a much broader meaning, covering many thousands of other organisms that are usually seen only by those who have been trained to look for them. Whereas the layman thinks of plants in terms of green organisms with roots, stems, leaves, flowers, fruits, and seeds, the plant kingdom actually includes many plants having no such structures and completely devoid of the green coloring material *chlorophyll* that characterizes the larger forms of plant life.

Although the great majority of nongreen plants are less conspicuous and typically much smaller than green seed-bearing plants, they are no less abundant or less important. Actually nongreen plants are far more numerous than green plants. As has been pointed out by Transeau, Sampson, and Tiffany (1940), nearly 80 per cent of the known species of plants are green, yet there are fewer individual green plants than nongreen plants—as illustrated by the fact that there are over 15,000 times as many individual plants in a single cake of compressed yeast as there are corn plants in a thousand-acre cornfield.

A few hundred seed-bearing plants—such as Indian pipe (*Monotropa*) and beechdrops (*Epifagus*)—have no chlorophyll (Fig. 1), but the vast majority of nongreen plants are organisms of the type known as *fungi*. The following list classifies the major subdivisions of the plant kingdom and shows the position of the fungi (**) with respect to other types of plants.

Subkingdom Thallophyta. Plant body not differentiated; no vascular tissue.

CHLOROPHYLLOUS THALLOPHYTA

CHLOROPHYTA. Green algae.
CYANOPHYTA. Blue-green algae.
EUGLENOPHYTA. Euglenoids; flagellates with green plastids.
CHRYSOPHYTA. Yellow-green and golden-brown algae; diatoms.
PYRROPHYTA. Dinoflagellates.
PHAEOPHYTA. Brown algae.
RHODOPHYTA. Red algae.

NONCHLOROPHYLLOUS THALLOPHYTA

SCHIZOPHYTA. Unicellular nongreen Thallophytes; reproduce by cell division.
  EUBACTERIALES. True bacteria.
  ACTINOMYCETALES. Actinomycetes.
**MYXOMYCOPHYTA. Myxomycetes; slime molds.
**EUMYCOPHYTA. True fungi; Usually consists of filamentous hyphae.
  PHYCOMYCETES. Sporangium fungi (algal fungi).
  ASCOMYCETES. Ascus (sac) fungi.
  BASIDIOMYCETES. Club fungi.
  FUNGI IMPERFECTI. Imperfect fungi.

Subkingdom Embryophyta. Embryo develops from zygote in archegonium or embryo sac.

BRYOPHYTA. Bryophytes.
  HEPATICAE. Liverworts.
  ANTHOCEROTAE. Horned liverworts.
  MUSCI. Mosses.
TRACHEOPHYTA. Plants with conducting tissues (xylem and phloem).
  PSILOPSIDA. Mostly fossils; few living species.
  LYCOPSIDA. Lycopods and quillworts; living species and fossils.

SPHENOPSIDA. Horsetails; extinct Sphenophyllales and Calamites.

PTEROPSIDA.

   FILICINEAE. Ferns.

   GYMNOSPERMAE. Gymnosperms (naked seed plants).

   ANGIOSPERMAE. Angiosperms (flowering plants).

FIG. 1. *Beechdrops* (Epifagus virginiana), *a flowering plant that does not contain chlorophyll. Like the fungi, which are also nonchlorophyllous, such plants must depend upon an external source of energy-containing organic compounds. This particular nongreen plant is a parasite on beech roots.*

The majority of fungi are small and inconspicuous. However, a few types, such as the mushrooms, shelf fungi, and puffballs, have large and prominent reproductive structures. Most of the members of the Subkingdom Embryophyta and all algae of the Subkingdom Thallophyta contain chlorophyll and hence, unlike the fungi, are capable of synthesizing sugar from carbon dioxide and water. Because of their lack of chlorophyll, all fungi are dependent upon some external source of sugar or other utilizable carbon-containing compound as a source of energy and assimilable carbon.

The great majority of fungi obtain their food from dead organic material and hence are known as *saprophytes;* a relatively small percentage derive their food directly from other living organisms and are known as *parasites.* Some fungi are able to live either as saprophytes or as parasites, some live only as saprophytes, and others, known as *obligate parasites,* grow only on other living organisms. The latter cannot be cultured on artificial media in the laboratory, but since most (if not all) of the plant-parasitic fungi studied are incapable of synthesizing one or more vitamins or essential amino acids, it is quite possible that ways of culturing them will eventually be found and they will drop out of the category of obligate parasites.

In their parasitism the fungi are not restricted to the higher plants, since man, domesticated animals, and insects may be parasitized by various fungi, and there are numerous instances of fungi being parasitized by other (sometimes closely related) fungi. The great emphasis in comparatively recent years on the relation of fungi to the diseases of economic plants has served to focus attention on the species that parasitize plants, which, as stated previously, are not representative of the majority of fungi. This emphasis is of great value to the agriculturist, though it usually results in a somewhat one-sided concept of the fungi. A spectacular discovery such as penicillin calls immediate attention to another type of fungi, although there are many less dramatic ways in which the activities of fungi can be successfully directed toward man's benefit.

A few of the many species of bacteria (which, like the fungi, contain no chlorophyll) are able to oxidize reduced inorganic compounds such as hydrogen sulphide or ferrous oxide. The energy derived from this oxidation is utilized in the reduction of carbon dioxide with the resultant formation of sugar—a process known as *chemosynthesis.* Thus the chemosynthetic bacteria are completely independent of the photosynthetic process of green plants. A few bacteria possessing a pigment known as *bacterial chlorophyll* are also independent of green plants as the ultimate source of their food. Because of the great number of biochemical similarities between bacteria and fungi it might be suspected that there are counterparts of the chemosynthetic and photosynthetic bacteria among the fungi. No such fungi have yet been described; accordingly it may be said that all known fungi obtain their energy and assimilable carbon from some external source.

Some fungi have the capacity to utilize a great variety of organic compounds, whereas others are restricted to a rather limited number. Several attempts have been made to correlate the chemical structure of organic compounds with their utilization by fungi (Nageli, 1881; Tamiya, 1932) but no clear picture has resulted, although it has been found that some compounds may be respired yet not be used in assimilation.

In view of the great variety of organic compounds that fungi utilize or synthesize, it is not surprising that many enzyme systems are found among the fungi. In the past the respiratory activities of fungi have all too often been viewed primarily as simple oxidations in which a wide variety of carbon compounds are oxidized completely to carbon dioxide and water. Such oversimplification is apt to be quite misleading in that it allows for no recognition of the truly complex synthetic capacities of these organisms. Raistrick, Birkinshaw, Clutterbuck, and other English researchers have isolated and identified a large number of complex synthetic substances of fungi. In view of the paucity of workers in the field of fungus biochemistry and the relatively few fungus species that have been studied, it is reasonable to expect that many more such materials will be found. Most of these metabolic products of fungi are now regarded as of academic interest only. It must be remembered, however, that over a decade had to elapse before the full implications of the discovery of penicillin became generally apparent.

Morphology of Fungi

Although in certain features of their nutrition the fungi are remarkably uniform, there is considerable morphological diversity in the group. The vegetative body of most species is composed of many filaments (*hyphae*) which for a single individual are referred to collectively as the *mycelium*. Although it is sometimes possible to determine the large group to which a species belongs merely by making a microscopic examination of the mycelium, most mycelia are so similar in appearance that their characteristics are of little diagnostic value. Certain wood-rotting fungi form an exception to this and can be identified by keys based solely on mycelial characters.

The principal differentiating characteristics of these organisms are found in their reproductive structures. Unlike seed-bearing green plants, most species of fungi reproduce by means of minute structures known as *spores.* Many fungus species may, nevertheless, be propagated in culture by transplanting a portion of the mycelium to a suitable substratum. Although a great many spores consist of but one cell, some species develop spores consisting of two or more cells. The size, shape, color, wall markings, and number of cells of spores are characteristic features that are commonly used in making an identification. Some spores are vegetative, that is, developing from vegetative hyphae without the advent of any sexual process. Others are sexual spores, developing only as part of a sexual process.

The nature of the spore-bearing structures must also be determined in order to identify fungus species. Spores may be borne either singly, in chains, in clusters, within spore cases (*sporangia*), in sacs (*asci*), or on special club-shaped hyphal cells (*basidia*). These structures may occur singly on the mycelium or clustered together in a fruiting body, which is often characteristic for a particular type of fungus. The common cultivated mushroom is representative of fungi whose spore-bearing hyphae are grouped together in a definite fruiting body. Even though a mushroom appears to be a complex structure with a high degree of organization, it is basically filamentous. If a bit of mushroom tissue is dissected under a lens it will be found to consist of interlaced, compacted hyphae.

Classification of Fungi

The classification of a group of organisms as large and diverse as the fungi is naturally the occasion for differences of opinion. An examination of several textbooks of mycology will reveal that such differences do exist; however, the present work makes no attempt to discuss the merits of the various systems of classification. The fungi are here considered to consist of four large natural classes plus a fifth large artificial group containing a more or less heterogenous mixture of forms, whose complete life histories are in some cases unknown. For the most part, the four natural classes possess well-marked characteristics which set off each as a distinct entity, whereas the fifth group, the Fungi Imperfecti, consists of a large aggregation of unrelated forms grouped together under a common heading simply because their perfect (sexual) stages are either unknown or infrequently encountered. The classification of the imperfect fungi into a single large group is highly arbitrary, the existence of such a classification being justified only on the grounds that it serves to provide some type of organization in an otherwise extremely unwieldy mass of material. The five large groups of fungi are:

MYXOMYCETES (Mycetozoa). Slime fungi or slime molds.
PHYCOMYCETES. Sporangium fungi or algalike fungi.
ASCOMYCETES. Ascus, or sac, fungi.
BASIDIOMYCETES. Basidium or "club" fungi.
FUNGI IMPERFECTI (Deuteromycetes). Imperfect fungi.

MYXOMYCETES. The principal feature that distinguishes the more than three hundred species of Myxomycetes from all other groups of fungi is the vegetative phase, although the reproductive structures are also quite distinctive. During the vegetative phase representatives of this class consist of naked multinucleate masses of protoplasm called *plasmodia.* The plasmodium may be variously colored, but the majority of slime molds have yellow-pigmented plasmodia. The myxomycete plasmodium exhibits a very rapid, amoeboid type of movement, constantly changing shape and ingesting small food particles such as bacteria, spores, and bits of the mycelia of other fungi. The plasmodium may be quite small or it may spread in a thin fan-shaped structure over an area of several square inches (Fig. 2); it may be reticulate or it may form a continuous sheet over the substrate. Little exact information is available concerning the nutrition of Myxomycetes, because scant success has been achieved in maintaining these organisms in pure culture.

After an active vegetative period (the duration depending on the species as well as on environmental conditions) in which the plasmodium moves about and grows larger, it becomes quiescent and develops spore-bearing structures. With the exception of one species (*Ceratio-myxa fruticulosa*), the spores of Myxomycetes are borne within a spore case. On the basis of their structure spore cases are classified as *sporangia, aethalia,* or *plasmodiocarps* (Fig. 3). Though usually small and incon-spicuous, these spore cases are among the most beautiful and delicate structures of the plant kingdom.

The mature spores usually germinate quite rapidly under suitable conditions, from one to four flagellated *swarm cells* emerging from each spore. These cells may ingest bacteria and other small objects, may divide, or may become amoeboid, but eventually they function as *gametes,* which by fusion in pairs form *zygotes* that are the immediate forerunners of plasmodia.

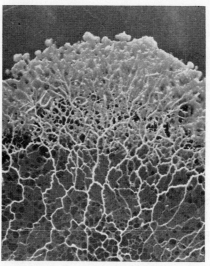

FIG. 2.   *Portion of plasmodium of* Physarella oblonga, *a slime mold.*

With their amoeboid plasmodia, their motile swarm cells, and their ability to ingest solid food particles, the Myxomycetes obviously have close affinities with the animal kingdom and hence should probably not be classified among the true fungi. Indeed, some investigators prefer for them the name Mycetozoa (fungus animals), because it implies a closer relationship with the animal kingdom than with the plant king-dom. Thought to be closely allied with the Myxomycetes are the Acrasiae, a small group of organisms in which the vegetative stage is a *pseudoplasmodium*—so called because it is not a multinucleate structure like the myxomycete plasmodium but an aggregation of discrete amoeboid cells that move and act as a unit.

Several pathogens of economically important seed plants formerly classified with the Myxomycetes are no longer recognized as members

FIG. 3. *Fruiting bodies of Myxomycetes.* Top: *Pseudoaethalium of* Lycogala epidendrum. Middle left: *Sporangia of* Hemitrichia clavata. Middle right: *Sporangia of* Stemonitis fusca. Bottom left: *Sporangia of* Craterium minutum. Bottom right: *Plasmodiocarp of* Hemitrichia serpula.

of this class. Slime molds, usually found on decaying wood, leaves, and similar organic debris, are not parasitic at least so far as the higher plants are concerned. The economic importance of this class is not easily assessed, for the activities of the Myxomycetes may be either detrimental or beneficial to man's interests. Howard and Currie (1932a, 1932b) have shown that plasmodia can destroy the fruiting structures, spores, and mycelia of a number of wood-rotting fungi—undoubtedly a beneficial activity but one that is difficult to evaluate, since its extent under natural conditions cannot be measured. On the other hand, although they are not generally considered by mushroom growers a particularly serious menace, plasmodia may occasionally damage a crop of cultivated mushrooms. Much of our information concerning the chemical and physical properties of protoplasm is derived from studies of myxomycete plasmodia because they afford ample quantities of easily obtained protoplasmic material.

PHYCOMYCETES. The Phycomycetes are more commonly encountered than the Myxomycetes, since they occur in a much wider range of habitats and have about five times more species. One of the most common members of the class is the ordinary black mold, *Rhizopus nigricans* (Fig. 4), which may be isolated from moldy bread, fruits, and vegetables, spoiled canned foods, soil, and a variety of other habitats. Some Phycomycetes are saprophytic, others are parasitic; some grow only in aquatic habitats, others only in the ground; some are plant-parasitic, other insect-parasitic.

The majority of the more commonly seen Phycomycetes have well-developed mycelia in which there are no cross walls (*septae*), except in old mycelia or where reproductive structures are formed. Unlike those of the Myxomycetes, the filaments have a firm outer wall; thus, the mycelium of most Phycomycetes can be likened to a many-branched continuous tube inside which are found cytoplasm and many nuclei. This type of mycelium is characteristic of the class, and an unknown fungus can usually be included in the Phycomycetes simply on the basis of the presence or absence of cross walls in the mycelium. Because there are a number of morphological similarities between some members of this class and certain of the green algae, the Phycomycetes are sometimes called the "algalike," or "algal," fungi. Because the asexual spores of most Phycomycetes are formed in a spore case or sporangium, the name "sporangium fungi" would seem more acceptable, being a more descriptive term without implying an algal ancestry.

The Phycomycetes have been variously subdivided into smaller groups. Fischer (in Rabenhorst, *Kryptogamen-Flora*) recognizes three subclasses—Archimycetae, Zygomycetae, and Oömycetae—and Schroeter (in Engler and Prantl, *Pflanzenfamilien*) combines the Archimycetae with the Oömycetae and thus recognizes but two subclasses. Gäu-

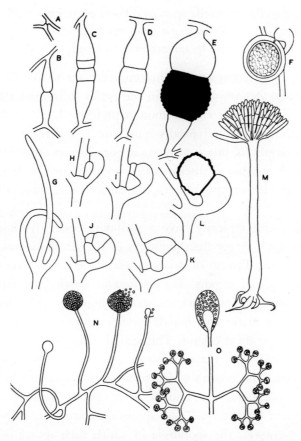

Fig. 4. *Spores and spore-bearing structures of Phycomycetes. A, B, C, D, E: Successive stages in zygospore development of* Rhizopus nigricans, *a heterothallic zygomycete (redrawn from De Bary, 1887). F: Antheridium, oögonium, and mature oöspore of* Pythium debaryanum, *an oömycete (redrawn from Fitzpatrick, 1930). G, H, I, J, K, L: Successive stages in zygospore development of* Zygorhynchus heterogamus, *a homothallic zygomycete (after Blakeslee, 1913). M:* Syncephalastrum *(redrawn from Gwynne-Vaughan and Barnes, 1927). N:* Mucor *(redrawn from Waksman and Starkey, 1931). O:* Thamnidium *(redrawn from Henrici, 1930).*

mann (1926), on the other hand, classifies the Archimycetae as a separate group co-ordinate with the Phycomycetes, Ascomycetes, and Basidiomycetes. For the purposes of this brief discussion Fischer's arrangement will be used, although, the trend among many mycologists today is to subdivide the Phycomycetes into developmental series based upon the flagellation of their spores. In accordance with this more modern view three series are recognized:

> Series *Uniflagellatae:* motile sporangiospores posteriorly uniflagellate.
> Series *Biflagellatae:* motile sporangiospores biflagellate.
> Series *Aplanatae:* motile sporangiospores lacking.

The larger, more conspicuous Phycomycetes are to be found in the Oömycetes and Zygomycetes (or in the Series Biflagellatae and Series Aplanatae, if the newer classification is preferred).

The Archimycetes are typically quite small, and many are aquatic. Some are saprophytic, others growing as parasites on other fungi, algae, and insects. A number of diseases of economic plants, such as clubroot of cabbage and brown spot of corn, are caused by members of this subclass.

The Oömycetes typically have a well-developed mycelium and in general are much larger than members of the Archimycetes. Many of them are aquatic. Typical of this subclass is the development of well-differentiated sexual organs. The *antheridia* (male gametangia) and *oögonia* (female gametangia) are morphologically quite distinct, and so, also, are the male and female gametes (*sperms* and *oöspheres*) which develop in these organs. This sexual differentiation, a condition known as *heterogamy,* makes the two sexes easily distinguishable in the Oömycetes. The zygotes which form as the result of the fusion of sperms and oöspheres are known as *oöspores.* Asexual spores are formed in many Oömycetes. These spores are commonly motile and are known as *zoospores;* the sporangia in which such spores develop are called *zoosporangia.* Both saprophytic and parasitic species are found in this subclass. The causal agents of such well-known diseases as white blister of crucifers and downy mildew of grapes are Oömycetes.

The Zygomycetes are commonly terrestrial. Extensive mycelia are usually developed by members of this subclass. Both sexual and asexual spores are formed, but in all instances they are nonmotile (hence the series name Aplanatae). Sexuality exists in the Zygomycetes, but, in contrast to the Oömycetes, it is impossible to distinguish the gametangia as male and female on morphological grounds; the gametes also are morphologically indistinguishable—a condition usually referred to as *isogamy*. The sexual spore (*zygospore*) characteristic of this subclass forms as the result of the fusion of two gametangia and their multinucleate protoplasmic contents.

Since male and female sexual structures cannot be distinguished, but sexuality obviously exists, the sexes are usually referred to as "plus" and "minus." Some species are *homothallic* (both sexes occurring on the same mycelium), others are *heterothallic* (different sexes occurring on different mycelia). Asexual spores are borne in small sporangia that develop at the ends of special hyphae known as sporangiophores. The common black molds, such as species of *Rhizopus* and *Mucor,* are Zygomycetes as are members of the genera *Entomophthora* and *Empusa*—organisms that occur almost exclusively as parasites of insects.

ASCOMYCETES.   Although mycologists differ widely in their estimates of the number of species of Ascomycetes, they are generally agreed that this is the largest natural class of fungi. With the exception of such organisms as the yeasts, Ascomycetes have well-developed mycelia, which, however, differ from those of the Phycomycetes in that the hyphae are regularly septate, each cell usually having but a single nucleus. There is great diversity within the class in both size and complexity of structure: some members such as the yeasts are one-celled; others develop an extensive mycelium from which a reproductive structure weighing several pounds may be derived. All members of this class develop sexual spores (*ascospores*) in a saclike structure, the *ascus* (Fig. 5). The usual number of ascospores per ascus is eight, but there are species in which exceptions to this number occur. In some Ascomycetes the sexual organs (antheridia and ascogonia) which develop prior to ascus formation are well differentiated and easily distinguishable one from the other; in others they are morphologically similar, and in still others one of the sex organs may be abortive.

The *conidium,* the asexual spore of the Ascomycetes, is developed by a great many species. Conidia are formed by abstriction at the ends of specialized hyphae called *conidiophores.*

The Ascomycetes may be divided into two subclasses on the basis of whether or not the asci are aggregated in special structures. In the sub-

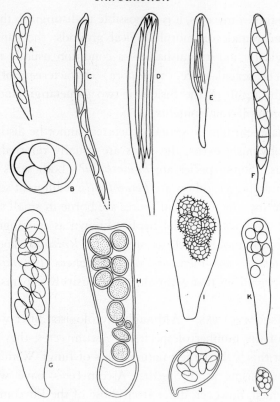

FIG. 5. *Asci and ascospores.* A: Hypoxylon coccineum. B: Saccharomy-ces cerevisiae. C: H. borinquensis (*redrawn from Jump, 1937*). D: Rhy-tisma acerinum. E: Nematospora phaseoli (*redrawn from Wingard, 1925*). F. Sphaerostilbe aurantiicola (*redrawn from Luttrell, 1944*). G: Rhyparo-bius sexidecimsporus (*redrawn from Seaver, 1942*). H: Taphrina defor-mans (*redrawn from Martin, 1940*). I: Ascodesmis microscopica (*redrawn from Seaver, 1942*). J: Uncinula fraxini (*redrawn from Salmon, 1900*). K: T. potentillae (*redrawn from Martin, 1936*). L: *ascus stage of* Penicil-lium brefeldianum (*redrawn from Dodge, 1933*).

class Hemiascomycetae (also called Protoascomycetae) the asci may develop singly or in groups but are never aggregated in special struc-tures; in the larger subclass Euascomycetae the asci are always ag-gregated in or on special structures called *ascocarps* (Fig. 6). Well-known members of the Hemiascomycetes are the yeasts and the parasitic fungi (*Taphrina* spp.) which cause leaf curl in various green plants.

In some species of the subclass Euascomycetae the ascocarps are unique, with characteristics that alone may be sufficient for species identification. On the basis of the form of the ascocarp developed, the Euascomycetae may be divided into three series:

Series *Plectomycetes:* ascocarp a cleistothecium.
Series *Discomycetes:* ascocarp an apothecium.
Series *Pyrenomycetes:* ascocarp a perithecium.

The *cleistothecium* type of ascocarp, found in the Plectomycetes, is completely closed, with the asci sometimes irregularly arranged within. Fungi that develop cleistothecia are the common blue and green molds, *Penicillium* and *Aspergillus,* and the parasitic fungi that are the causal agents of the plant diseases known as powdery mildews—a common example is *Microsphaera alni,* the causal agent of powdery mildew of lilac.

An *apothecium* is a disklike or cup-shaped ascocarp (or one derived from a fundamentally cup-shaped structure) which may or may not be stalked; the asci are arranged in a palisade within the cup. The Discomycetes include a large number of species. In some the ascocarps are small (1.0 mm. or less); in others, such as *Urnula craterium* and various species of *Morchella* and *Helvella,* they are large (10–15 cm.) and conspicuous. There are both saprophytic and parasitic species of Discomycetes.

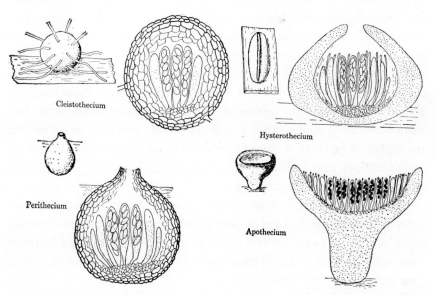

Cleistothecium

Hysterothecium

Perithecium

Apothecium

Fig. 6. *Diagrammatic representation of types of ascocarps, shown in surface view and in vertical section. (From Wolf and Wolf, 1947.)*

The Pyrenomycetes include those Ascomycetes whose asci are developed in a flask-shaped structure, the *perithecium*. The latter is not completely closed but has a small opening called the *ostiole*. Perithecia often are about 1 millimeter in diameter. A variation of the typical perithecium, known as an *hysterothecium,* occurs in some species; in this structure the ascocarp is elongated horizontally and opens by means of a slit rather than a small pore. The Pyrenomycetes are quite numerous (10,000 to 20,000 species have been estimated) and include both saprophytic and parasitic species.

Since the Euascomycetae are an extremely large subclass, no attempt will be made here to classify them further. For additional details of their classification, consult Gäumann (1926), Wolf and Wolf (1947), Bessey (1950), or Alexopoulos (1952).

BASIDIOMYCETES. The Basidiomycetes or "club fungi" are those fungi in which the sexual spores (*basidiospores*) are borne externally on special club-shaped cells, called *basidia* (Fig. 7), which may develop singly or in layers known as *hymenial layers*. Usually four basidiospores develop on each basidium, although exceptions to this number may occur in some species. Basidiospores germinate and form hyphae which, though at first multinucleate, eventually become septate and uninucleate; such hyphae constitute the *primary mycelium.* The initial phase of the sexual process occurs when primary mycelia of opposite mating type grow in close proximity and two cells fuse. The nuclei of the cells that fuse do not unite; a *secondary* or *dikaryotic* mycelium then develops in which the cells are typically binucleate. In some Basidiomycetes the process of mating is often followed by the formation of clamp connections, which are unique processes developed at the septae of mycelia. A mycelium with clamp connections is immediately identified as a basidiomycete, although their absence does not exclude an organism from the class.

Since sexuality in the sense of recognizable male and female structures is completely lacking in the Basidiomycetes, the term "mating types" seems far more accurate than "sexes." This terminology becomes even more logical when dealing with those Basidiomycetes in which four discrete mating types occur.

Basidia may be formed directly from cells of the secondary (binucleate) mycelium or—as in the smuts and rusts—from spores which developed from the secondary mycelium. Young basidia are binucleate but the two nuclei soon fuse; from the fusion nucleus are derived four nuclei (through meiosis) which become the nuclei of the four basidio-spores. Conidia are developed in some members of this class, but asexual spores are not so common in the Basidiomycetes as in the Ascomycetes.

The Basidiomycetes are divided into two subclasses, Heterobasidiomycetes and Homobasidiomycetes (also called Holobasidiomycetes). In the Heterobasidiomycetes the basidia are septate except in two orders; they develop directly from a vegetative cell or from a spore (*teliospore*). In those species in which organized fruiting bodies are formed, basidia are nearly always on the free surface of the fruiting body. Both saprophytic and parasitic species are found in this sub-

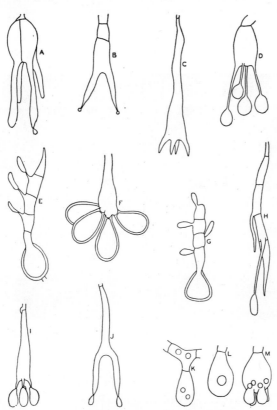

FIG. 7. *Types of basidia, highly magnified.* A: Tremella aurantia. B. Corticium sterigmaticum. C: Aleurodiscus *sp.* D: Lycoperdon *sp.* E: Septobasidium. F: Melanogaster variegatus. G: Ustilago. H: Auricularia. I: Hymeniales. J: Dacrymyces. K, L, M: *Stages in development of basidium of* Tulasnella. (*Redrawn from Rogers, 1934.*)

FIG. 8.   Hericium coralloides, *a Basidiomycete in which the basidiocarp is a spiny structure with the hymenial layers covering the spines.*

FIG. 9.   Stereum *sp., a Basidiomycete in which the hymenial layer covers a plane surface.*

class, which includes the "jelly" or "trembling" fungi, the rusts, and the smuts. The last two types of fungi include some of the most important parasites of man's economic plants.

In the Homobasidiomycetes the basidia, which develop from vegetative cells, are nonseptate and usually club-shaped. In this subclass are found the largest of all the fungi. Typically these fungi develop special-

Fig. 10.   Calvatia craniformis. *This puffball is a Basidiomycete in which the hymenial layers remain enclosed until maturity.*

Fig. 11.   Pleurotus sapidus, *a Basidiomycete in which the hymenial layer covers the surfaces of the lamellae (gills).*

Fɪɢ. 12.   Clavaria *sp. This coral fungus is a Basidiomycete in which the hymenial layer covers the corallike branches of the basidiocarp.*

Fɪɢ. 13.   Fomes applanatus, *a Basidiomycete in which the hymenial layer lines small tubes* (pores). (*Courtesy C. E. Taft.*)

ized fruiting structures (*basidiocarps*) on or in which the basidia and basidiospores form. With few exceptions the basidia are grouped in definite layers (*hymenial layers*) that cover plane surfaces, lamellae or gills (as in the mushrooms), or coralloid (spiny) structures (as in *Clavaria* or *Hydnum*), or that serve as lining of small tubes (as in the pore fungi), or of closed fruiting structures, as in the puffballs (Figs. 8–13). The most conspicuous part of a species of this subclass is the basidiocarp. Generally an extensive mycelium is formed which develops largely within the substrate (soil, wood, organic debris) and hence is commonly not seen. Both saprophytes and parasites occur in this subclass; some of the most destructive parasites of timber trees are Homobasidiomycetes.

FUNGI IMPERFECTI. In this group are included the asexual stages of certain species known to have perfect (sexual) stages and those fungi in which the perfect stage has not been observed. In some classifications the Fungi Imperfecti are considered a class coordinate with the Phycomycetes, Ascomycetes, Basidiomycetes, and Myxomycetes. This classification is obviously unsound because the only characteristic common to all species of Fungi Imperfecti is the apparent absence or rarity of their sexual stages. But since the majority of the fungi once classified as Fungi Imperfecti and now reclassified on the basis of observed sexual stages have proved to be Ascomycetes, it would seem preferable to place them in a category close to the Ascomycetes. The classification of the Imperfect Fungi, based as it must be on the characteristics of the asexual stages, is highly artificial, and the fact that two "species" are placed in the same genus does not necessarily mean that they are closely related. Discovery of their perfect stages may result in their being properly reclassified in widely separated genera. Because the mycologist must deal with a great many Imperfect Fungi, a convenient system of classification has been developed. In a natural class such as the Ascomycetes, the species are grouped into orders, families, genera, and species. A similar classification is employed for the Fungi Imperfecti. In this group, however, they are referred to as *form orders, form families,* and so forth. This convention provides a workable system, but one should bear in mind that the members of Fungi Imperfecti are not species but merely asexual phases of species, and that the classification of two form species in the same genus, family, or order does not necessarily denote close relationship.

Nearly all of the Fungi Imperfecti develop conidia (Fig. 14), and the arrangement of the conidia-bearing hyphae (*conidiophores*) serves as a useful characteristic in determining the order to which a species belongs:

Sphaeropsidales: conidia developed in variously shaped *pycnidia*.
Melanconiales: conidia developed on *acervuli*.
Moniliales: conidia developed on separate conidiophores or on conidiophores which are compacted into *synnemata* or *sporodochia*.
Mycelia Sterilia: conidia lacking.

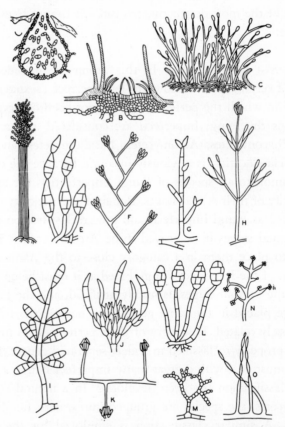

FIG. 14.   *Spores and spore-bearing structures of Fungi Imperfecti.* A: *Pycnidium of* Ascochyta pisi. B: *Acervulus of* Colletotrichum cereale. C: *Sporodochium of* Tubercularia. D: *Coremium of* Stysanus. E. Alternaria. F: Stachybotrys. G: Trichosporium. H: Verticillium. I: Spondylocladium. J: Fusarium. K: Cephalosporium. L: Macrosporium. M: Monilia. N: Trichoderma. O: Fusidium. (A *redrawn from Wolf and Wolf, 1947;* B *redrawn from Stevens, 1913; remainder redrawn from Gilman, 1945.*)

The Sphaeropsidales and Moniliales each contain four form families; the Melanconiales, one form family. The Mycelia Sterilia are not divided into families. Within each form family further subdivisions are made on the basis of conidial color, conidial shape, and number of cells per conidium. Some characteristic fruiting-body types are shown in Figure 14.

As we have seen, the Fungi Imperfecti constitute a large group. Bender (1931) reported that there are 1331 form genera, and Wolf and Wolf (1947) state that between 15,000 and 20,000 form species have been named. Both saprophytes and parasites occur in this group.

Identification of Fungi

Unfortunately there is no single volume that can be used in identifying fungus species. Before the identities of some fungi can be determined, it is often necessary to consult several different works. Because many fungus groups are quite large, it is not uncommon to find a lengthy taxonomic treatise devoted to a single genus or family. Once the family or genus has been determined for a particular organism, the more highly specialized treatise must be used for species identification.

To identify the family to which an unknown fungus belongs, the key of Martin (1936) will be found quite useful, and Clements and Shear's *Genera of Fungi* (1931) may be used for identification of genus. For an excellent guide to the literature dealing specifically with the identification of fungi the work of Bessey (1950), which contains an entire chapter devoted to this phase of mycology, should be consulted. Species determination is in many instances a time-consuming and difficult task, often requiring the advice and opinion of the specialist.

Number of Fungi

Estimates of the number of fungus species have been made from time to time. About seventy-eight thousand species are listed in Saccardo's *Sylloge Fungorum,* but Bisby and Ainsworth (1943) have suggested a much lower figure. These and the estimates of Wolf and Wolf (1947), Gwynne-Vaughan and Barnes (1927), and Bessey (1935) are listed in Table 1.

Table 1.—Some estimates of the number of species of fungi

	Saccardo	Bisby and Ainsworth	Gwynne-Vaughan and Barnes	Bessey	Wolf and Wolf
Myxomycetes (and related forms)	750	450			450?
Phycomycetes	1500	1000	800		1500
Ascomycetes	26,150	12,120	15,000	35,000	25,000–35,000
Basidiomycetes	24,700	13,460	13,000	24,500	20,000–25,000
Fungi Imperfecti	24,200	10,500	many thousands	25,000	15,000–20,000

Of the estimates listed in Table 1, the highest (Bessey) is only 84,500. Martin (1951) has suggested that an estimate of 100,000 is excessively conservative and that the total number may be as high as the number of species of vascular plants—approximately 205,000. He bases his suggestion in part on analyses of lists of host plants and in part on the species of fungi cited in Seymour's *Host Index* (1929) as parasites of these particular plants. Martin further substantiates his view by pointing out that at least some of Saccardo's species have been shown to embrace two or more clearly defined species. He adds that many economically unimportant vascular plants have received little study with regard to the fungi that parasitize them, and that our knowledge of nonparasitic fungi is grossly incomplete. It seems reasonable to predict that, as more facts are accumulated, Martin's views will probably be substantiated and that the fungi will eventually be recognized as bearing the same relationship to the plant kingdom (on the basis of numbers of species) as insects bear to the animal kingdom.

Isolation and Laboratory Cultivation of Fungi

Most mycological work of an applied or physiological nature involves the isolation of fungi and their maintenance in pure culture. For this work the pure-culture techniques of the bacteriologists are employed, but with different media from those commonly used for bacterial cultures. A very common method of isolating fungi is to place, with sterile forceps or needle, a bit of "infected" material on the surface of sterile agar medium in a petri dish and to allow the fungus to grow on the surface of the medium. With this method a mixed culture of several fungi and bacteria is most frequently obtained. The components of the mixed culture can then be separated by removing spores from discrete clusters, by removing bits of hyphae from the edges of colonies, or by making spore suspensions in sterile water and then making streak- or dilution-plate cultures in order to obtain discrete colonies of the various organisms. Since all fungi do not grow equally well on the same type of medium, several types of media are commonly used in isolation work. Cultures of fungi which develop large, fleshy fruiting structures can frequently be obtained in pure culture by transferring a bit of material from the exposed tissue of a freshly broken sporophore to a suitable medium. For the isolation of unicellular organisms such as yeasts, the dilution method is generally satisfactory.

Sometimes it is necessary to obtain cultures derived from a single spore. Indeed, Hagem (1908)* early expressed the opinion that pure cultures from single spores are prerequisites for any investigation. The most satisfactory method of obtaining single spores involves the use of a micromanipulator, although several other methods have proved successful. The details and merits of the various single spore isolation methods are reviewed by Hildebrand (1938).

Once a fungus has been obtained in pure culture it can usually be kept pure by the transfer of spores or bits of mycelia to fresh, sterile medium at regular intervals. Stock cultures are generally maintained on agar slants in test tubes, the type of nutrients in the medium depending on the fungus that is being cultured and also to a considerable extent on the personal choice of the investigator. For the maintenance of yeasts and many filamentous fungi a simple medium such as the following is satisfactory: dextrose, 20 grams; KH_2PO_4, 5 grams; Difco Yeast Extract, 7 grams; agar, 20 grams; distilled water, 1000 milliliters. Media are often made from fruit or vegetable decoctions (grape agar, prune decoction agar, carrot agar, potato dextrose agar). There are also a great many synthetic media, such as Czapek's agar.

* Cf. Hildebrand, 1938.

How often fresh cultures of a fungus should be made depends on the individual organism. Some fungi remain viable even when the agar has dried to a horny mass; others must be transferred frequently in order to keep them alive. The characteristics of some fungi change markedly with prolonged maintenance in the vegetative state; with such fungi it is often desirable to maintain the culture by other means than the simple subculturing described above. The more commonly used methods for the conservation of stock cultures are discussed in Chapter 8.

Literature Cited

Alexopoulos, C. J. 1952. *Introductory mycology.* Wiley, New York.

Bary, A. de. 1887. *Comparative morphology and biology of the fungi, mycetozoa and bacteria.* Trans. by H. E. Garnsey. Clarendon Press, London.

Bender, H. B. 1931. The genera of Fungi Imperfecti: North American species and hosts, with particular reference to Connecticut. Unpublished thesis, Yale University.

Bessey, E. A. 1935. *A textbook of mycology.* Blakiston, Philadelphia.

———. 1950. *Morphology and taxonomy of fungi.* Blakiston, Philadelphia.

Bisby, G. R., and Ainsworth, G. C. 1943. The numbers of fungi. *Trans. Brit. Mycol. Soc.* 26:16–19.

Blakeslee, A. F. 1913. Conjugation in the heterogamic genus Zygorhynchus. *Mycol. Centralbl.* 2:241–244.

Clements, F. E., and Shear, C. L. 1931. *The genera of fungi.* H. W. Wilson, New York.

Dodge, B. O. 1933. The perithecium and ascus of Penicillium. *Mycologia* 25:90–104.

Fischer, A. 1892. "Phycomyceten" (in Rabenhorst, *Kryptogamen-Flora von Deutschland, Oesterreich, und der Schweiz;* Band 4:1–505). Edward Kummer, Leipzig.

Fitzpatrick, H. M. 1930. *The lower fungi, Phycomycetes.* McGraw, New York.

Gaümann, E. 1926. *Vergleichende Morphologie der Pilze.* Gustav Fischer, Jena.

Gilman, J. C. 1945. *A manual of soil fungi.* Iowa State Coll. Press, Ames. 2d ed., 1957.

Gray, W. D. 1938. The effect of light on the fruiting of Myxomycetes. *Am. Jour. Bot.* 25:511–522.

Gwynne-Vaughan, H. C. I., and Barnes, B. 1927. *The structure and development of the fungi.* Cambridge Univ. Press, Cambridge.

Hagem, O. 1908. Untersuchungen über Norwegische Mucorineen. *Videnskapselskapets-Skrifter. Mat. naturv. Klasse 1907* (7): 1–50.

Henrici, A. T. 1930. *Molds, yeasts, and actinomycetes.* Wiley, New York.

Hildebrand, E. M. 1938. Techniques for the isolation of single microorganisms. *Bot. Rev. 4:*627–664.

Howard, F. L., and Currie, M. E. 1932a. Parasitism of myxomycete plasmodia on the sporophores of Hymenomycetes. *Jour. Arnold Arbor. 13:*270–283.

———. 1932b. Parasitism of myxomycete plasmodia on fungus mycelia. *Jour. Arnold Arbor. 13:*438–447.

Jump, J. A. 1937. A new fungus in *Ficus nitida* Thunb. *Jour. Agr. Univ. Puerto Rico 21:*573–576.

Luttrell, E. S. 1944. The morphology of *Sphaerostilbe aurantiicola* (B. and Br.) Petch. *Bull. Torrey Bot. Club 71:*599–619.

Martin, E. 1936. Morphological and cultural studies of *Taphrina potentillae*. *Bot. Gaz. 98:*339–347.

———. 1940. The morphology and cytology of *Taphrina deformans*. *Am. Jour. Bot. 27:*743–751.

Martin, G. W. 1936. A key to the families of fungi exclusive of the lichens. *Univ. of Iowa Studies in Nat. Hist. 17:*83–115.

———. 1951. The numbers of fungi. *Proc. Iowa Acad. Sci. 58:*175–178.

Nageli, C. 1881. Ernährung die niederen Pilze durch Kohlenstoff- und Stuckstoffverbindungen. *Bot. Mitt. 3:*395–485.

Rogers, D. P. 1934. The basidium. *Univ. of Iowa Studies in Nat. Hist. 16:*160–182.

Saccardo, P. A. 1882–1931. *Sylloge fungorum omnium hucusque cognitorum*. 25 vols.; published by author, Pavia, Italy.

Salmon, E. S. 1900. A monograph of the Erysiphaceae. *Mem. Torrey Bot. Club 9:*1–292.

Schroeter, J. 1897. "Pilze" (in Engler and Prantl, *Die natürlichen pflanzenfamilien*). Wilhelm Englemann, Leipzig.

Seaver, F. J. 1942. *The North American cup fungi*. Published by author, New York.

Seymour, A. B. 1929. *Host index of the fungi of North America*. Harvard Univ. Press, Cambridge, Mass.

Stevens, F. L. 1913. *The fungi which cause plant disease*. Macmillan, New York.

Tamiya, H. 1932. Ueber die Verwendbarkeit von verschiedenen Kohlenstoffverbindungen im bau und Betriebstoffwechselphysiologie von *Aspergillus oryzae*: IV. *Acta Phytochemica 6:*1–129.

Transeau, E. N., Sampson, H. C., and Tiffany, L. H. 1940. *Textbook of botany*. Harper, New York.

Waksman, S. A., and Starkey, R. L. 1931. *The soil and the microbe*. Wiley, New York.

Wingard, S. A. 1925. Studies on the pathogenicity, morphology and cytology of *Nematospora phaseoli*. *Bull. Torrey Bot. Club 52:*249–290.

Wolf, F. A., and Wolf, F. T. 1947. *The fungi:* Vol. I. Wiley, New York.

I

BENEFICIAL ACTIVITIES

OF FUNGI

2 · *The Destruction of Organic Waste*

DECAY OF ORGANIC MATERIAL due to fungus activity may be beneficial to man's interests in some circumstances and detrimental in others. The capacity of fungi (and bacteria) to bring about the decay of organic material through their various digestive and respiratory processes benefits man in three very important ways: (1) organic debris is continuously being removed from man's environment; (2) large quantities of carbon dioxide—so important to photosynthesis—are released to the atmosphere and made available again for use by green plants in the synthesis of sugar; and (3) *humus,* a very important soil constituent, is formed from waste organic material through the activities of microorganisms. These three processes are of inestimable value to man. If the fungi and bacteria should suddenly lose their capacity for bringing about the decay of organic debris, life would become exceedingly burdensome and disagreeable and, conceivably, might cease altogether.

Removal of Organic Debris

Were it not for the ability of nonchlorophyllous plants to decompose waste organic material, the earth in a very short time would be covered to an astonishing depth with an accumulation of vegetable debris and other waste products that had their origin either directly or indirectly in plant material. Transeau, Sampson, and Tiffany (1940) estimate that there are about 1,000,000 leaves on a large elm tree, and sometimes as many as 7,000,000. If fungi and bacteria were not active in the destruction of leaves at the end of the growing season the dead leaves would fall to the ground and eventually would accumulate to such an extent that the tree might be completely covered. The harmful effect of completely covering a chlorophyll-containing plant with dead leaves is self-evident.

An incalculable amount of organic material is decomposed annually through the activities of nonchlorophyllous plants. Estimates may serve to give some notion of the magnitude of this decaying action. If we take Transeau's conservative figure (1,000,000 leaves per large elm tree) and then calculate the weight of a single leaf crop, we find that more than 400 pounds of leaves are formed annually. Thus the total destruction (by bacteria and fungi) of the annual crop of leaves from a large elm tree involves the biological oxidation of over 200 pounds of carbon. This figure may appear small and relatively unimportant, but in ten years over 600 million pounds of leaves would be formed by 150,000 elm trees—the estimated number that have died in one decade in Columbus, Ohio, as the result of the virus disease phloem necrosis. The destruction of 600 million pounds of waste organic material by microorganisms would seem to be a tremendous accomplishment, yet this figure almost fades into insignificance when one considers the annual leaf crop of all the trees on earth. Truly man is greatly benefited by the unceasing decay activities of fungi and bacteria. Were it not for these activities, all living things might be suffocated; at best the human race would become a group of rakers and burners, barely able to keep their heads above the accumulating leaves.

Equally poignant examples might be drawn from agriculture, where only a small portion of certain crops is harvested for use; an even more striking example is uncultivated vegetation where entire plant bodies eventually become organic debris. Another source of organic debris is the decomposition of waste paper, running into many thousands of tons annually, and averaging about 150 pounds per square mile over the entire land area of the continental United States.

Hundreds of similar examples could be mentioned, painting a dismal picture of how a particular type of waste material might accumulate, much to our annoyance and discomfort. That this accumulation of debris does not happen is due to the ubiquity of fungi (Figs. 15–17) and bacteria, and to their capacities for rapidly destroying organic materials of all types.

FIG. 15. *Mycelium of a Basidiomycete growing just underneath the bark of a decaying beech log.*

FIG. 16. *Hardwood forest litter with the loosely packed, dry upper layer removed. Note the white fungus mycelium and the leaves in various stages of decay.*

FIG. 17.   *A piece of badly decayed hardwood. Discarded during lumbering operations, this piece of wood may now be easily crumbled with the fingers. The ruler measures 6 inches.*

Return of Carbon Dioxide to the Atmosphere

The importance of carbon dioxide to all living things cannot be overemphasized. The reduction of this gas (through photosynthesis) by the hydrogen of water in the chloroplasts of green plants results in the formation of sugar, which furnishes the immediate energy needs of all plants and animals. Each growing season tremendous quantities of atmospheric carbon dioxide diffuse into green plants, making photosynthesis possible. As a result, the carbon is chemically bound, first in sugar and eventually in other carbohydrates, proteins, fats, and in all of the myriad compounds of which living cells are composed. Some of the carbon bound during photosynthesis returns to the atmosphere as a result of plant respiration; however, the annual amount of carbon chemically bound in a green plant during photosynthesis far exceeds the quantity returned to the atmosphere. If the photosynthetic rate is initially high, the atmosphere in the immediate vicinity of the plant will become temporarily depleted of carbon dioxide and photosynthesis will automatically slow down. Under such conditions carbon dioxide concentration may become the limiting factor in photosynthesis, but only temporarily, because the supply is replenished by diffusion from other areas into the depleted region.

Other than annoyance and discomfort, no serious effects would accompany the accumulation of organic debris, provided that an unlimited quantity of carbon dioxide were available. But the supply is definitely limited and could be readily exhausted if not returned to the atmosphere. Waksman and Starkey (1931) have pointed out that although carbon is one of the most important elements in the life of plants and animals, it comprises only a small fraction of the earth's surface (lithosphere, hydrosphere, and atmosphere). Since the quantity is limited a continuous recirculation of carbon is essential to life.

Numerous mechanisms are responsible for the return of carbon dioxide to the atmosphere: respiration of plants and animals; freeing of carbon dioxide in the erosion of rocks; volcanic eruptions; combustion of coal, gas, and petroleum; and combustion of plant and animal residues. Although it is impossible to evaluate these processes accurately, it is safe to assume that the major role is played by fungi and bacteria. Figure 18 diagrammatically illustrates the principal features of the

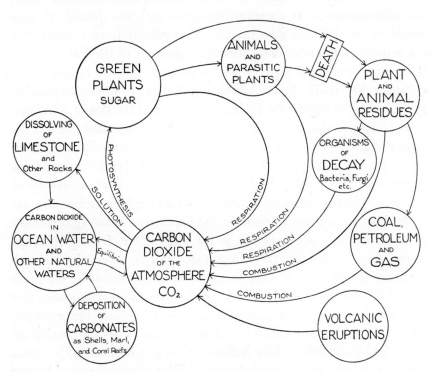

Fig. 18. *The carbon cycle in nature. (From Transeau, Sampson, and Tiffany, 1940.)*

carbon cycle and shows the most important processes that contribute to the return of carbon to the atmosphere for use in the synthesis of sugar.

Schroeder (1919) estimated that the amount of carbon dioxide involved annually in photosynthesis (exclusive of photosynthesis in the ocean) is 80 trillion kilograms (88,105,726,872 tons) and that of this quantity 58 trillion kilograms (64,867,829,140 tons) are organically bound. Since the atmosphere contains only about 0.03 per cent carbon dioxide, it is apparent that, on the basis of Schroeder's estimates, considerable depletion of the world supply of carbon dioxide occurs annually as a result of photosynthesis. Lundegårdh (1931) states that the figure estimated for the quantity of carbon dioxide annually bound organically represents $\frac{1}{35}$ of the total atmospheric carbon dioxide, and believes that if decay should cease, life too would cease in a short time. Lundegårdh is certainly correct in his general concept, but he does not take into account the fact that the ocean contains over one hundred times more carbon (as dissolved carbon dioxide and carbonates) than the atmosphere; it is therefore doubtful that the period of time would be as short as that implied. Lundegårdh further states that the activity of the cellulose-destroying organisms of the soil is one of the most important biological processes on earth, and if inhibited would endanger life itself. In an earlier publication (1924) Lundegårdh pointed out that during the Carboniferous Period the rate of formation of organic material exceeded the rate of decay, and that the world's supply of coal corresponds to four times the total carbon dioxide content of our present atmosphere. He adds that perhaps even today on moors, where the rate of decay is slow, there is a gradual accumulation of organically bound carbon at the expense of atmospheric carbon dioxide.

Without attempting to discount the importance of decay organisms in the return of carbon dioxide to the atmosphere, Lundegårdh's extreme views concerning their importance can be accepted only with some reservation. Before such views can be fully evaluated, one needs some knowledge of the magnitude of the various other processes that result in an increase in atmospheric carbon dioxide. For example, Martin (1930) states that the average amount of carbon dioxide excreted by human beings daily is about 26 ounces, or about 593 pounds annually. With a world population of 2 billion, the total annual human respiratory carbon dioxide is 593 million tons,* or slightly less than 1 per cent of the amount organically bound each year as a result of photosynthesis. If, as Franck and Loomis (1949) have estimated, the total annual animal respiratory carbon dioxide is less than that of plants, something less than 23 billion tons of carbon dioxide would return to the atmosphere annually as a result of respiration. This figure represents only about 36 per cent of the amount of carbon dioxide bound annually in photosynthesis.

Another factor that might be expected to contribute greatly to the increase of atmospheric carbon dioxide is the combustion of coal, gas, and petroleum products. A few calculations, however, reveal that this contribution is not too significant. The total amount of coal (anthracite and bituminous) mined in the United States in 1947 was 675 million tons. If the carbon content of coal is taken at 65 per cent, complete combustion of all of the coal mined in the United States in 1947 would result in the return of 1,605,825,000 tons of carbon dioxide to the atmosphere—a mere 2.4 per cent of the amount organically bound annually. The total world production of coal in 1945 (exclusive of China, for which there were no figures available) was 1,420,420,000 tons—the equivalent of 3,379,179,180 tons of carbon dioxide, or about 5.2 per cent of the quantity organically bound annually in photosynthesis. From such calculations it becomes apparent that unless the quantities of carbon dioxide annually returned to the atmosphere through such agencies as volcanic eruptions, freeing of carbon dioxide from rocks, and combustion of gas and petroleum are equivalent to at least 60 per cent of the quantity annually bound organically, the great bulk of carbon dioxide must be returned to the atmosphere through the respiration of microorganisms. Franck and Loomis (1949) estimate that about 80 per cent of the annual plant synthesis is broken down by microorganisms.

One other point should be mentioned. If there were no organisms of decay, the earth's supply of nitrogen in a form available to green plants would diminish, since nitrogen would be bound into proteins and other nitrogenous plant compounds simultaneously with the binding of carbon into organic compounds. In the decay of such materials some

---

* The estimate of Franck and Loomis (1949) of about 0.3 billion tons is probably more nearly correct, since Martin's measurements were probably made with adults.

of this nitrogen would become part of the assimilatory products of the decay organisms and hence be unavailable to green plants. However, some nitrogen is freed as ammonia and eventually may be converted to available form (nitrates) through the activities of the nitrifying bacteria.

Humus Formation

In the absence of decay-causing microorganisms, we could, of course, as Thaysen and Bunker (1927) pointed out, burn the organic debris that would accumulate. This burning would result in the removal of debris and also in the return of carbon dioxide to the atmosphere. However, if organic waste were actually disposed of in this fashion, man's agricultural pursuits would soon suffer, since it is from waste organic matter that the important soil constituent *humus* is formed. Waksman (1938) states that humus is important in soil processes in three ways: (1) *physical,* in that it modifies soil color, texture, structure, moisture-holding capacity, and aeration; (2) *chemical,* in that it influences the solubility of certain soil minerals, forms compounds with certain elements (such as iron) which makes them more available to plants, and increases the buffering properties of the soil; (3) *biological,* in that humus is a source of energy for microorganisms and makes the soil a better medium for the growth of higher plants.

Humus is not a single, simple chemical compound but rather a mixture of many organic compounds that are continuously being decomposed by soil microorganisms. As listed by Waksman, the properties of humus are as follows:

1. Humus is dark brown to black, and practically insoluble in water, although a part may form a colloidal suspension in pure water. Humus dissolves in dilute alkali solutions, especially on boiling, giving a dark-colored extract; a large part of this extract precipitates when the solution is neutralized with mineral acids. Certain humus constituents may also dissolve in acid solutions and be precipitated at about pH 4.8.
2. Humus contains a larger amount of carbon than plant, animal, and microbial bodies, the carbon content frequently being as high as 58 per cent.
3. The nitrogen content of humus is usually 3 to 6 per cent, but in high-moor peat may be as low as 0.5 to 0.8 per cent and in subsoils as high as 10 to 12 per cent.

4. Humus of many soils and humus of sea bottoms contain carbon and nitrogen in a ratio of about 10:1. This ratio, however, may vary with many factors.
5. It is in a dynamic rather than a static condition, since it is constantly being formed from organic residues and constantly being further decomposed by microorganisms.
6. It is a source of energy for various microorganisms, and as it is decomposed, carbon dioxide and ammonia are continuously evolved.
7. It has a high capacity of base exchange; it combines with various inorganic soil constituents; it absorbs water, and swells; it possesses other properties that make it a valuable constituent of substrates that support plant and animal life.

Although the chemical nature and origin of the constituents of humus has by no means been elucidated, its importance in soil fertility is recognized. Also recognized is the vital role played by microorganisms in the formation of humus through the decomposition of organic materials and through the synthesis of substances that also become part of the humus.

Thus far bacteria and fungi have been discussed as the causal agents in the decay of organic waste, although our concern is primarily with fungi and their activities. It is difficult to evaluate the separate roles of bacteria and fungi in humus formation, since both organisms are ubiquitous and unceasingly active. Probably the interrelated activities of both organisms are essential to humus formation, since fungi and bacteria occur in great numbers wherever humus is formed. It would therefore be pointless, in view of our present state of knowledge, to ascribe greater or lesser importance to the activities of either of these organisms. Nonetheless it is possible to make certain conjectures regarding their relative roles under specific conditions. For example, since certain bacteria are able to live with little or no molecular oxygen, the partial decomposition of organic materials under these circumstances is unquestionably due largely to the activities of such bacteria rather than to the presence of oxygen. The fungi, which in general are highly aerobic organisms, are involved primarily in the partial decay of organic materials under conditions of adequate oxygen supply, although the recent work of Cantino (1949) has demonstrated that a water mold, *Blastocladia pringsheimii,* can dissimilate glucose in an atmosphere consisting entirely of carbon dioxide. Although it has long been held

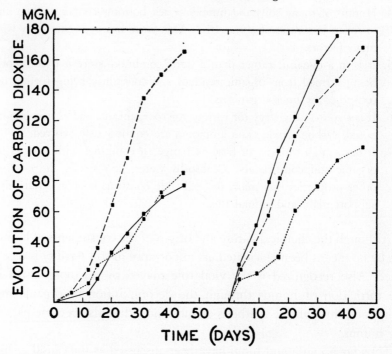

FIG. 19.   *Comparative growth of cellulose-decomposing bacteria* (———),
fungi (_____), *and actinomycetes* (. . . . .) *in neutral soil. Curves show
growth at 30 per cent of the moisture-holding capacity of the soil* (left)
and at 50 per cent (right). (*After Dubos; redrawn from Waksman and
Starkey, 1931.*)

that the destruction of submerged organic waste was due entirely to
anaerobic bacteria, further investigations may well demonstrate that
a number of fungi also contribute to this process. The work of Dubos *
illustrates the fact that different organisms may be responsible at different times and under different conditions for the decay processes occurring in the soil. Dubos' results, presented graphically in Figure 19,
show the relation of soil moisture content to the type of microorganism
most active in the decay process.

Present knowledge of the oxygen relations of fungi indicates that
the destruction (either complete or partial) of organic waste by the
majority of fungi occurs primarily under more or less well-aerated conditions such as exist on the surface or in the uppermost layers of the soil.
That there are great numbers of fungi in the soil is quite evident to

* See Waksman and Starkey (1931).

anyone who has plated out a small sample and isolated the various fungi that appear. Gilman (1945) in his *Manual of Soil Fungi* listed more than 500 species distributed through 139 genera of Phycomycetes, Ascomycetes, and Fungi Imperfecti, and in a later edition (1957) has increased this list materially. As Gilman points out, the question arises whether a fungus isolated from a soil sample is in reality a soil inhabitant or merely the result of the accidental lodgement of a spore in the sample. This question, however pertinent in Gilman's studies, is of little significance to our discussion in view of the overwhelming evidence that a great many species of fungi are soil-inhabiting.

Types of Organic Compounds Decomposed

The role of fungi as active agents in the destruction of organic debris—whether in connection with the removal of organic waste, the return of carbon dioxide to the atmosphere, or the formation of humus—involves the biological degradation of plant materials. Of these, cellulose is the most abundant. Constituting 50 per cent or more of the cell wall material of plants, it represents the major portion of all vegetable debris.

Like starch, cellulose is a complex carbohydrate known as a polysaccharide, consisting of a large number of glucose molecules; unlike starch, cellulose cannot be digested by the green plants in which it is synthesized. Though many fungi are able to digest cellulose, great difficulty has been encountered in the demonstration *in vitro* of a cellulose-digesting enzyme system. As a result, relatively little is known about the cellulose-digesting enzyme (or enzymes), commonly referred to as cellulase or cytase, although its existence is beyond question. First described by De Bary (1886), this enzyme was reported to be capable of dissolving plant cell walls. Ward (1888) and Behrens (1898) confirmed De Bary's findings. Later von Euler (1912) studied the enzyme more thoroughly and obtained his enzyme preparation by extracting with water the mycelium of *Merulius lacrymans,* a basidiomycetous fungus commonly associated with dry rot of timber. Pringsheim (1932) believes that the enzymic digestion of cellulose involves two enzymes: (1) *cytase,* which brings about the hydrolysis of cellulose to a disaccharide (cellobiose), and (2) *cellobiase,* which catalyzes the hydrolysis of the cellobiose molecule to two molecules of glucose. If

Pringsheim is correct, there is a remarkable parallelism between enzymic hydrolysis of cellulose and enzymic hydrolysis of starch, since the latter polysaccharide is enzymatically degraded through a series of dextrin intermediates to a disaccharide (maltose), which in turn may be hydrolyzed to glucose. Other investigators do not believe that cellulose digestion proceeds in quite the orderly fashion described by Pringsheim.

As noted in a later chapter, it is possible to prepare concentrates of certain fungus enzymes on a large scale, notable examples being *amylase* (obtained from various species of *Aspergillus*) and *invertase* (usually obtained from yeast). Thus far large-scale production has not been accomplished with cellulose-digesting enzymes, which would pave the way for rather spectacular developments in the utilization of cellulosic wastes, most of which are now left to decay. Thus it would seem that research on the production and concentration of enzymes for large-scale industrial use could well be pointed in the direction of a cellulose-digesting enzyme. In recent years at least one U. S. manufacturer has successfully prepared a concentrate of this enzyme, but the work is still on an experimental basis and large-scale production does not appear imminent. Galloway and Burgess (1937) state that with this enzyme some type of linkage with the living organism that synthesized it is essential. Although it may be true that *in vivo* the enzyme is operative only in close proximity with the living organism, it does, like amylase, diffuse out of the organism and hence under proper conditions should yield to isolation in almost pure form. Aside from its unquestioned economic implications, such an enzyme would also provide a valuable tool for further studies on the nature of cellulose, concerning which there is yet much to be learned.

Despite the many failures encountered in the isolation of cellulase, its occurrence in many fungi is an established fact and can be readily demonstrated by culturing the proper fungus on a sterile piece of filter paper or cotton cloth. Galloway and Burgess state that about half of the "commonly occurring fungi" possess the capacity for digesting cellulose. In their survey of the cellulolytic activity of 453 cultures of fungi (the majority of which were Fungi Imperfecti) White and others (1948) obtained similar findings. From the tabular data presented by the latter investigators it is difficult to judge in certain instances whether or not cellulose was actually destroyed, but these instances are represented only by those fungi whose cellulolytic capacities apparently were slight. A very considerable body of literature indicates that a great many fungi are capable of digesting cellulose; for further references consult Chaps. 21 and 22 on wood decay and deterioration of textiles.

Cellulose-digesting species have been demonstrated among all of the large groups of fungi except the Myxomycetes. Definite information about the activities of this curious group is lacking, primarily because the Myxomycetes have not yet been readily obtained in pure culture. When plasmodia of Myxomycetes are allowed to spread over the surface of moist filter paper, the cellulose is certainly digested, but whether the digestion is accomplished by the Myxomycetes or by associated microorganisms has not been determined. The extent to which Phycomycetes digest cellulose is also uncertain. White and his co-workers (1948) were unable to demonstrate cellulose digestion with six members of the order Mucorales, and concluded that members of that order were noncellulolytic. Whiffen (1941) has shown that seven of nine species of Chytridiales studied can decompose cellulose. In all probability further investigations will reveal that there are still other cellulolytic Phycomycetes. Among the fungi that digest cellulose most rapidly are members of the Ascomycetes (e.g., species of *Chaetomium*, especially *C. globosum*) and the Basidiomycetes. The occurrence of cellulose destroyers in the Fungi Imperfecti has already been discussed in connection with the investigations of White and his co-workers.

Although not so abundant as cellulose, lignin is another important constituent of plant cell walls. Less is known of the chemistry of lignin than of cellulose, and as a chemical compound it is virtually useless to the chemical industry. It poses a major problem in the manufacture of paper from wood cellulose. In the process large quantities of lignin are freed, thereby creating a tremendous waste-disposal problem. Lignin is generally more resistant to decay than cellulose, but in spite of its greater resistance, it is decomposed by a number of fungi, especially certain species of wood-rotting Basidiomycetes. The enzyme instrumental in the decomposition of lignin is commonly referred to as *ligninase.* The synthesis of this enzyme (or enzymes) has been reported by Garren (1938) for *Polyporus abietinus,* by Bayliss (1908) for *P. versicolor,* by Nutman (1929) for *P. hispidus,* and by Zeller (1916) for *Lenzites saepiaria.*

Lignin has often been considered the most important substance in the formation of humus, probably because lignin is decayed rather less rapidly than certain other of the common plant constituents. Figure 20 illustrates diagrammatically the factors involved in humus formation. Lignin is undoubtedly quite important, yet it would seem that the other plant materials which are decomposed are probably no less important.

Table 2.—Principal constituents of coniferous wood

Constituent	Per Cent
Cellulose	54.10
Hemicelluloses	
Hexosans	3.06
Pentosans	12.25
Lignin (including acetyl groups)	30.60

After von Euler (1923).

Although cellulose and lignin are the most abundant materials in plant waste (Table 2), there are many other substances occurring in smaller amounts which may also be destroyed by fungi. Among such materials are suberin, cutin, starch, sugar, the hemicelluloses and pectins, and certain nitrogenous compounds that are constituents of protoplasm. Fungal degradation of all these materials, except cutin and suberin, can be easily demonstrated. Many different species have been reported to be capable of forming *hemicellulases* and *pectinases;* the formation of *amylases* (starch-digesting enzymes) by fungi has long been known and utilized. Commercial production of fungal amylases has been conducted on a large scale for many years, especially in Oriental countries (Chap. 14). The capacity to digest a variety of nitrogen-containing organic compounds is probably possessed by all fungi. Robbins (1937), in his classification of fungi into four groups based upon the types of nitrogen compounds they may utilize, combines in one group a large number of species that obtain their nitrogen only from organic sources. However, members of the other three groups may also utilize many organic nitrogenous compounds.

The problem of the natural disappearance of suberin and especially cutin is a puzzling one, for the enzymic digestion of these materials has

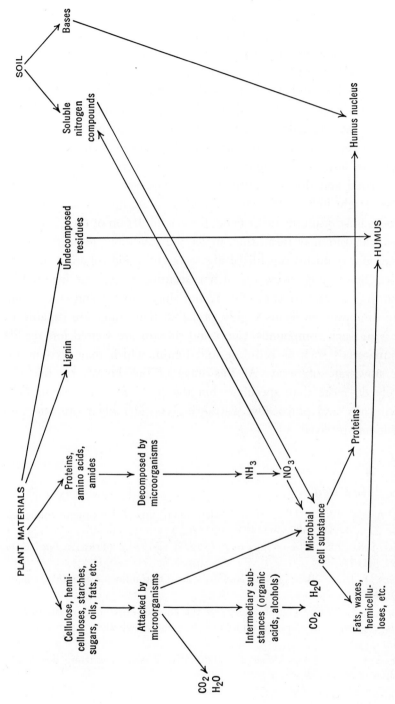

FIG. 20. *Diagrammatic representation of the process of humification. (After Waksman, 1938.)*

never been clearly demonstrated. This fact has often been used as an argument in support of the mechanical theory of cuticular invasion of plants by pathogens. Priestley (1921) has reported that certain peat deposits consist largely of cuticular, endodermal, and corky materials of heath-inhabiting plants. In his study of the bogs of the Huron River Valley, Transeau (1905) states: "The peat formed through the agency of the bog sedges and their attendant plants has a fibrous and matted appearance. The structures of the various stems, roots, and leaves have suffered but slight alteration. They were originally strongly cuticularized and this has aided in their preservation." * Such reports as these might indicate that suberin and cutin are not digested at all by microorganisms; on the other hand, the accumulation of these materials in peat deposits may mean that, under the conditions peculiar to peat formation, organisms capable of digesting cutin and suberin could not survive. Since fungi grow on such a seemingly resistant material as asphalt (Gray and Martin, 1947), and since suberin and cutin eventually disappear, it seems highly probable that fungi are capable of destroying such compounds. Cutin and suberin are wetted less readily than materials such as cellulose and lignin, which may account for their slow rate of decay. At this stage of our knowledge one can scarcely do more than speculate, but the problem is important both academically and practically, warranting considerably more attention than it has received.

Literature Cited

Bary, A. de. 1886. Uber einige Sclerotinien und Sclerotinienkrankheiten. *Bot. Zeit.* 44:377–387, 393–404, 409–426, 433–441, 449–461, 465–474.

Bayliss, J. S. 1908. The biology of *Polystictus versicolor* (Fries). *Jour. Econ. Biol.* 3:1–24.

Behrens, J. 1898. Beitrage zur Kenntnis der Obstfaulin. *Centralbl. f. Bakt., Abt. 2, 4*:514.

Cantino, E. C. 1949. The physiology of the aquatic Phycomycete, *Blastocladia pringsheimii,* with emphasis on its nutrition and metabolism. *Am. Jour. Bot.* 36:95–112.

Euler, A. C. von. 1923. Ueber die quantitative Zusammensetzung des Nadelholzes. *Cellulosechemie* 4:1–11.

* Pp. 372–373.

Euler, H. von. 1912. Zur Kenntnis der Cellulase. *Zeit. angew. Chem.* 25:250–251.

Franck, J., and Loomis, W. E. 1949. *Photosynthesis in plants.* Iowa State Coll. Press, Ames.

Galloway, L. D., and Burgess, R. 1937. *Applied mycology and bacteriology.* Leonard Hill Ltd., London.

Garren, K. H. 1938. Studies on *Polyporus abietinus:* I. The enzyme-producing ability of the fungus. *Phytopathology* 28:839–845.

Gilman, J. C. 1945. *A manual of soil fungi.* Iowa State Coll. Press, Ames. 2d. ed., 1957.

Gray, W. D., and Martin, G. W. 1947. The growth of fungi on asphalt-treated paper. *Mycologia* 39:587–601.

Lundegårdh, H. 1924. Kreislauf der Kohlensäure in der Natur.

———. 1931. *Environment and plant development.* Trans. from 2d German edition by E. Ashby. E. Arnold, London.

Martin, H. N. 1930. *The human body.* Holt, New York.

Nutman, F. J. 1929. Studies on wood destroying fungi: I. *Polyporus hispidus* Fr. *Ann. Appl. Biol.* 16:40–64.

Priestley, J. H. 1921. Suberin and cutin. *New Phyt.* 20:17–29.

Pringsheim, H. 1932. *The chemistry of the monosaccharides and of the polysaccharides.* McGraw, New York.

Robbins, W. J. 1937. The assimilation by plants of various forms of nitrogen. *Am. Jour. Bot.* 24:243–250.

Schroeder, H. 1919. Die jährliche Gesamtproduktion der grünen Planzendecke der Erde. *Die Naturwissenschaften* 7:8–12, 23–29.

Thaysen, A. C., and Bunker, H. J. 1927. The microbiology of cellulose, hemicelluloses, pectin, and gums. Oxford Univ. Press, London.

Transeau, E. N. 1905. The bogs and bog flora of the Huron River Valley. *Bot. Gaz.* 40:351–375.

———, Sampson, H. C., and Tiffany, L. H. 1940. *Textbook of botany.* Harper, New York.

Waksman, S. A. 1938. *Humus. Origin, chemical composition and importance in nature.* Williams & Wilkins, Baltimore.

——— and Starkey, R. L. 1931. *The soil and the microbe.* Wiley, New York.

Ward, H. M. 1888. A lily disease. *Ann. Bot.* 2:319–382.

Whiffen, A. 1941. Cellulose decomposition by the saprophytic chytrids. *Jour. Elisha Mitchell Sci. Soc.* 57:321–330.

White, W. L., Darby, R. T., Stechert, C. M., and Sanderson, K. 1948. Assay of cellulolytic activity of molds isolated from fabrics and related items exposed in the tropics. *Mycologia* 40:34–84.

Zeller, S. M. 1916. Studies in the physiology of the fungi: II. *Lenzites saepiaria* Fr. with special reference to enzyme activity. *Ann. Mo. Bot. Gard.* 3:439–519.

3 · *Mycorhizae*

IN THE PRECEDING CHAPTER it was pointed out that a great many fungus species inhabit the soil. Accordingly it would be logical to expect that under normal conditions fungi and the roots of higher plants would grow in close association. Actually if the proper species (fungus and green plant) are in proximity and if environmental conditions are favorable, in many instances the root tip and fungus mycelium enter into such a close relationship that discrete morphological structures consisting of both root tissues and fungus are formed. According to Hatch (1937), the European foresters of the 1800's apparently had seen and sketched these compound structures without knowing their true significance. Kelley (1950) claims that Pfeffer (1877) should be considered the true discoverer of these fungus roots, and Rayner (1945) gives credit to the Polish botanist Kamienski (1881). But our knowledge of this phase of botany actually had its beginning with the work of Frank (1885a, 1885b), who pointed out that a curious relationship existed between fungi and the smaller roots of higher plants, resulting in a compound structure composed of both root tissue and fungus mycelium. Frank termed this structure a fungus-root (*Pilzwurzel*), or *mycorhiza* and suggested that it might be of fundamental importance in the nutrition of trees. Subsequent observations by later investigators have shown that Frank's concept of the morphological nature of mycorhizae was correct and that these structures are in fact discrete organs similar to lichen thalli in that they are composed of two members.

It is now known that fungi grow in close association with members of all the great groups of plants. But though this relationship is basically the same in all instances, the structures arising from it are not. It is obviously impossible for Thallophytes and Bryophytes to form mycorhizae since they do not have roots. The term *mycothallus* may be applied to the structure developed by these rootless plants, but when the association involves an alga and a fungus, the term *lichen* is more commonly used.

Prevalence and Distribution of Mycorhizae

Since the publication of Frank's work in 1885—which, incidentally, started a controversy as to whether or not mycorhizae are of widespread occurrence—many studies of these interesting complex structures have appeared. Despite McDougal's statement (1922) that they are merely abnormal pathological structures and are of infrequent occurrence, it is now known that mycorhizae are prevalent throughout the plant kingdom and world-wide in distribution. This fact has been adequately demonstrated by the works of Janse (1896) in Java, Samuel (1926) in Australia, Asai (1934) in Japan, Hesselman (1900) in the Arctic, Doak (1927) in Indiana, and Rayner (1938) in Africa. McDougal and Glasgow (1929), in their examination of the roots of 33 species from 19 genera of the Compositae, found mycorhizae present in 89.4 per cent of the genera and 84.8 per cent of the species. Samuel found mycorhizae in the roots of 27 species of legumes and 30 species of grasses. Janse, in his investigations of the plants of Java, found mycorhizae in 69 of the 75 species examined. Hatch, whose investigations of fungus roots have been concerned primarily with those of trees, has said that no woody plants (exclusive of the relatively few parasitic woody plants) have been demonstrated to be devoid of mycorhizae. McArdle (1932), in his study of the mycorhizae of conifer seedlings, reported that in three nurseries where he conducted his investigations abundant mycorhizae were found on the roots of practically all the seedlings examined. Reports such as those of Jones (1924) and Gerdemann (1955) indicate that mycorhizae may well

be prevalent among crop plants. Thus the evidence points overwhelmingly to the fact that fungus-root formation is not an exceptional
occurrence but, on the contrary, may well prove to be the rule. Yet
we still do not know whether certain plants are mycorhizal, and Kelley
(1950) rightly points out that there should be more investigations
like those conducted by Janse.

Actually we possess relatively little exact information about the
structure and activities of roots in their natural environments. Most
physiological studies of roots are conducted with plants that have been
reared in sand or water or perhaps in sterilized soil. Since these conditions may not even approximate the natural environment of the vast
majority of roots, botanists may be less aware of root processes than is
generally supposed. For example, there is no real evidence that root
hairs commonly occur on young roots growing in their typical habitats.
Our current ideas about the physiological processes of roots—including those concerned with the relative frequency of root hairs and mycorhizae—may undergo considerable revision after further research.

Fungi Involved in the Formation of Mycorhizae

In view of the great prevalence of fungi of all classes in the
soil, it is not surprising that fungi capable of entering into the mycorhizal relationship are found in several groups—the Phycomycetes,
Ascomycetes, Basidiomycetes, and Fungi Imperfecti. In addition to
species that can be placed with certainty in one or another of the groups
above, certain fungi have been designated by the name *Mycelium
radicis.* Thus Melin (1921) named a mycorhizal fungus from Scotch
pine *Mycelium radicis sylvestris,* and Hatch (1934) named a fungus
with black hyphae *Mycelium radicis atrovirens.*

So far a much greater number of species of Basidiomycetes (chiefly
in the family Agaricaceae) are reported to be mycorhizal than any of
the other groups of fungi, but this weight of opinion stems from the
fact that mycorhizae of trees have received more attention than those of
herbaceous plants, as well as from the fact that the mycelia of various species of Agaricaceae are commonly associated with tree roots.
Mycorhizal fungi associated with various species of orchids are members of the genus *Rhizoctonia* (Fungi Imperfecti), while those associated with members of the Ericaceae (heath family) have been iden-

tified as species of *Phoma* (Fungi Imperfecti). On the basis of what is known about heath and orchid mycorhizae it might appear that a high degree of specificity exists in the establishment of the mycorhizal relationship. However, Kelley (1950) believes that "strictly speaking there are no mycorrhizal fungi: there is only a mycorrhizal state," adding that apparently there is no specificity in mycorhizal endophytism but that a mycorhiza can be formed by one of several fungi.

Thus Kelley views the establishment of the mycorhizal relationship as a more or less casual event that occurs when the root tip comes into contact with any one of a number of different fungi. This view is strengthened by observations which indicate that several different species of fungi may have the capacity to form mycorhizae with a single species of seed-bearing plant. An example is provided by the work of McArdle (1932), who reported that *Tricholoma personatum, Lycoperdon gemmatum, Clitocybe diatreta,* and *C. rivulosa* var. *angustifolia* all formed mycorhizae with seedlings of both northern white pine and Norway spruce. McArdle also reported that eight other species of fungi were thought to be capable of forming mycorhizae with these two tree species.

Apparently some of the early investigators considered that sufficient proof of the mycorhiza-forming capacity of a fungus species obtained if sporocarps of the fungus were found growing close to the plant, or if strands of mycelium could be traced from sporocarps to mycorhizae. Today such proof is considered adequate only (1) if the fungus is isolated from a fungus-root association, obtained in pure culture and subsequently identified, or (2) if mycorhizae can be synthesized, using known species of fungus and higher plant. Most proof is obtained by the latter method because of the many difficulties inherent in the isolation of a single fungus species from a small root that has been in contact with soil in which several hundred other species of fungi may have been growing. Such synthesis consists of making pure cultures of both the fungus and the higher plant, introducing inoculum from the fungus culture into the seedling culture, and examining the latter for the presence of mycorhizae after a sufficient period. The manipulations are relatively simple: seeds are surface sterilized, allowed to germinate under sterile conditions (e.g., on sterile agar), and then transferred aseptically to a cotton-stoppered flask or bottle containing sterilized soil or other suitable rooting medium. After the seedlings have become well established, inoculum from a pure culture of the fungus under test is introduced into the flask, employing the usual pure-culture techniques. The weakness of this method is that even though a fungus may form mycorhizae with a certain species of seed-bearing plant under laboratory conditions, described above, there is no proof that the same species of fungus will form mycorhizae under natural conditions.

Types of Mycorhizae

Two general types of mycorhizae, based upon structure, are recognized: (1) those in which the hyphae of the fungus member are intracellular with respect to the other member, and (2) those in which the greater part of the fungus mycelium occurs as a mantle around the root tips, with intercellular hyphae growing between the cells of the outer root tissues. Mycorhizae in which the hyphae are intracellular are known as *endotropic mycorhizae.* Figure 21, a photomicrograph of a longitudinal section of an endotropic mycorhiza of the tulip poplar (*Liriodendron tulipifera*), shows the coils of intracellular hyphae within the living cells of the root. The second type is the *ectotropic mycorhiza,* in which the hyphae within the root are never inside the cells but are always intercellular. In the latter type the greater part of the mycelium invests the root tip with a covering sheath or mantle; hyphae from the mantle penetrate the root centripedally to

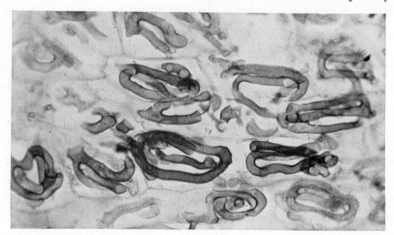

FIG. 21. *Longitudinal section of an endotropic mycorhiza of* Liriodendron tulipifera *showing coiled intracellular hyphae that are nonseptate and thus phycomycetous in character.* (*Photograph by K. D. Doak.*)

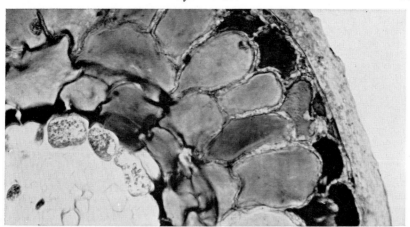

FIG. 22. *Highly magnified cross-sectional view of an ectotropic mycorhiza of* Pinus taeda. *Note the fungus mantle from which the hyphae of the Hartig net penetrate as far as the endodermis. (Photograph by K. D. Doak.)*

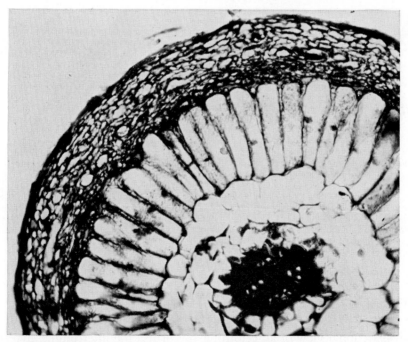

FIG. 23. *Portion of a cross-sectional view of an ectotropic mycorhiza of* Betula lutea. *Note that the epidermal cells are radially elongated and that the hyphae of the Hartig net extend inward only as far as the inner limits of the epidermal cells. (Photograph by K. D. Doak.)*

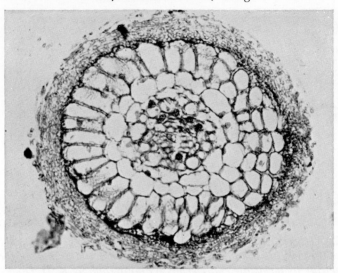

FIG. 24.   *Cross-sectional view of an ectotropic mycorhiza of* Castanea japonica. (*Photograph by K. D. Doak.*)

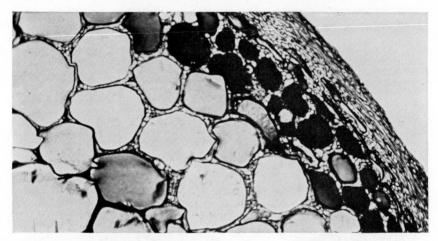

FIG. 25.   *Cross-sectional view of an ectotropic mycorhiza of* Tsuga canadensis. (*Photograph by K. D. Doak.*)

varying depths between the cortical cells depending on the species involved. The thickness of the mantle varies with the mycorhiza. In a cross-sectional view of an ectotropic mycorhiza the intercellular hyphae that extend inward from the mantle frequently have the appearance of a network, commonly referred to as the *Hartig net*. The depth to which these hyphae penetrate apparently varies with the species of

Fɪɢ. 26. Above: *Small roots of* Pinus taeda *with numerous dichoto-mously branched mycorhizae.* (*Courtesy P. J. Kramer.*) Below: *Coralloid compound mycorhizae* (Rootknollen) *of* Alnus incana × *1.5.* (*Courtesy G. W. Blaydes and A. Heilman.*)

plant and fungus involved. A very highly magnified cross-sectional view of a portion of an ectotropic mycorhiza of loblolly pine (*Pinus taeda*) is shown in Figure 22. Cross-sectional views of ectotropic my-corhizae of *Betula lutea, Castanea japonica,* and *Tsuga canadensis* are shown in Figs. 23, 24, and 25.

Various mycorhizae that appear to be intermediate between the ectotropic and endotropic types have been described. Often called *ectendotropic* mycorhizae, they are sometimes considered to be a third category of fungus roots. But Hatch and Doak (1933) concluded that such forms were transitional between the true endotropic and ectotropic types and included them with the latter.

Since the presence of the fungus mantle causes the root tips to appear swollen, ectotropic mycorhizae can usually be recognized by macro-scopic examination of the root system. Such mycorhizae are often dichot-omously branched and sometimes are so profusely branched that the re-sultant structure is coralloid (Fig. 26); these features, of course, also aid in identification. The endotropic forms are not so easily distinguished, unless they are quite swollen, and this fact may account for some of the earlier opinions that mycorhizae are of infrequent occurrence. Endo-tropic mycorhizae are formed on many herbaceous plants; both types are formed on woody plants.

The invasion of small roots by the hyphae of soil-inhabiting fungi does not always result in the formation of mycorhizae; occasionally structures that only superficially resemble mycorhizae may be formed. Such roots, often referred to as *pseudomycorhizae,* have been encoun-tered by various investigators. Apparently these roots result from true parasitism, and since more and more evidence is accumulating that true mycorhizae represent a mutualistic relationship between fungus and root, it would be advisable to drop this term from usage.

In some instances fungi may be associated with rhizomes (under-ground stems) in much the same manner as they are with roots. The resultant structure is obviously not a mycorhiza but is referred to as a *mycorhizome.*

Nature of the Mycorhizal Relationship

Of the many scientific controversies involving mycorhizae, the greatest number have concerned whether or not the fungus-root association is symbiotic in the sense of being a mutualistic relationship—that is, one in which each member benefits from the other's presence. Almost as soon as the morphological characteristics of mycorhizae were elucidated, the question arose whether the nonfungal member of the association was harmed or benefited by the presence of the fungus. That the fungus obtains food and other essential materials from the host plant can hardly be denied, especially in endotropic mycorhizae, in which the fungus member may not be in contact with anything other than the living cells of the other member of the association. In ectotropic mycorhizae it is possible (but hardly probable) that the fungus obtains nothing material from the root-bearing member, since hyphae may extend outward from the mantle into the soil where presumably they may be in contact with a variety of nutritive materials. Thus in most instances the fungus benefits from such an association. But the primary question of whether or not the nonfungal member of the association receives any benefit from it has not yet been satisfactorily answered.

In some situations mycorhizae might be beneficial to the nonfungal member whereas in others no benefits would be derived at all; in still other instances the relationship might be harmful to the nonfungal member. Certainly it requires little imagination to see how the very delicate biological balance existing between these two members, might be upset in such a way that one or both members might be harmed or even destroyed. Thus some change in environmental conditions or a mutation in a mycorhizal fungus might result in its becoming a parasite that damages or destroys the other member. A mutation might also render the fungus incapable of maintaining the mycorhizal relation. Such a turn of events is likely enough in biological relationships. Furthermore, it is believed that the intracellular hyphae of certain endotropic mycorhizae may be destroyed and their contents digested and presumably utilized by the root cells that they inhabited. There is reason for believing that the reverse can also occur.

Various theories have been proposed to explain the mycorhizal relationship. The principal ones concern parasitism, humus, and mineral salts.

PARASITISM THEORY. Adherents of the parasitism theory regard the invasions of roots by fungi, with the subsequent formation of compound structures, as nothing more than parasitic attacks. One of the first proponents of this theory was Robert Hartig (1888), who regarded mycorhizae as being more or less of exceptional occurrence and said, "I see in mycorrhizal fungi nothing more than parasites which live on a tree but do not kill it. . . ." Various investigators have supported this theory, among them McDougal (1914, 1922) and Burges (1936); the latter, in his discussion of the significance of mycorhizae states: "The presence of the fungus in a mycorhizal association is to be regarded as an example of controlled parasitic attack. The fungi concerned are weak pathogens whose activity is curbed by the reactions of the host cells."

Any attempt to disprove either Hartig's or Burges' statement regarding the parasitic nature of these fungi is quite pointless since these fungal activities obviously fit rather well into the usual concept of parasitism. However, merely to call them parasites evades the important question of their significance and fails to establish whether the harmful effects of a weak parasitic attack outweigh some of the benefits accruing from a mycorhizal relationship. The latter point cannot fully be settled for all such associations until we have much more information on the possible beneficial effects on the nonfungal member. A situation in which the host is more benefited than harmed by a parasite is certainly not without precedent; for example, certain plants that are infected with one virus are known to be more resistant to other more harmful viruses; a human patient infected with syphilis is more benefited than harmed when invaded by an attenuated malarial parasite.

Hartig's endorsement of the parsitism theory undoubtedly carried considerable weight among his contemporaries because of his high standing in the developing field of plant pathology. But his reputation and dogmatic position notwithstanding, relatively few investigators accept the parasitism theory in its strictest sense of excluding all possible benefits to the nonfungal associate. Kelley (1950) consulted 118 papers in which the authors expressed a definite opinion and found that only 14 favored the parasitism theory. Most investigators accept the view that mycorhizae are in some way beneficial to the root-bearing member of the association; the principal differences of opinion concern the nature of the beneficial action. A number of theories purporting to explain this point have been advanced.

HUMUS THEORY. Frank (1885a, 1885b, 1888) observed that the abundance of mycorhizae was directly related to the quantity of humus in the soil. His observations led him to believe that mycorhizae are organs which are concerned with the utilization of forest humus and resulted in his proposal of the humus theory to explain the significance of the mycorhizal relationship. Frank found that when beech seedlings were placed in pot cultures in meadow soils, garden soils, humus, sterilized humus, and sand, development of mycorhizae either was not profuse or did not occur at all except in cultures containing forest humus. From the humus theory has arisen the view that mycorhizae make possible the absorption and utilization of the organic compounds (especially organic compounds of nitrogen) present in humus. The nitrogen-nutrition theory has been accepted by many investigators, especially Melin, whose work on mycorhizae in Sweden has extended over a considerable period.

The work of Rayner (1922) also seems to present evidence that mycorhizae may be involved in nitrogen nutrition, but not in the sense that they make organic nitrogen compounds available to the seed-bearing associate. This investigator reported that seedlings of *Calluna vulgaris* (family Ericaceae) thrived on silica gel medium containing no nitrate and were, on the average, healthier than the controls—a result attributed to the ability of the endophyte (a member of the genus *Phoma,* Fungi Imperfecti) to fix atmospheric nitrogen. Ternetz (1907), who worked with five varieties of *Phoma radicis* that form mycorhizae with certain species of Ericaceae (heaths), claimed that these fungi could fix atmospheric nitrogen. Regarding the various species of Ericaceae with which she worked, Rayner states that "As in the Orchidaceae, root formation by seedlings is dependent upon early infection by the endophyte, failing which, development ceases and the plant perishes in the seedling stage." The claims of Rayner and Ternetz concerning the fixation of nitrogen by these endophytic fungi must be accepted with some caution, although it is significant that Duggar and Davis (1916) reported nitrogen fixation with *Phoma betae* and Jones and Smith (1929) with *Phoma radicis callunae.* In all reported instances of attempts to determine whether or not a particular fungus is capable of fixing atmospheric nitrogen, investigators have worked with the fungus in pure culture and, on the basis of results obtained with such a method, have often reported the fungus to be incapable of fixing nitrogen. There is some question whether this method is adequate for determining if a mycorhizal fungus can fix nitrogen, since pure-culture conditions are obviously different from symbiotic relationship with another organism. In general, when dealing with parasitism, our primary concern with the effect of the parasite on the host may prevent consideration of the reverse relationship. Moreover, two organisms living together may have certain capabilities which neither possesses alone.

The findings of McArdle (1932) do not indicate that mycorhizae play any part in the utilization of organic nitrogen by white pine or Norway spruce. He reported that when seedlings were grown under conditions where the only nitrogen source was organic, the presence of mycorhizae did not alleviate the nitrogen deficiency.

MINERAL SALT THEORY. This theory was first advanced by Stahl (1900), who maintained that trees growing in soils deficient in mineral elements are somehow aided by mycorhizae in the absorption of these elements. Stahl's theory has been extended by Hatch (1937), who explained salt absorption by mycorhizae chiefly on the basis of the increased absorbing surface afforded by such structures. Kelley (1950) states that Stahl's theory has not met with favor among modern investigators, pointing out that Stahl believed the significance of mycorhizae lay in their relationship to transpiration. Stahl (like most of the physiologists of his time) held that the entry of mineral salt into a plant was directly related to the plant's rate of transpiration, and that establishment of the mycorhizal relationship was most necessary to plants having a limited transpiration stream. It is now generally believed that mineral salt entry occurs quite independently of water entry, and that Stahl's ideas regarding mycorhizae and transpiration cannot be accepted.

Although Stahl's concept of the means by which mycorhizae might aid in a greater entry of mineral salt into the plant may be erroneous, the theory of a relationship between the two should not be discarded. Working with *Pinus echinata* growing in soils with different base-exchange capacities, Routien and Dawson (1943) suggested that mycorhizae may increase the salt-absorbing capacity of roots primarily by adding to the supply of exchangeable hydrogen ions derived, in part, from the carbonic acid formed during the respiratory activities of the fungus. Finn (1942) found a greater quantity of nitrogen and potassium in white pine seedlings having mycorhizae than in seedlings without them, and McComb (1943) states: "Without mycorrhizae pines acquired phosphorus with difficulty." Kramer and Wilbur (1949), using a mineral salt solution containing radioactive phosphorus, present good evidence that greater amounts of this element enter roots of loblolly pine (*Pinus taeda*) and red pine (*P. resinosa*) with mycorhizae than enter similar roots without them (Fig. 27).

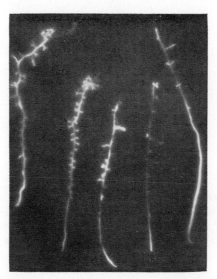

FIG. 27. *Radiographs of pine root systems showing greater accumulation of radioactive phosphate in roots with greater numbers of mycorhizae. (Courtesy P. J. Kramer.)*

The work of Kramer and Wilbur might be criticized on the grounds that they made no attempt to relate increased phosphate uptake with increased absorbing surface; the later work of Harley and McCready (1950) is not subject to this criticism, since their data is presented as phosphate uptake per unit of surface area. The latter workers used short apical lengths of beech roots that were excised and sorted into mycorhizal and nonmycorhizal groups. These excised tips were then placed in an inorganic salt solution containing P^{32} as phosphate, the solution being aerated through sintered glass. When quantitative measurements of radioactive phosphorus were made at suitable intervals with a Geiger counter, it was found that the rate of phosphorus uptake of mycorhizal roots exceeded that of nonmycorhizal roots on the basis of both surface area and fresh weight. Harley and McCready's data are presented graphically in Fig. 28.

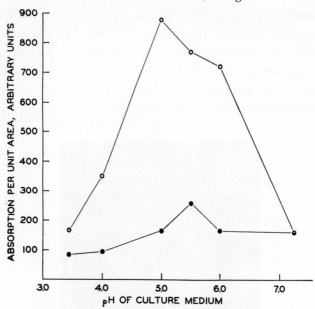

FIG. 28. *Comparison of the amounts of phosphorus absorbed per unit area by mycorhizal and nonmycorhizal root tips in solutions containing radioactive phosphate and buffered with phthalate at various pH values. Mycorhizal tips, o———o; nonmycorhizal tips, •———•. (Redrawn from Harley and McCready, 1950.)*

There seems little doubt that in some instances fungus roots are associated with increased uptake of mineral salts. Whether this increased uptake is due simply to increased absorbing surface or to some other cause is not yet clear.

OTHER THEORIES. In addition to the theories discussed above, various others have been advanced to explain the significance of fungus-root relationships. Thus the beneficial effects of mycorhizae have been ascribed to the capacity of the fungus to synthesize (from organic constituents of the soil) various carbonaceous materials which then become available to the nonfungal member of the association. This explanation seems especially plausible for nongreen plants such as Indian pipe (*Monotropa sp.*), where the entire root system is involved in a mycorhizal relationship.

With the availability in recent years of an increasing amount of information about growth-promoting substances, it is not surprising that a theory has been proposed which attributes the beneficial action of mycorhizae to the production of such substances by fungi. A discussion of this and other theories may be found in the work of Kelley.

Known and Suspected Beneficial Effects of Mycorhizae

Despite the differences of opinion about the nature of the benefits to the seed-plant member of the mycorhizal association, more and more evidence is accumulating that some sort of benefit is derived. Criticism of the disproportionate amount of research on fungus roots of tree mycorhizae, primarily those of conifers is justifiable, especially when the apparent beneficial effects of certain tree mycorhizae are ascribed to all mycorhizae. On the other hand, it should be borne in mind that the ectotropic type of mycorhiza commonly formed on pines and other conifers is peculiarly well adapted to studies on the nature of the mycorhizal relationship. In such studies it is not difficult to maintain small conifer trees in pure culture for several years, whereas faster-growing, bulkier plants such as hardwood trees and many herba-

FIG. 29. *Indian pipe, a seed plant that has no chlorophyll. Commonly called a saprophyte, this plant is actually a parasite on a fungus. (Courtesy C. W. Ellett.)*

ceous plants, are difficult to maintain for any prolonged period of time. Another explanation of the great preponderance of studies on coniferous mycorhizae is that much of the modern afforestation and reforestation effort is concerned with conifers.

An outstanding example of benefits to a seed-bearing plant from the presence of a fungus in its root system is provided by the Indian pipe, a plant devoid of chlorophyll (Fig. 29). Unless we are completely to revise our present ideas about the physiological processes of seed plants and postulate a new set of processes for Indian pipe, we must assume that under normal growth conditions this plant is almost completely dependent on the fungus associated with its roots. Since the entire root system is involved, anything that enters the roots of Indian pipe must do so by way of the fungus hyphae that envelop the roots. In this particular instance proponents of the parasitism theory would have a difficult problem, for they could not argue that the plant might grow more vigorously without such root infection, since without chlorophyll it could not synthesize the sugar essential for growth. Commonly called a saprophyte, Indian pipe would be more correctly termed a parasite—on the fungus infesting its root system.

A curious relationship exists between the tuber of *Gastrodia elata,* a Japanese orchid, and *Armillaria mellea,* a common parasitic gill fungus (Rayner, 1945). Apparently the erratic production of flowering shoots by this orchid was not understood until it was discovered that they are formed only by tubers that are invaded by rhizomorphs of *A. mellea.* Thus the completion of the life cycle of *G. elata* is dependent on fungus invasion. Though the relationship is not understood the beneficial effects are obvious. It is possible that mechanisms similar to those of mycorhizae are involved.

By far the greatest amount of evidence to support the view that mycorhizae are beneficial is derived from studies of coniferous trees, especially species of pine. Much of the evidence is circumstantial, but in a number of instances is supported by experimental results that are difficult to ascribe to any source other than the beneficial effects of mycorhizae—though it must be admitted that a causal relationship has not been demonstrated. Thus Samuel (1926) reported that when *Pinus insignis* was planted in recently cleared ground, plants that were healthy had mycorhizae whereas these structures were either lacking or poorly developed in stunted specimens.

On the basis of experience with an extensive planting of trees in the Great Plains region, Chester (1942) stated that it is necessary to supply suitable mycorhizal fungi on prairie soils that usually lack such organisms. His viewpoint possibly derived in part from experimental results such as those obtained by Hatch (1937), who attempted to culture white pine (*Pinus strobus*) in soil taken from a treeless prairie region in Wyoming. Prairie soil was mixed with sand, dispensed in six pots, and sterilized; after sterilization twenty germinated white pine seeds were placed in each pot. The pots were then protected from contamination by fungus spores. The seeds were planted in August. By November all seedlings were small, yellow, and without mycorhizae. Half the pots were then inoculated from pure cultures of four fungi known to form mycorhizae. By the following spring the seedlings in the inoculated and the control pots were markedly different. All plants were harvested and examined in late May or early June; seedlings from inoculated pots possessed abundant mycorhizae, were larger and more vigorous, and had longer and greener needles than the control seedlings. The latter had no mycorhizae. Comparative data from the two series are presented in Table 3; they show that seedlings with mycorhizae weighed more, had a smaller root-shoot ratio, and contained greater quantities of nitrogen,

Table 3.—Comparison of mycorhizal and nonmycorhizal seedlings of Pinus strobus *cultured in prairie soil*

	Dry Weight of Seedling (mg.)	Root-Shoot Ratio	Nitrogen		Phosphorus		Potassium	
			(mg./ seedling)	(%, dry wt.)	(mg./ seedling)	(%, dry wt.)	(mg./ seedling)	(%, dry wt.)
Averages from two pots of mycorhizal seedlings	404.6	0.782	5.00	1.241	0.789	0.1957	3.02	0.744
Averages from three pots of nonmycorhizal seedlings	320.7	1.138	2.64	0.849	0.236	0.0735	1.38	0.425

From Hatch (1937).

phosphorous, and potassium than the control seedlings without mycorhizae. In connection with Hatch's experiment, the works of Kramer
and Wilbur and of Harley and McCready already cited (see Fig. 28)
should be re-emphasized, since they afford additional evidence that the
presence of mycorhizae results in the movement of greater amounts of
phosphate into the plant.

Rayner (1934) pointed out that the introduction of small quantities
of suitable material (inoculum) into seedbeds of pine induces formation
of mycorhizae similar to those in the inoculum, resulting in "stimulation" of the seedlings to vegetative growth. Where mycorhiza development is defective, Rayner added, the condition can be relieved and
growth of trees stimulated by inoculating seedbeds with small amounts
of material containing active mycorhizae of the species. In a later publication (1938) this investigator reported a number of observations
made in various parts of the world which strongly indicate that mycorhizae are noticeably beneficial to certain conifers:

NORTHERN RHODESIA.   In attempts to establish plantings
of a number of species of pine exotic to Northern Rhodesia, success
was encountered with only one species when the soil was not inoculated. Of the species observed (*Pinus canariensis, P. caribea, P. halepensis, P. pinaster, P. palustris, P. patula, P. taeda,* and *P. teocote*), *P.
halepensis* was the only one that grew beyond the seedling stage without
the addition of soil inocula. When soil from an established plantation
of *P. radiata* a thousand miles away in Southern Rhodesia was transported to Northern Rhodesia and used to inoculate nursery beds of
P. longifolia and experimental plots of *P. caribea, P. halepensis,* and
P. taeda, remarkable stimulation of growth occurred.

BUITENZORG, JAVA.   From the Forest Research Institute
it was reported that *Pinus merkusii* is "completely dependent on the
presence of mycorrhizal infection" for normal development. Inoculation with roots, with humus obtained beneath pines, or with pure cultures of the proper fungus produced vigorous growth in plants nearest
the point where inoculation was made. Infection spread rapidly from
plant to plant after the mycorhizal fungus was established in the soil.
Boletus granulatus, or a closely related species, was considered the most
important mycorhizal fungus for *P. merkusii.*

NYASALAND. The Forestry Department of Nyasaland recorded that in many species positive results followed soil inoculation from old, thriving stands of *P. patula* and *P. radiata*. Of the species observed, only *P. longifolia* grew without soil inoculation.

NEW ZEALAND. Positive results were obtained with *P. radiata* when seedbeds were inoculated with sporophores of *Boletus luteus, Seleroderma bovista,* and *Rhizopogon rubescens* and *Boletus*-infested soil from a healthy stand of trees. There were no mycorhizae on plants from control (uninoculated) plots.

Reports similar to those of Rayner have been recorded from other regions. Melin (1917), studying what appears to be a case of seedling dependence on mycorhizae, found that pine and spruce seedlings that started from wind-distributed seeds in recently drained peat bogs grew normally only when infected with mycorhizal fungi. Those seedlings not so infected showed symptoms of nitrogen deficiency and eventually died. Kessell (1927) reported several pine nursery failures in western Australia that were attributed to the absence of proper mycorhizal fungi in the soil. Seeds germinated and seedlings at first appeared healthy but soon ceased to grow, turned yellow, and finally died. Examination of the roots revealed that mycorhizae were absent. When small portions of soil from established nurseries were introduced into the seedbeds of unhealthy pines, recovery, accompanied by development of mycorhizae, took place.

But tests with more than one species of tree do not always yield results like those reported by Rayner. For example, Morrison (1956) conducted experiments with *Nothofagus menziesii* (silver beech) and *Pinus radiata* (Monterey pine) in which mycorhizal and nonmycorhizal individuals were cultured in a similar series of soils. He found that in infertile soils the growth of *P. radiata* was increased when mycorhizae were present, whereas their presence on the roots of *N. menziesii* did not produce any beneficial results.

Mosse (1957), on the other hand, compared the growth of mycorhizal and nonmycorhizal apple trees and found, in five experiments extending over a three-year period, that mycorhizae were beneficial to apple trees. Seedlings whose roots were associated with an endophytic fungus were larger, sturdier, and greener and had a higher potassium, iron, and copper content but considerably lower magnesium content than seedlings without mycorhizae.

Oliveros * (1932) reported that *Pinus insularis,* which is native to the highlands of the Philippines, could not be established in the Philippine lowlands from seeds, but that if seedlings were transplanted from nurseries located in the highlands (the natural habitat of the trees), they grew more luxuriantly in the lowlands than in their native environment. It was impossible to raise *P. insularis* from seeds at low altitudes until the seedbeds were inoculated.

The findings of Oliveros raise the question whether distribution of certain plant species might not be governed in part by the distribution of fungi capable of forming mycorhizae with those species. According to Hatch (1937), "Every afforestation project involving the establishment of members of the Abietineae, Fagaceae, Betulaceae, Salicaceae, the genus *Hickoria* (*Carya*), and a few other trees by seeds in new nurseries is predestined to failure unless provision is made for the introduction of suitable mycorrhizal fungi along with the trees." White (1929) suggested that mycorhizae might be a factor in the distribution of species of strawberry. Although he offered no evidence in support of this statement, he did point out that strawberry roots contain an endophytic fungus of the *Phoma* type, and that *Fragaria chiloensis,* one of the parent species from which all cultivated strawberries are derived, has a sharply restricted distribution.

But if mycorhizae are in any way associated with the distribution of certain higher plants, the absence of such plants in a particular area may not be entirely attributable to the lack of proper fungi. For example, according to Pramer (1956), several investigators have presented evidence of the failure of a number of pine species to develop in Wareham Heath soil because of antagonism between soil microorganisms and mycorhizal fungi. A diffusible toxic factor capable of preventing the establishment of the mycorhizal relationship was shown to be present in the soil.

Summary

From the foregoing brief account three facts are apparent: (1) the mycorhizal habit is prevalent throughout the plant kingdom, (2) mycorhizae are world-wide in distribution, and (3) in many

* Cf. Hatch, 1937.

instances the possession of mycorhizae benefits the seed-bearing member of the association. Yet we know very little concerning the manner in which the fungus brings about the beneficial action. If this action were due simply to nitrogen fixation, as suggested by the findings of Rayner and others, the mechanism would be easily understood; however, results such as those obtained by Hatch indicate that a more complex mechanism is involved, since greater amounts of potassium and phosphorus, as well as nitrogen, accumulate in mycorhizal pine seedlings than in nonmycorhizal seedlings. Moreover, it is difficult to understand how a nonchlorophyllous plant such as Indian pipe could exist and grow unless it obtained certain energy-containing compounds from the fungus associated with its roots. The theory that the higher plant benefits from the synthesis of growth-promoting substances by the fungus is not without merit, since a number of fungi have been found to synthesize such substances.

In the present state of our knowledge no single theory that purports to explain the beneficial effects of mycorhizae is completely acceptable, and thus the significance of mycorhizae cannot be fully explained. This problem will be elucidated only after much careful experimental work and further investigation of the mycorhizae. In the interim it would seem advisable on purely practical grounds to disseminate and apply the information gained thus far to afforestation and reforestation efforts.

Literature Cited

Asai, T. 1934. Über das Vorkommen und die Bedeutung der Wurzelpilze in Landpflanzen. *Jap. Jour. Bot.* 7:107–150.

Burges, A. 1936. On the significance of mycorrhiza. *New Phyt.* 35:117–131.

Chester, K. S. 1942. *The nature and prevention of plant diseases.* Blakiston, Philadelphia.

Doak, K. D. 1927. Mycorrhiza bearing species in the vicinity of Lafayette, Indiana. *Proc. Ind. Acad. Sci.* 37:427–439.

Duggar, B. M., and Davis, A. R. 1916. Studies in the physiology of the fungi: I. Nitrogen fixation. *Ann. Mo. Bot. Gard.* 3:413–437.

Finn, R. F. 1942. Mycorrhizal inoculation of soil of low fertility. *Black Rock Forest Paper* 1:116–117.

Frank, A. B. 1885a. Ueber die auf Wurzelsymbiose beruhende Ernährung gewisser Bäume durch unterirdische Pilze. *Ber. d. deutsch. bot. Ges.* 3:128–145.

Frank, A. B. 1885b. Neue Mittheilungen über die Mycorhiza der Bäume u. der Monotropa Hypopitys. *Ber. d. deutsch. bot. Ges. 3:*xxvii–xxxii.

———. 1888. Ueber die physiologische Bedeutung der Mycorhiza. *Ber. d. deutsch. bot. Ges. 6:*248–269.

Gerdemann, J. W. 1955. Relation of a large soil-borne spore to phycomycetous mycorrhizal infections. *Mycologia 47:*619–632.

Harley, J. L., and McCready, C. C. 1950. The uptake of phosphate by excised mycorrhizal roots of the beech. *New Phyt. 49:*388–397.

Hartig, R. 1888. Die Pflanzenlichen Wurzelparasiten. *Forst- und Jagd-Zeit. 64:*118–123.

Hatch, A. B. 1934. A jet-black mycelium forming endotropic mycorrhizae. *Svensk Bot. Tidskr. 28:*369–383.

———. 1937. The physical basis of mycotrophy in *Pinus. Black Rock Forest Bull. No. 6.*

———, and Doak, K. D. 1933. Mycorrhizal and other features of the root systems of *Pinus. Jour. Arnold Arbor 14:*85–99.

Hesselman, H. 1900. Om mykorrhizabildingar hos arktiska växter. *Bihang till Svenska Vetensakad. Handl. 26, Afd. III:* 1–46.

Janse, J. 1896. Les endophytes radicaux de quelques plantes Javanaises. *Ann. Jard. bot. Buitenz. 14:*53–201.

Jones, F. R. 1924. A mycorrhizal fungus in the roots of legumes and some other plants. *Jour. Agr. Res. 29:*450–470.

Jones, W. N., and Smith, M. L. 1929. On the fixation of atmospheric nitrogen by *Phoma radicis callunae,* including a new method for investigating nitrogen-fixation in microorganisms. *Brit. Jour. Exp. Biol. 6:*167–189.

Kamienski, F. 1881. Die Vegetationsorgane der *Monotropa hypopitys* L. *Bot. Zeit. 39:*458–461.

Kelley, A. P. 1950. Mycotrophy in plants. Chronica Botanica Company, Waltham, Mass.

Kessell, S. L. 1927. Soil organisms: The dependence of certain pine species on a biological soil factor. *Empire For. Jour. 6:*70–74.

Kramer, P. J., and Wilbur, K. M. 1949. Absorption of radioactive phosphorus by mycorrhizal roots of pine. *Science 110:*8–9.

McArdle, R. E. 1932. The relation of mycorrhizae to conifer seedlings. *Jour. Agr. Res. 44:*287–316.

McComb, A. L. 1943. Mycorrhizae and phosphorus nutrition of pine seedlings in a prairie soil nursery. *Res. Bull. Iowa Agr. Exp. Sta. 314:*582–612.

McDougal, W. B. 1914. On the mycorhizas of forest trees. *Am. Jour. Bot. 1:*51–74.

———. 1922. Mycorhizas of coniferous trees. *Jour. For. 20:*255–260.

———, and Glasgow, O. 1929. Mycorrhizas of the Compositae. *Am. Jour. Bot. 16:*224–228.

Melin, E. 1917. Studier över de norrländska myrmarkernas vegetation med särkild hansyn till deras skogs-vegetation efter torrläggning. Akad. Avhandl., Uppsala.

Melin, E. 1921. Über die Mykorrhizenpilze von *Pinus silvestris* L. und *Picea abies* (L.) Karst. *Svensk Bot. Tidskr. 15:*192–203.

Morrison, T. M. 1956. Mycorrhiza of silver beech. *New Zealand Jour. For.* 7:47–60.

Mosse, B. 1957. Growth and chemical composition of mycorrhizal and non-mycorrhizal apples. *Nature 179:*922–924.

Oliveros, S. 1932. Effect of soil inoculation on the growth of Benguet pine. Dept. of Agr. and Nat. Res. of the Philippine Islands, *The Makiling Echo 11:*205–214.

Pfeffer, W. 1877. Ueber fleischfressende Pflanzen und über die Ernährung durch Aufnahme organischer Stoffe überhaupt. *Landwirt. Jahrb. 6:*969–998.

Pramer, D. 1956. The case of Wareham Heath. Abstr. in Proc. of the 13th Meeting, Soc. of Ind. Microbiol.

Rayner, M. C. 1922. Nitrogen fixation in the Ericaceae. *Bot. Gaz. 73:*226–235.

———. 1934. Mycorrhiza in relation to forestry: I. Researches on the genus *Pinus,* with an account of experimental work in a selected area. *Jour. Soc. For. Great Brit. 8:*96–125.

———. 1938. The use of soil or humus inocula in nurseries and plantations. *Empire For. Jour. 17:*236–243.

———. 1945. *Trees and toadstools.* Faber, London.

Routien, J. B., and Dawson, R. F. 1943. Some interrelationships of growth, salt absorption, respiration, and mycorrhizal development in *Pinus echinata* Mill. *Am. Jour. Bot. 30:*440–451.

Samuel, G. 1926. Note on the distribution of mycorrhiza. *Trans. Roy. Soc. South Australia 50:*245–246.

Stahl, E. 1900. Der Sinn der Mycorrhizenbildung. *Jahrb. wiss. Bot. 34:* 539–668.

Ternetz, C. 1907. Über die Assimilation des atmospherische Stickstoffes durch Pilze. *Jahrb. wiss. Bot. 44:*353–408.

White, P. R. 1929. Mycorrhiza as a possible determining factor in the distribution of strawberry. *Ann. Bot. 43:*535–544.

4 · *Industrial Mycology*

FERMENTATION METHODS
SELECTION OF THE ORGANISM
MAINTENANCE OF STOCK CULTURES
INOCULUM FOR LARGE-SCALE FERMENTATIONS
RAW MATERIALS

EXCEPT PERHAPS IN AFFORESTATION EFFORTS, in which the desired mycorhiza-forming species of fungus may be introduced with the tree species, man ordinarily does not control the conditions under which the activities of fungi occur. It is obvious that under natural conditions pure cultures of fungi are not found, and that changes in both quality and quantity of the fungus flora may occur with changes in environment. As a result of these changes, the rates of decay and formation of mycorhiza and carbon dioxide are subject to considerable fluctuation. In contrast to the fungus activities that result in these natural and uncontrolled processes, a number of other fungus activities, if allowed to take place under properly controlled conditions, can be profitably directed toward man's benefit.

The demand for several fungus metabolic products, as well as for the entire fungus body, has warranted their production on a large scale. Examples are citric acid, gluconic acid, penicillin, gallic acid, ethyl alcohol, mold amylase, yeast invertase, and irradiated yeast products. In addition, large-scale production of itaconic acid and kojic acid has recently been initiated. With each important discovery in the field of fungus biochemistry, additions to the above list will doubtless be made.

Most of the industrial processes involving the large-scale production of fungus materials may be referred to as fermentations.* The establishment of such processes on a production scale frequently presents problems not commonly encountered in the synthesis of chemical compounds. Not the least of these problems is that of preventing the introduction of undesired microorganisms. Since the entrance of contaminating organisms must be prevented, or at least held to a minimum, particular attention must be given to the design and maintenance of plant and equipment. A small break in a pipeline or other piece of equipment, an improperly packed valve, a rough spot in a pipeline where nutrient materials from a previous fermentation may lodge, or a short length of unsterilized pipe—all add to the chances for contamination by undesirable microorganisms.

With few exceptions, yields of desired end products of fungus fermentations may be substantially decreased or even destroyed if contaminating organisms enter the fermentation medium and utilize part or all of the raw materials (usually carbohydrates) intended for use by the desired organism. In extreme cases a contaminant may grow so rapidly that the growth of the preferred organism is almost completely suppressed. Even if the yield is not too seriously affected (as in alcoholic fermentations), the presence of contaminants may impart undesirable characteristics to the end product, as in alcoholic fermentations conducted for the preparation of beverage alcohol.

The maintenance of sterile conditions in processes employing a single species or strain of fungus often presents great difficulties. But these difficulties are also encountered in such bacterial fermentations as the acetone-butyl-alcohol fermentation and the 2,3-butanediol fermentation. It is a relatively simple matter to keep contaminants out of a cotton-stoppered flask or a test tube culture, but in a 50,000-gallon tank the problem assumes magnified proportions, and can be solved only through close cooperation of the mycologist and the engineer, understanding of the details of the process by the production operator, careful laboratory control, and rigid enforcement of all sanitary precautions.

The establishment of a fermentation process on an industrial scale is generally accomplished in four steps:

1. *Experimental laboratory fermentations* are made in test tubes or small flasks. They are typically concerned with the determination

---

* Here, as in the ensuing sections, the term *fermentation* is applied to both anaerobic processes (true fermentations) and aerobic processes (so-called oxidative fermentations).

of medium reaction, aeration, optimum temperature conditions, and concentration of carbon, mineral salt, and nitrogen sources with respect to the rate of fermentation and yield of the desired end product. The testing of different fungus strains and species is also commonly conducted with small-scale laboratory fermentations.

2. *Large-scale laboratory fermentations* are usually the second step, and employ large flasks or bottles or, in some instances, special metal containers designed to simulate on a small scale the proposed large-scale plant equipment. When the shift is made from the first step to the second, it is often discovered that optimum conditions for small fermentations are not necessarily suitable for large ones, and these results may have much to do with influencing the final design of plant equipment.

3. *Pilot-plant fermentations* follow next. These are conducted on a larger scale than the largest laboratory fermentations and with apparatus more closely approximating plant equipment. Pilot-plant experiments determine the feasibility of large-scale production, establish some of the operating conditions, and establish data for the design of large-scale plant equipment.

4. *Plant-scale fermentations* represent the final step in the establishment of a fermentation on an industrial basis, the type of equipment employed varying with the particular fermentation process.

Fermentation Methods

Four methods of obtaining fungus fermentations are used in industry. The cultures may be grown in bottles or flasks, shallow pans or trays, deep vats, or rotating drums.

BOTTLE METHOD. In the bottle-culture method spores of the fungus being used are introduced onto the surfaces of relatively small amounts of liquid medium in horizontally placed cotton-stoppered bottles (milk bottles have frequently been used), and the cultures then incubated at proper temperature. After a suitable period of incubation, the fungus mycelium that develops on the surface is filtered off, and the desired product recovered from the liquid medium. The disadvantages of this method are numerous: (1) for sustained large-volume production, literally thousands of bottle cultures must be incubating simultaneously, necessitating the maintenance of extensive incubation space in which temperature and humidity can be closely controlled; (2) many of the operations can be accomplished only with hand labor, which adds greatly to the expense of the process; (3) cleaning and sterilizing the fermentation equipment between runs add unnecessary time and cost to the operation. A large-scale bottle-culture operation is economically possible only when the value of the fermentation product justifies the additional cost involved.

Thus far the only extensive use of this method has been in the early stages of development of the penicillin industry. One advantage of the method is that contamination by undesirable microorganisms rarely occurs if reasonable care is employed; even if a few bottles become contaminated, little loss of materials is involved since each bottle contains only a small quantity of fermentation medium.

SHALLOW-PAN METHOD.   The shallow-pan method involves the growth of the desired fungus in shallow layers of medium in large metal pans or trays. The medium may be a liquid, as in the early production of citric acid, or a solid (steamed wheat bran), as in the production of mold amylase. Devised primarily for use with highly aerobic fungi, this method affords a large surface area in relation to the depth of the fermentation medium. This ratio is quite important, for when the medium is properly inoculated, a mycelial mat (Fig. 30) soon forms over its entire surface; since the medium is not agitated or aerated, only its top layer is in contact with the mat, and if the depth of the medium is too great, the diffusion of nutrient materials into the layer under the mat and of metabolic products away from it may be seriously retarded.

The shallow-pan method has two disadvantages. (1) Literally acres of pans would be required for sustained large-volume production. (2) Unless the trays are tightly covered, which would in part defeat the purpose of this method, or are placed in specially designed cabinets during the incubation period, contamination may occur very easily. The method is therefore not suitable for use with any fungus which may be easily overrun by contaminating microorganisms or which synthesizes materials easily destroyed by them. Thus, as usually employed, it would be entirely unsuitable for use in the making of penicillin, since the optimum conditions for the production of this material are also quite favor-

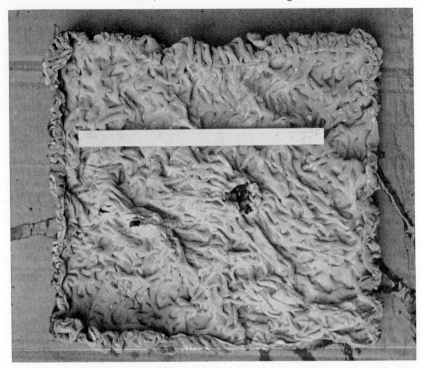

FIG. 30. *Mycelial mat of* Aspergillus terreus *which formed on the surface of liquid medium in a tray 8 x 8 inches.*

able for the growth of a variety of common bacteria, some of which synthesize the enzyme *penicillinase,* which quickly destroys penicillin. But contamination ceases to be much of a problem if a fermentation is conducted under conditions (such as a highly acid reaction of the medium) which prevent or inhibit the growth of organisms other than the desired one.

The advantage of this method is that a large surface area of medium may be exposed—a very desirable feature when the organism being used is highly aerobic.

DEEP-VAT METHOD. Fermentations involving the use of the deep-vat method are conducted in large tanks or vats constructed of tile, wood, or metal; of these materials, metal (stainless steel, copper-bearing steel, etc.) seems to be most satisfactory. Depending on the type of fermentation, (1) the vats may be open or covered; (2) the medium may be unaerated or aerated during fermentation; and (3) the medium may or may not be mechanically agitated.

The alcoholic fermentation may be conducted in open tanks, since fermentation occurs at a rapid rate, with virtually anaerobic conditions being developed soon after inoculation (thus precluding the possibility of any aerobic contaminants becoming established), and since yeast growth and metabolic activities are not easily suppressed by other organisms. But if the fermentation becomes badly contaminated, the yield may be reduced, or undesirable odors or flavors (produced by the contaminants) may be present in the end product. For this reason many alcohol plants use covered tanks only, since the chances for contamination are thus markedly reduced, and since these vessels can be more readily sterilized than open tanks. Another advantage of the use of covered vats is that it makes possible the recovery of gaseous by-products that might otherwise be lost. For example, in the course of the alcoholic fermentation carbon dioxide is evolved in great quantity; in localities where there is sufficient demand, it is economically feasible to recover this gas, compress it, and thus produce solid carbon dioxide (dry ice). In many breweries the carbon dioxide formed during fermentation is recovered and later used for further carbonation of the beverage.

Fungi such as yeast may grow and ferment sugar readily when they are completely submerged in a liquid medium, but most filamentous fungi are highly aerobic organisms and can survive and utilize sugar efficiently under these conditions only if the medium is aerated. This can be accomplished by agitating the medium with motor-driven propellers, but more commonly by passing air through the medium by means of a sparging system mounted near the bottom of the tank. To aerate deep-vat fermentations large volumes of sterile air are supplied to each vat; to be most effective the air should pass into the liquid as fine bubbles, requiring the use of an air-sparging system, such as porous carbon tubes or pipes with very fine perforations. The air must be sterilized prior to its entry into the system by passing it through a sterilized cotton or glass-wool filter in which the contaminants of the air stream are mechanically entrapped, or by passing it through liquids that not only entrain the contaminants but may destroy their viability.

Excessive foaming resulting from aeration is usually controlled by the addition of a suitable antifoaming agent to the medium, depending on the type of fermentation, the organism used, the type of medium, and the rate of aeration. Stefaniak and others (1946) studied the performance of several antifoams in the penicillin fermentation and found that

Nopco Defoamer and Vegifat Y were the most effective, although they were also the most toxic to *Penicillium chrysogenum.* These investigators stated that 3 per cent octadecanol in lard oil appeared to be most satisfactory. An antifoam composed of lard and Vegifat has proved effective in acid-hydrolyzed corn mash used in the 2,3-butanediol fermentation conducted with *Aerobacter aerogenes,* a bacterium. Soybean oil and lime mixtures may sometimes control excessive foaming in the alcoholic fermentation of malt-converted small-grain mashes.

Not all fungus strains may be used in deep-vat fermentations, since the behavior of different strains of the same species of organism may be quite different when submerged in the medium than when in bottle or shallow-pan culture. This particular problem was encountered in connection with penicillin production, and many strains were tested before one suitable for submerged culture production was found. This problem was for a long time a source of difficulty in citric acid fermentation; recent reports, however, indicate that strains have been found or developed which yield well in submerged culture.

A filamentous fungus growing in shallow-pan or bottle culture forms a mat on the surface of the medium. This mat is sometimes very thick and tough, and the fungus commonly sporulates quite heavily. By contrast, filamentous fungi in well-aerated or agitated submerged cultures usually grow as small, discrete, roughly spherical colonies that are tumbled about by the movement of the medium. Burkholder and Sinnott (1945) have shown that the appearance of the submerged colonies of one species of fungus may differ markedly from similarly submerged colonies of another species (Fig. 31).

The advantages of the deep-vat method of conducting a fermentation are: (1) a relatively large amount of medium may be fermented in one container, thus obviating the necessity for the extensive plant layouts that would be inevitable in large-scale production operations using either the bottle or shallow-pan culture method; (2) much expensive and inefficient hand labor is eliminated; (3) sterilization of the fermentation equipment is readily accomplished, especially when covered vessels are used; and (4) the rate of fermentation is frequently more rapid than in shallow-pan cultures, since the fungus colonies are moved about through the medium (with the exception of the alcoholic fermentation, which is conducted anaerobically and without agitation), and hence the diffusion of nutrient materials and metabolic products through the medium cannot retard the fermentation process.

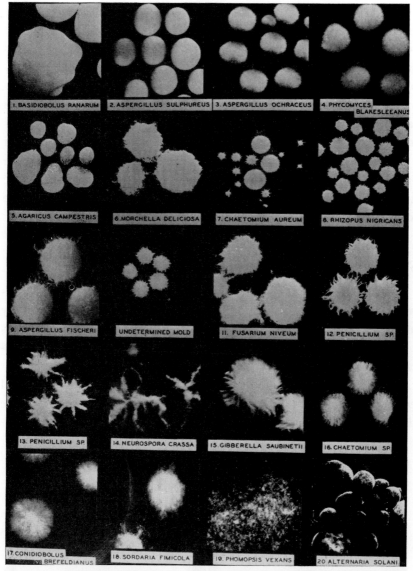

FIG. 31. *Appearance of colonies of different species of fungi when growing submerged in liquid medium. (From Burkholder and Sinnott, 1945.)*

ROTATING-DRUM METHOD. The equipment used in this method consists of a horizontally mounted metal drum or tank which is rotated during fermentation. Baffles on the inner wall of the tank serve as efficient agitators of the medium. As in the deep-vat method, the fungus does not form a solid mat that floats on the surface of the medium but consists of small, discrete colonies that are submerged. Diffusion gradients are eliminated and a rapid fermentation results, since the fungus colonies are moved about through the medium continuously. Sterile air may be introduced into the drum as it rotates, thus increasing the degree of aeration. In gluconic acid fermentation, which has been successfully conducted in rotating drums, it has been found that the rate of fermentation is greatly increased when air is introduced into the drum at a rate sufficiently rapid to build up pressure within the drum. The rotating-drum method has been used (with moistened wheat bran instead of a liquid medium) in the production of mold bran, a source of amylase and other enzymes. Lockwood and Moyer (1938) state that the rotating drum is the only type of fermentation equipment in which it is possible to separate aeration and agitation effects.

Selection of the Organism

The selection of a suitable organism for use in an industrial fermentation is extremely important. Often the organism is chosen only after extensive screening tests with a great number of different species or different strains of the same species. The literature on fungus fermentations reveals many widely divergent reports on yields and fermentation rates obtained by different investigators under essentially identical environmental conditions with the same species of fungus. Many of these discrepancies can be attributed to the use of different strains, which are

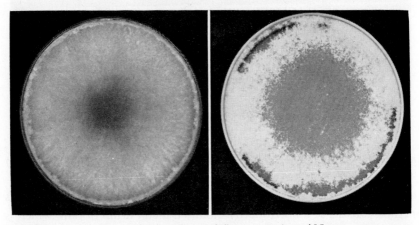

FIG. 32. *Petri plate cultures of two different strains of* Neurospora crassa. *Although they appear different in culture they are morphologically indistinguishable. The strain shown at the left is incapable of synthesizing the amino acid lysine; the one at the right cannot synthesize proline.*

morphologically inseparable from each other and whose differences can be demonstrated only by biochemical means. Accuracy in species identification is, of course, essential, but equally important is the need for recognizing that two individuals of the same species are not necessarily alike in all respects. Hence it should not be assumed that two cultures of different origin (even if they are both quite typical representatives of the same species) will behave in similar fashion. Although two fungi may be morphologically and culturally indistinguishable, they may differ considerably in some physiological process or biochemical synthesis (Fig. 32). One may cite the difference between strains of distiller's yeast, *Saccharomyces cerevisiae:* some strains ferment very rapidly and hence are quite useful when a rapid fermentation is desired (e.g., in the production of industrial alcohol, in which neither odor nor flavor are critical factors), whereas others ferment relatively slowly. Table 4 shows the differences between two yeast strains cultured under identical conditions.

Table 4.—*Fermentation rates of two strains of* Saccharomyees cerevisiae

Temp. (°F.)	Cumm. CO_2/Min./10^8 Cells	
	Strain #1	Strain #31
72	28.0	9.0
80	51.5	23.5
86	56.5	27.5
90	74.0	32.5
96	90.5	35.5
100	104.5	41.5

Some strains of yeast have the capacity to ferment sugar quite readily even under conditions of high alcohol concentration, whereas sugar utilization by other strains is markedly inhibited by the same concentration of alcohol. Strains of the latter type cannot efficiently be used to ferment sugar solutions of very high concentration, since an inhibitory concentration of alcohol is soon developed, and further sugar utilization is prevented or greatly retarded. Figure 33 shows the percentage of sugar utilization in two strains which differ in their capacities to tolerate alcohol.

Gross differences in physiological activities between different strains of the same species, comparable to those just discussed in connection with strains of *S. cerevisiae,* have been recorded for almost every species of microorganism used in an industrial process. Usually these differences are merely concerned with degree or rate of completion of a particular

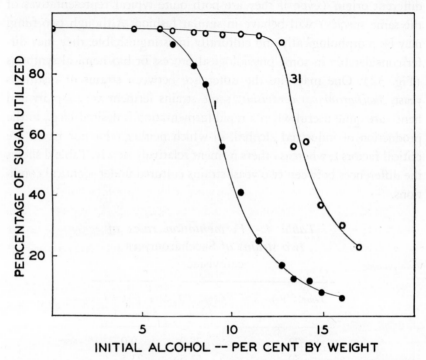

FIG. 33.   *Differences in alcohol tolerances of two strains of* Saccharomyces cerevisiae. (*Based on data of Gray, 1941.*)

process, but sometimes they involve the need for careful testing of strains to produce a high yield. Except for organisms used in closely guarded industrial processes, strains of a particular organism may be obtained from the investigator who isolated them or from an agency such as the American Type Culture Collection (Washington, D. C.) or the Central Bureau voor Schimmelcultures (Baarn, Holland).

Although it was necessary in the past to isolate many strains from their natural habitats to obtain a high-yielding strain for a particular process, recent work has demonstrated the efficacy of other methods. It has been shown, for example, that the mutation rate of fungi and other organisms can be greatly increased through the use of X-ray and ultraviolet radiation, mustard gases, radioactive compounds, and other mutagenic agents, thus producing a great many different strains from one parent strain. The testing of these induced mutants may reveal that some are more suitable and higher-yielding than the original strains. The method consists of treating a spore suspension with some mutagenic agent, plating out the suspension, and then testing the various fungi obtained—assuming that if the suspension was properly diluted, the colonies that appeared on the dilution plates each had their origin in a single spore. During the early phases of the development of the penicillin industry the selection of high-yielding, naturally occurring strains enabled the investigators to obtain increased yields of penicillin, but the really spectacular yield increases were made through the use of mutants derived from strains that had been subjected to X radiation or other treatment to increase the mutation rate. Unfortunately, mutants selected in the course of a strain-developing program may not possess all of the characteristics required for industrial usage. For example, in their studies of a group of high-yielding strains derived from *Penicillium chrysogenum* Q176 (see Chap. 8), Backus and Stauffer (1955) noted that a progressive decline in vegetative and reproductive vigor accompanied the increased capacity to synthesize penicillin.

Planned breeding programs may also be used to obtain improved strains of microorganisms. Lindegren and Lindegren (1943) have pointed out that two yeast strains may be hybridized to produce a third strain that combines the most desirable characteristics of each. Such a breeding program is applicable only to organisms having a known sexual stage and which readily complete their sexual life cycle in culture.

Maintenance of Stock Cultures

In any industry based on the activity of a microorganism, strains or species of organisms suitable for use are usually maintained in a permanent stock-culture collection, either for experimental purposes or as alternates to be used in production operations when preferred strains are lost or undergo undesirable changes in characteristics. Furthermore, in many industrial laboratories new isolates are continually being obtained and tested in a search for more suitable organisms. In all these operations one of the main problems is maintaining a large number of stock cultures. In the past this was accomplished largely by transferring spores or bits of mycelium from each culture to fresh agar slants (employing standard pure-culture techniques) at regular intervals—a time-consuming process that can be accomplished only by hand labor. When as many as several thousand cultures have to be transferred frequently, maintenance by such means can easily become a full-time job. In addition, the more frequently cultures are handled the greater are the chances for contamination and loss of cultures. Storage of fungus cultures on agar slants at room temperature or in an incubator involves frequent transfer because the agar medium dries out quickly; accordingly when a new culture is growing well and is free of contaminants, it is sometimes stored in a refrigerator and thus kept viable for a much longer time.

Even when cultures are stored at low temperatures to reduce the frequency of subculture, the method described above is relatively unsatisfactory, since it often results in the loss of one or more potentially valuable organisms. Another disadvantage of the method is that fungi maintained in this manner frequently lose certain of their desirable characteristics. For example, a fungus may with repeated subculturing lose its capacity to synthesize large quantities of a compound, and its capacity to sporulate.

Fortunately, more satisfactory methods for the preservation of stock cultures are coming into wider use. It has been found, for example, that stock cultures of many fungi can be conserved for long periods without transfer by completely covering the fungus growth on an agar slant with sterile mineral oil. Originally developed by Ungermann (1918) for use with bacterial cultures, this method has been employed successfully by Sherf (1943) with cultures of filamentous fungi. Fresh cultures are prepared on agar slants of suitable medium and after about ten days (the time depending on how rapidly the organism covers the surface of the agar slant) sufficient sterile mineral oil is added to cover the top of the slanted surface. The tubes are then replugged and stored at room temperature. Subcultures can be made by passing a sterile needle or loop through the oil layer, scooping up bits of fungus tissue, withdrawing the loop from the oil layer (allowing the excess oil to drain against the side of the tube), and then transferring the tissue to a fresh medium.

Buell and Weston (1947), in reporting the results of studies involving storage of a variety of fungi under oil, stated that some cultures were still viable after twenty-four months of storage. They pointed out that though the action of the oil is not fully understood, it does serve to prevent dehydration and to slow down metabolic activities. Storage under oil is an especially suitable method for maintaining cultures of fungi that usually do not sporulate in culture, since it reduces the necessity for frequent transfer, which is not so easily accomplished with this type of fungus as with readily sporulating types.

Wernham (1946), who successfully used the mineral oil preservation method with four fungus pathogens of corn (*Diplodia zeae, Gibberella zeae, Helminthosporium maydis,* and *Nigrospora oryzae*), subcultured from the oil-covered agar slants at intervals and found that all cultures were still viable after two years. Cultures so stored for fifteen months were used to prepare material for field inoculations with no apparent loss of pathogenicity, which suggests that this method may be better for maintaining stable cultures. Fungi cultured for long periods by the usual method often change, losing certain desirable characteristics, and thus become less valuable or even useless for a particular process. An example of such a change is given by Moyer and Coghill (1945) in the production of itaconic acid by fungus fermentation. They cite a study by Kinoshita (1929), who isolated an organism which he named *Aspergillus itaconicus* because of its capacity to synthesize itaconic acid. He deposited a culture of this organism with the Central Bureau voor Schimmelcultures, whence it was obtained by workers at the Northern Regional Research Laboratory (Peoria, Illinois) about fifteen years later. Testing of the culture at Peoria revealed that it had lost most of its itaconic acid–producing capacity, since only traces of this acid were formed. Fortunately, investigators in England found that itaconic acid was also synthesized by strains of *A. terreus.* Although some fungi are notably stable in culture, others like *A. itaconicus* undergo certain changes, making it extremely important to maintain cultures so that such changes are prevented or minimized. The report of Wernham seems to indicate that the use of the mineral oil method may be one answer to the problem of keeping fungi stable in culture, but further studies are required.

A promising method for preserving stock cultures of many fungi for long periods without transfer is the *lyophile* method, in which suspensions of viable fungus spores are frozen quickly and then subjected to vacuum desiccation while in the frozen state. Various bacteriologists have demonstrated that bacteria may be preserved in viable form through employment of the lyophile technique, and Wickerham and Andreasen (1942) have shown that yeasts may be so preserved. Raper and Alexander (1945) investigated the use of the lyophile process for the preservation of a large number of different microorganisms (1850 fungi other than yeasts, more than 900 yeasts, and about 400 bacterial cultures) and found that fungi preserved by lyophilization retained their biochemical and physiological characteristics in unaltered form. This discovery is of particular importance because of the difficulty of maintaining cultures in a stable and highly productive state. These investigators reported that strains of *A. terreus* preserved by the lyophile process produced undiminished yields of itaconic acid after forty months, and that penicillin-producing strains of *Penicillium chrysogenum* and *P. notatum* retained at original levels their capacity to produce penicillin. Raper and Alexander described their method of preparing spores for lyophilization as follows:

> Cultures were grown, in the usual manner, on Czapek's solution agar or malt extract agar in either test tubes or Petri dishes for one week to ten days, or until a sufficient quantity of conidia was produced. Approximately 0.25 cc. of sterile beef serum was placed in an agglutination tube, and spores or conidia were added from the culture to be lyophilized until the resulting suspension was comparatively dense. By means of a micropipette, approximately 0.05 cc. of the suspension was then dispensed into each of four previously labelled, sterile lyophil tubes (made of 4-inch lengths of 6 mm. Pyrex tubing sealed at one end). The cotton plugs were replaced and the excess cotton was burned off. The remaining portion of the plug was then pushed down into the tube to a depth of about one-half inch as a precaution against possible contamination during processing, and to prevent the cotton from being drawn into the apparatus during evacuation.*

The lyophile tubes were then attached by means of rubber sleeves to a manifold, which was connected with a vacuum pump and then lowered so that the ends of the tubes containing spore suspensions were submerged in a bath of dry ice and methyl cellosolve (temperature: $-40°$ to $-50°$ C). When the liquid in the tubes had frozen, the vacuum pump was started and the manifold lifted so that the tubes were raised above the surface of the bath to a level at which the tem-

* Raper and Alexander (1945), p. 502.

FIG. 34.   *Lyophilized spore suspensions of* Penicillium chrysogenum.

perature was about $-10°$ C., where they were held during the drying process (usually about $1\frac{1}{2}$ to 2 hours). When completely dry, the mass of serum and spores formed a compact cylindrical pellet (Fig. 34); at this time the tube was sealed off (still under reduced pressure) with a gas-oxygen flame. For further details concerning the apparatus used in this process, consult the report of Wickerham and Andreasen or that of Raper and Alexander. Horse serum and skim milk are some of the media that have been used for making spore suspensions.

Although lyophilization of fungus cultures requires apparatus and techniques not used in the older methods of maintaining stock cultures, it has several distinct advantages: (1) storage of stock cultures requires much less space, since the tubes are much smaller; (2) possibility of contamination during storage is eliminated because the culture tubes are sealed; (3) there is as yet no evidence that biochemical characteristics change when fungi are preserved by this method; and (4) a large number of replicate cultures can be prepared from a single large suspension of spores from the same source and used as inoculum for standard cultures over a long period. The disadvantage of the lyophile process is that it cannot be used for all types of fungi; some filamentous fungi, for example, do not sporulate and thus cannot be conserved by lyophilization.

A simpler technique for the preservation of fungus cultures, and one that requires no special apparatus, is to store the fungus spores in fine, dry, sterile soil in test tubes. The soil in the tube is sterilized either by dry heat or by autoclaving. (Caution: because heat transfer through soil is slow, it may have to be heated for periods longer than those used for the sterilization of medium, etc.) A heavy spore suspension is added and mixed with the soil by shaking—Foster (1949) recommends that the volume of the suspension be about one-tenth the volume of the soil. The inoculated tubes are then dried in a vacuum desiccator and stored in a cool dry place. A strong recommendation for this method is that a single culture can be used repeatedly, since very little soil need be removed to start a new culture.

Inoculum for Large-Scale Fermentations

Preparation of inoculum for large-scale bacterial and yeast fermentations, has never been a serious problem, since the active vegetative stages of these organisms consist of single cells that can be used directly for inoculation. But it is difficult to obtain large amounts of inoculum for industrial filamentous fungus fermentations because the vegetative stage of these fungi consists of mycelia whose strands are interlaced, forming a rather compact mass of tissue. Obviously the inoculation of large volumes of medium with a mat of this type would be inefficient, since the fungus tissue would come into contact with a relatively small amount of medium. Consequently, fungus spores have been used for inoculum, since they are often unicellular and can be dispersed throughout a large amount of fermentation medium, thus providing many points of inoculation. The use of spores as inoculum implies obtaining them in large quantity. In the published reports concerning the development of various fungus fermentations, considerable emphasis has been placed on the conditions favoring spore development. Several investigators have devised special "sporulation" media which differ in composition from those regularly employed for fermentations. Lockwood and Moyer (1938) make the general recommendation that liquid medium deficient in nutrients be employed for the production of spores used for inoculum, since a thick mycelial mat is usually formed if there is an abundance of nutrients.

The use of spores as inoculum is ordinarily an inefficient method if a fast fermentation is desired, because the spores must germinate and growth of mycelium must start before any significant amount of the desired metabolic activity can begin. This lag period in the fermentation can be eliminated by allowing the spores to germinate and then employing a suspension of pre-germinated spores as inoculum. This variation of procedure, however, does not solve the problems connected with the production of a large number of spores, for all too frequently a fungus strain which is valuable because of some heightened biochemical activity does not sporulate well.

A much better inoculating technique involves the use of a suspension of pieces of vegetative mycelium which have been fragmented under sterile conditions in a Waring Blendor. This method has numerous advantages over the spore-inoculum technique because it makes possible the use of fungi that sporulate poorly or not at all. Moreover, it eliminates the necessity for preparation of special sporulation media, and the lag that occurs while the spores are germinating. Inoculum so prepared consists of active vegetative mycelium which may start growing and fermenting as soon as it is introduced into the fermenter. Because of their small size and great number, the mycelial fragments may be distributed throughout the fermentation medium, thus effectively accomplishing inoculation at many points. This distribution of fungus material throughout the medium may be accomplished more easily and more uniformly with mycelial fragments than with spores, because the spores of some fungi can be wetted only with difficulty, thus preventing a uniform suspension. Savage and VanderBrook (1946), who applied the mycelial fragment inoculation technique to their work with two penicillin-producing organisms, reported that mycelia may be fragmented in a Waring Blendor with little injury to growth and fermentative capacities, since mycelial fragmentation seems to occur at the septae. They found that fragmented mycelium, even when diluted 1:40,000, could be adequately substituted in shaken flask cultures for unfragmented mycelium used at a 1:10 inoculum level. Dorrell and Page (1947) used the same technique and found that with *Helminthosporium oryzae* the replacement of spore inoculum with 1 per cent minced mycelium resulted in a twofold increase in mycelium yield in two-thirds of the cases. These investigators found that if 50 milliliters of a 5- to 6-day-old culture of *Gibberella zeae,* grown in a shaker flask, was minced for 1 minute in a Waring Blendor, about 1 to 1.5 million fragments per milliliter were obtained. Microscopic examination of the blended mycelium revealed that the fragments consisted of 3 to 10 cells, and Dorrell and Page stated that the fragments were wholly viable and capable of growth at many points. From these reports it would seem that the fragmented-mycelium inoculum method is greatly superior to the older spore inoculum method and will probably largely replace it in many fermentations.

Raw Materials

For the successful production of fungus-synthesized compounds the organism used in the fermentation must be cultured in a medium containing certain materials requisite for the growth and metabolic activities of that particular organism. In general the medium must contain (1) a carbon source (carbohydrate), (2) a nitrogen source, and (3) certain mineral elements. In addition, it is sometimes necessary to supply other substances which have beneficial effects upon growth and metabolism. An example of this type of substance is corn-steeping liquor, which is commonly added to the medium used in fungus fermentations.

The necessity for addition of materials other than the carbon source apparently depends on the degree of purity of the material used as a carbon source. In a fermentation in which a crude, unrefined material is used, it is usually unnecessary to add a nitrogen source or minerals as such, since these are present in adequate amounts in the carbon-containing material—the production of alcohol from grain mashes is an example. Since ground whole grain contains nitrogenous materials, minerals, and vitamins, in addition to a great quantity of carbohydrate, it may be used for the alcoholic fermentation without any supplemental materials. When it is necessary to use a more highly refined carbon source, such as a purified sugar, both minerals and a nitrogen source must be added. The quantity and quality of these added materials will vary with the organism and type of fermentation, so no general statement can be made which will be applicable to all fermentations; specific details will be considered in connection with the fermentations discussed in later chapters.

In certain special fermentations still other materials must be added to the medium because the desired biosynthetic reaction will not occur at all or will occur in greatly lessened amounts unless some other reaction is blocked. The addition of material will partially or completely block the competing reaction. An example is the glycerol fermentation that is accomplished by adding sulphite or bisulphite to block the reaction in which acetaldehyde is reduced to ethyl alcohol. If this reduction is not prevented, very little glycerol will be formed. In certain other fermentations (penicillin fermentation and microbiological synthesis of steroid hormones) chemical precursors of the desired end product are added to the medium.

Exclusive of water, the greatest portion of the material contained in a fermentation medium is the material added as the carbon source, since it is from the carbon-containing compound that the energy used in the various fungus metabolic processes is derived. It is also from the carbon source that the fungus metabolic products are principally derived through a series of biochemical transformations. The carbon compound usually supplied is a carbohydrate, typically a sugar such as dextrose or sucrose, although there are a few exceptional cases in which starch or some other polysaccharide is used. The carbohydrate-containing materials that have been used most widely in fungus fermentations are blackstrap molasses (a by-product of the sugar industry), the various cereal grains, or low to high grades of refined sugars obtained from grains,

Table 5.—Alcohol production per ton of raw material

Raw Material	Gal./Acre	Gal./Ton
Sugar beet	287.0	22.1
Sugar cane (La.)	268.0	15.2
Jerusalem artichokes	180.0	20.0
White potatoes	178.0	22.9
Sweet potatoes	141.0	34.2
Apples	140.0	14.4
Raisins	102.0	81.4
Grapes	90.4	15.1
Corn	88.8	84.0
Rice (rough)	65.6	79.5
Blackstrap molasses	45.0	70.4
Grain sorghum	35.5	79.5
Wheat	33.0	85.0

From Jacobs (1939).

sugar cane, or sugar beets. Almost any material that contains fermentable sugar in adequate quantities (or a material that can be readily converted to fermentable sugar) can be used as a carbon source, but crude raw materials often create additional refining problems. Some idea of the range of carbon sources in fermentations can be gained from Table 5, which lists certain agricultural raw materials that can be used for the production of ethyl alcohol by fermentation.

It is possible that, in the future development of industrial mycology, cellulose—the most abundant carbohydrate in the world—will be widely used as a carbon source in various fermentations. Though many fungi can digest cellulose, its widespread use as a source of carbon would require more efficient methods for hydrolyzing cellulose than those now used. Various techniques have been proposed for the acid hydrolysis of cellulosic waste materials and the subsequent use of the sugar solution as a fermentation medium, but at present industrial use of cellulose is limited despite the vast quantities available.

Literature Cited

Backus, M. P., and Stauffer, J. F. 1955. The production and selection of a family of strains in *Penicillium chrysogenum*. *Mycologia* 47:429–463.

Buell, C. B., and Weston, W. H. 1947. Application of the mineral oil conservation method to maintaining collections of fungus cultures. *Am. Jour. Bot.* 34:555–561.

Burkholder, P. R., and Sinnott, E. W. 1945. Morphogenesis of fungus colonies in submerged shaken cultures. *Am. Jour. Bot.* 32:424–431.

Dorrell, W. W., and Page, R. M. 1947. The use of fragmented mycelial inoculum in the culture of fungi. *Jour. Bact.* 53:360–361.

Foster, J. W. 1949. *Chemical activities of fungi.* Academic Press, New York.

Gray, W. D. 1941. Studies on the alcohol tolerance of yeasts. *Jour. Bact.* 42: 561–574.

Jacobs, P. B. 1939. Alcohol from farm products. *Ind. & Eng. Chem.* 31:162–165.

Kinoshita, K. 1929. Formation of itaconic acid and mannitol by a new filamentous fungus. *Jour. Chem. Soc.* (Japan) 50:583–593 (in *Chem. Abstr.* 25 [1931]:5664).

Lindegren, C. C., and Lindegren, G. 1943. Selecting, inbreeding, recombining, and hybridizing commercial yeasts. *Jour. Bact.* 46:405–419.

Lockwood, L. B., and Moyer, A. J. 1938. The production of chemicals by filamentous fungi. *Bot. Rev.* 4:140–164.

Moyer, A. J., and Coghill, R. D. 1945. The laboratory-scale production of itaconic acid by *Aspergillus terreus*. *Arch. Biochem.* 7:167–183.

Raper, K. B., and Alexander, D. F. 1945. Preservation of molds by the lyophil process. *Mycologia 37:*499–525.

Savage, G. M., and VanderBrook, M. J. 1946. The fragmentation of the mycelium of *Penicillium notatum* and *Penicillium chrysogenum* by a high-speed blender and the evaluation of blended seed. *Jour. Bact. 52:*385–391.

Sherf, A. F. 1943. A method for maintaining *Phytomonas sepedonica* in culture for long periods without transfer. *Phytopathology 33:*330–332.

Stefaniak, J. J., Gailey, F. B., Garvis, F. G., and Johnson, M. J. 1946. The effect of environmental conditions on *Penicillium* fermentations with *Penicillium chrysogenum* X-1612. *Jour. Bact. 52:*119–127.

Ungermann, E. 1918. Eine einfache Methode zur Gewinnung von Dauerkulturen empfindlicher Bakterienarten und zur Erhaltung der Virulenz tierpathogener Keime. *Arb. a. d. Reichsgesundheitsamte 51:*180–199.

Wernham, C. C. 1946. Mineral oil as a fungus culture preservative. *Mycologia* 38:691–692.

Wickerham, L. J., and Andreasen, A. A. 1942. The lyophil process: its use in the preservation of yeasts. *Wallerstein Laboratories Communications 5:* 165–169.

5 · *Direct Utilization of Fungi as Food*

MUSHROOM CULTURE
FOOD YEAST

MANKIND HAS USED FUNGI as food for many centuries, and literature from ancient times to the present is liberally sprinkled with references to their use in the human diet. In early Roman society various edible fungi were held in high esteem, as attested by the extant writings of that period. In other societies, fungi were considered an important part of the diet yet apparently were not regarded as epicurean delicacies. Since Rolfe and Rolfe (1928) have listed many of the early works concerning the use of fungi as human food, no attempt will be made here to deal with the strictly historical aspects of this subject.

The vast majority of individuals who eat mushrooms are probably familiar with but a single edible species. Actually, however, the fleshy sporocarps of many species of Ascomycetes and Basidiomycetes may safely be eaten. Many laymen refer to the edible fungi as "mushrooms" and to the inedible or poisonous fungi as "toadstools." That these two terms are meaningless when applied in this way is well known to the mycologist, since a great many common so-called "toadstools" are in reality nonpoisonous and some are quite tasty. Various species of the genus *Coprinus,* frequently occurring in lawns are commonly relished by botanists and others familiar with this type of "toadstool." That the line of demarcation between mushrooms and toadstools is not very clear in many minds is evident from the recurrent reports of mushroom poisoning.

The percentage of poisonous species of fleshy fungi is in reality quite small. However, because the eating of a single poisonous mushroom may result in death or violent illness (Fig. 35), there is no margin for error, and the promiscuous eating of mushrooms collected by amateurs is a dangerous practice. The various handbooks or guides to common species of fleshy fungi generally distinguish between poisonous and edible species, so that no attempt will be made here to duplicate this information. Purported means of identifying poisonous and nonpoisonous

Toadstools Poison 11

What were thought to be mushrooms, but actually were toadstools poisoned a family of four and a household of seven yesterday afternoon at 149 S. Garfield-av.

Toadstools Fatal To Local Girl

A little girl who ate toadstools died in Children's Hospital at 5:30 p.m. Wednesday. Officials said it was the first death of toadstool pois-

Toadstool Poisoning Kills Girl

18-Month-Old Baby Dies In Hospital Here

Eighteen-months-old Betty Whittington, who ate toadstools mistaken by her parents for mushrooms, died late Wednesday afternoon of fungus poisoning which has left four other persons in hospitals.

FIG. 35. *The indiscriminate eating of mushrooms collected in their natural habitats not infrequently leads to news items such as those shown above.*

types have become part of our folklore and widely accepted as fact—not infrequently with fatal results. These alleged tests include such doubtful criteria as whether or not a silver spoon blackens when placed in the mushroom broth; whether or not the cap peels; whether or not the mushroom grows on wood, and other equally unreliable indications. Such myths persist despite the work of writers like Herrick (1948), and others who have pointed out that edibility or nonedibility cannot be established by casual inspection or folklore. Because there is no quick, easy method of determining whether a mushroom is edible or poisonous the best advice is: *Do not eat any mushroom other than the cultivated type unless you are absolutely sure of its identity as an edible species as affirmed by one of the recognized manuals written by an authority on the subject.*

Fig. 36. Agaricus campestris, *the common field mushroom. The commercial mushroom is usually a variety of this species. (After Gilman, 1940.)*

Although a great many species of fungi are edible, relatively few have been cultivated for food purposes. In the United States commercial mushroom culture for market is confined almost entirely to varieties of the field mushroom *Agaricus campestris* (Fig. 36), which because of their two-spored basidia are usually named *Agaricus bisporus.* Wild mushrooms, however, may occasionally be offered for sale.

Agaricus campestris is also cultivated in Europe, as are various species of truffles (*Tuber* spp.), and wild mushrooms reach the market there far more frequently than in the United States. Rolfe and Rolfe state that inspection of edible fungi entering the markets of St. Etienne, France, began in 1897, and a special ordinance restricted the sale to certain species; in 1921 new regulations were made permitting the sale of eighteen formerly proscribed species in addition to all species of the genera *Clavaria, Helvella, Morchella,* and *Tuber.* Truffles have been extensively cultivated in oak plantations in France, and the subterranean habit of these fungi has led to the development of rather unique methods of hunting them, involving the use of trained pigs or dogs (Ramsbottom, 1923; Rolfe and Rolfe, 1928). From the standpoint of number of species cultivated, mushroom culture has reached a greater degree of development in the Orient than in the West. Among those cultivated in the East are *Cortinellus berkeleyanus, Volvariella volvacea, Armillaria matsutake,* and species of *Pleurotus* and *Auricularia.*

Mushroom Culture

Mushrooms have been cultured in the open, in abandoned quarries and mines, in caves, under greenhouse benches, and in small wooden flats in the home—hardly the most efficient and economical method. In the United States they are generally produced in special sheds or mushroom houses built of wood, cinder block, hollow tile, cement block, or brick. Rettew and Thompson (1948) have noted that cement block and brick constructions are not satisfactory because the walls tend to sweat. Regardless of the material used, the construction must allow for adequate control of temperature, humidity and ventilation.

The substratum in which the mycelium grows and on which the mushrooms eventually develop is known as compost; in this country composted horse manure is used almost exclusively for this purpose. In the preparation of compost, manure is allowed to undergo a natural fermentation process in which many organisms, both fungi and bacteria, probably play a part. According to Lambert (1938), who has prepared an excellent review of the subject of mushroom culture, the objective in the composting of manure is to prepare a medium that is more suitable for the growth of the mushroom mycelium than for the growth of the many other microorganisms whose presence in material of this type is unavoidable. During the composting process such easily decomposed materials as sugars, starch, and hemicelluloses disappear at a much more rapid rate than the more resistant cellulose and lignin. At the same time insoluble nitrogen compounds accumulate, probably as a result of the assimilatory processes of the microorganisms in the fermenting manure. Styer (1930) and Waksman (1932) have shown that lignin and insoluble proteins are readily utilized by the mushroom mycelium. Therefore, in properly prepared compost in which these materials are present in relatively high concentration the mushroom mycelium should grow much more rapidly than other fungi that cannot utilize lignin and insoluble proteins so readily.

For discussions concerning investigations of the chemical changes that occur during composting, the works of Hebert and Heim (1909, 1911) and Waksman and his co-workers (1931a, 1931b, and 1932) may be consulted. The potential mushroom grower more interested in the proper procedure for preparing compost will find this information available in works devoted to mushroom culture, such as those of Duggar (1905b, 1915) and Rettew and Thompson.

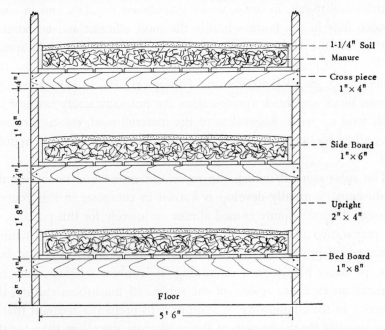

FIG. 37.   *Diagram of cross-sectional view of mushroom beds arranged in tiers. (Redrawn from Rettew and Thompson, 1948.)*

FIG. 38. *Sporocarps of* Agaricus bisporus *on compost in mushroom bed. These beds are arranged in tiers; the lower part of the tier next above is visible in the upper part of the photograph. (Courtesy F. G. Thompson, Mushroom Supply Co.)*

With increasing farm mechanization an obvious need has arisen for the development of procedures for preparing compost from materials other than horse manure. Various attempts have been made to prepare "artificial compost." Procedures of this type have been described by Hutchison and Richards (1923), Jenkins (1935), and Waksman, Tenney, and Diehm (1929). Although some success has been achieved in the preparation of artificial compost, Lambert states that the yields of mushrooms obtained on such material are only about 50–70 per cent of the yields obtained from manure compost. Rettew and Thompson list the following as ingredients of an artificial compost: 1000 lb of baled straw, 1000 lb of chopped tobacco stems, 1000 lb of soil (casing type), 500 lb of fresh manure, 50 lb of calcium cyanamide, 50 lb of bone meal, and 100 lb of gypsum (added on the last turning). These authors state that satisfactory yields of mushrooms have been obtained on compost prepared from the materials listed above but do not recommend it for commercial production.

When compost is ready for use it is sometimes placed in beds on the ground, but more often in large wood trays arranged in tiers with enough space between them to allow easy access for handling the compost, watering, and picking the crop (Figs. 37 and 38). With this tier arrangement a large surface area can be obtained in a comparatively small building.

After the compost is placed in the beds, it is kept for a week or more at a temperature of 130F in order to eliminate insects; it is then planted with material containing living mushroom mycelium; such material is termed *spawn*. In earlier practice the spawn consisted merely of compost permeated with mycelium (sometimes taken from a previous crop); and was in no sense a pure culture of the desired fungus but varied greatly in quality as inoculum. Today most spawn is a pure culture of the mushroom mycelium growing in bottles on cereal grains, tobacco stems, bran, or other suitable material. A pure culture spawn may be started by implanting a small piece of mushroom sporocarp tissue on proper medium, a method devised by Duggar (1905a), or it may be started with spores obtained from a mature mushroom. European mycologists first succeeded in obtaining germination of mushroom spores (Costantin, 1894; Costantin and Matruchot, 1894; Repin, 1897); in the United States this result was later achieved by Ferguson (1902).

Once the mycelium (spawn) is introduced into the mushroom bed, it grows through the compost at a slow or rapid rate, depending on a number of environmental conditions. If these conditions are not properly adjusted, extraneous fungi may grow more rapidly than the desired species, thus producing a crop of "weed" fungi or at least reducing the mushroom yield. Beach (1937) has listed a few of the conditions that may be more favorable for the growth of so-called weed fungi than for mushroom mycelium.

Mushroom mycelium may grow in medium having a reaction in the range of *p*H 3.4 to *p*H 9.0 (Bechman, 1929; Frear, Styer, and Haley, 1928); the optimum *p*H value varies with the composition of the medium. Growth will occur over a wide temperature range, but the optimum temperature is about 77F, as shown by Lambert (1932) and Duggar (1905a), who have established the cardinal temperatures for growth as follows:

Minimum 35F

Optimum 77F

Maximum 90F

Percentage of moisture in the compost also affects the rate of mycelial growth. Lambert (1938) states that in an average compost 160 per cent moisture is the optimum value; as with pH, the optimum moisture percentage varies with differently prepared composts.

It has long been a practical necessity for mushroom growers to spread a shallow layer of casing soil over the compost in mushroom beds. Lambert has studied the effects of different types of casing soils on yield and concludes that heavy soils produce better yields than sandy soils; he also recommends use of a soil that is nearly neutral in reaction. Why the addition of casing soil influences sporocarp development is not definitely known, but differences in CO_2 or O_2 concentrations between casing soil and compost may be critical factors. According to Klebs (1900), vegetation and reproduction are mutually antagonistic processes; hence, on the basis of his hypothesis, the specific effect of the casing soil may be to provide an environment favorable for growth in every respect except one—nutrients are lacking, and as a result the reproductive phase is initiated.

The environmental conditions under which mushrooms will develop are restricted to a much narrower range than those governing growth of mycelium. Thus, though the mycelium will grow in the temperature range of 35–90F, typical sporocarps develop only in the range of 45–75F. This development does not occur at equal rates throughout the effective range, and Lambert (1930) has shown that the rate of growth of the sporocarp increases with an increase in temperature. For example, the sporocarp of the white variety of *A. bisporus* reaches full growth in six days at 70F, whereas at 50F it reaches full growth only after twenty-two days. By proper adjustment of temperature and other conditions, it is possible for the mushroom grower to control, over a relatively wide range, the time of sporocarp development in his various houses in order to meet special market or labor conditions.

There is some difference of opinion about the effects of humidity on mushroom development: Stoller (1936) has indicated that high humidity may result in the production of deformed sporocarps, whereas Lambert (1938) has asserted that "normal" sporocarps may develop in caves under conditions of over 95 per cent relative humidity.

In 1933 Lambert published the results of experiments which show that a 1 per cent concentration of carbon dioxide in the air will affect sporocarp development, and that if the concentration is as high as 5 per cent, all development will be arrested. Since large quantities of carbon dioxide are formed as a result of the respiration of the mushroom mycelium and of the numerous other microorganisms inhabiting mushroom beds, some means of ventilating mushroom houses should be provided in order to prevent the accumulation of carbon dioxide in inhibitory concentrations.

DISEASES, WEEDS, AND INSECT PESTS.   Mushroom growing, like any other agricultural pursuit, is sometimes beset with difficulties arising from the presence of parasitic fungi and bacteria, insect pests, and weeds. Ware (1935) in his bulletin on mushroom culture gives a bibliography of the literature concerned with mushroom diseases, and Beach (1937) lists the twelve principal disease organisms and weed fungi, the characteristics of the diseases, the sources of the causal organisms, and the environmental conditions favoring the development of the parasitic forms as well as the weed fungi, which are not parasitic but do cause yield reductions. Bubble disease of mushrooms, caused by *Mycogone perniciosa* (Fungi Imperfecti), was formerly a major disease of mushrooms, but Beach states that it has become less serious since the factors favoring it have become better known, and that the most important disease now is brown spot, caused by a species of *Verticillium* (Fungi Imperfecti). Brown spot primarily affects the quality of mushrooms, but may eventually lead to a dry, leathery decay of

Table 6.—Principal diseases of cultivated mushrooms

Disease	Causal Organism
Bubbles	*Mycogone perniciosa*
Verticillium disease; brown spot	*Verticillium* sp.
Bacterial spot; brown blotch	*Bacterium tolaasi*
Bacterial pit	*Bacterium* sp.
Mildew; soft decay	*Dactylium* sp.
Damping-off	*Fusarium* spp.

the sporocarp. Some of the diseases listed by Beach are presented in Table 6.

In addition to their susceptibility to a variety of diseases, and reduced yields that may be caused by the presence of weed fungi, mushrooms may also be damaged or killed by insects. The insects commonly responsible for mushroom damage are discussed by Thomas (1931), who also makes recommendations for their control.

THE MUSHROOM INDUSTRY IN THE UNITED STATES. Although the mushroom industry is probably less than one hundred years old, it is of considerable size. Figure 39 shows that in the twenty-four

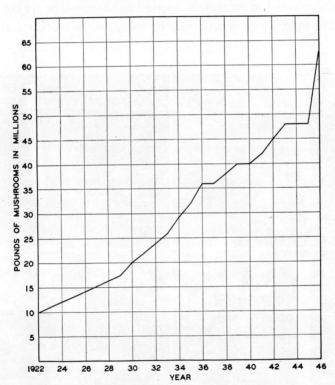

FIG. 39. *Annual production of cultivated mushrooms in the United States, 1922–46. (Redrawn from Rettew and Thompson, 1948.)*

year period from 1922 to 1946, the total annual production of mushrooms in the United States increased more than sixfold, with the trend still upward. Pennsylvania leads all other states in mushroom production with more than half of the total annual United States production in

1946. The industry is more or less concentrated in the area of Kennett Square in Philadelphia, a fact associated with the proximity of horse barns in the early days of horse-drawn street cars.

CULTIVATION OF NEW TYPES OF EDIBLE MUSHROOMS. Mushroom growers, like other agriculturists, have always been interested in obtaining new and better varieties and species of plants. In the United States at least, the greatest effort has been directed toward the selection of better varieties, but perhaps entirely different species might be more desirable and more easily culivated. Among the most prized of the wild mushrooms are the species of *Morchella* (Fig. 40), which are commonly referred to as morels, sponge mushrooms, or spring mushrooms. The morels may occasionally be found on the market during the

FIG. 40.   *Some common species of* Morchella. Upper left: M. crassipes. Upper right: M. esculenta. Lower left: M. angusticeps. Lower right: M. hybrida.

early spring, but the supply is very limited because they have only a short season and must be collected in their natural habitat. In some cities morels may be purchased at any season of the year in frozen-food packs, but for anyone who has tasted a fresh morel, the frozen product leaves much to be desired. The morels, especially *Morchella esculenta,* would be excellent species to have in cultivation, for their tissues are firm and many people prefer them to the common cultivated mushroom for flavor. So far attempts to establish morels in cultivation have not had wide success.

The morels may easily be obtained in pure culture either from ascospores or from bits of ascocarp tissue, and the mycelium grows readily on a variety of different media. The conditions favorable for ascocarp development, however, have not been determined, and there are few reports of ascocarps being formed in culture. This problem is exceptionally challenging in applied mycology. The individual or firm that first develops a successful method for cultivating morels will become a major factor in the mushroom industry. Citations of studies in the laboratory cultivation of morels may be found in the works of Heim (1936), Costantin (1936a, 1936b), Falk (1920), and Brock (1951).

Another species not now in cultivation but well worth some attention is *Pleurotus ostreatus,* the oyster mushroom, so-called because of its decidedly oyster-like flavor and firm texture. Typically it grows on decaying wood, which is no serious obstacle, since several types of mushroom are cultivated on wood in the Orient.

In recent years there have been several attempts to produce a food product from the mycelium of *Agaricus bisporus* instead of using the fruiting body. Such attempts involve growing the mycelium in submerged culture in liquid medium and using the mycelial pellets so formed for the purpose of adding a mushroom flavor to foods. Szuecs (1954) has received a patent on his process for enhancing mushroom mycelium flavor, but Beesch and Shull (1955) state that the lack of mushroom flavor of sufficient intensity and consumer acceptability has thus far handicapped the development of a large-scale production of mushroom mycelium for food by the submerged culture method. For further details of the process, the work of Sugihara and Humfeld (1954), who reported on the submerged culture of twenty species of mushrooms, should be consulted.

Food Yeast

Famine has long been a recurring chapter in the history of the human race. Notwithstanding the great discoveries and technological advances that have marked man's progress no substitute for food has yet been developed. The threat of starvation is still an ever-present human problem. Indeed, the prolonged depletion of many agricultural lands and the consequent conversion of large areas of formerly productive farm land to wasteland must inevitably diminish the total quantity of food produced by present agricultural methods. Growing urbanization and industrialization of farm land areas further contribute to the decrease in acreage used for food production. Paralleling the constant shrinking of arable land is the steady rise in world population, and these two conflicting trends present an alarming prospect. For example, it has been estimated that the population of the United States is currently increasing at the rate of 1 person every 12 seconds; if such a rate is maintained, it will result in an annual population increase in this country alone of 2,628,000. Similar population increases occurring in other countries are beginning to threaten the world's food supply. Such food problems will probably arise much sooner in certain underdeveloped areas of the world which undergo very rapid industrialization, since in these areas public health measures instituted in order to provide adequate labor for the industrial machine will lead to "explosive" population increases by reducing the infant mortality rate or by gradually increasing the average life expectancy.

Thus far at least the United States has been more fortunate than other countries in having more good agricultural land than is necessary to maintain an adequate food level for the population. But we even are still affected by famine in distant lands because starvation is one of the powerful and inexorable factors leading to world conflict. Such conflicts often result in a temporary redistribution of food and other necessities, but they also destroy tremendous quantities of the world's resources. There are many who advocate the sharing of a country's surplus food among its less fortunate neighbors—a simple and humanitarian solution to the problem, but a temporary solution at best, leading ultimately to a reversal of the roles of "have" and "have-not" nations.

Three realistic solutions to the approaching problem are suggested: (1) an ever-increasing world production of food, (2) a more efficient world utilization of the food now being produced, and (3) a slowing down of the present world rate of population increase. Of the three solutions offered, the first two seem to have the only chances for success; accordingly, any process or method that substantially increases the world's total food production or conserves the energy of food already produced should merit serious consideration.

The large-scale production of yeast for food purposes, though not a complete solution to the approaching world food problem, does provide a means of increasing food supplies and of converting cheap carbohydrate into protein without great loss of the energy of the carbohydrate. It also provides an opportunity to alleviate or eliminate undesirable nutritional conditions in certain protein-poor areas of the world, especially those in which there are abundant supplies of cheap carbohydrate. Perhaps the agriculture of the future will include the conversion of carbohydrates and inorganic nitrogen salts into edible and nutritious protein through the use of yeasts or other fungi. One writer (Yin, 1949) has referred to such processes as "microbial farming."

Like all other living organisms, man's food consists of carbohydrates, fats, and proteins, and a balanced diet should contain these essential elements. If supplied with carbohydrate, man's body cells can synthesize fat, but they are unable to synthesize proteins from carbohydrate. Hence man must be supplied with proteins obtained from other organisms or with amino acids, the chemical compounds from which proteins are synthesized. In the over-all picture of world food supply, carbohydrates are abundant; in a country such as the United States there is no shortage of either proteins or fats. But in many other areas protein is scarce and very expensive, and thus unavailable to a large portion of the population. If the carbohydrate in such regions could be cheaply converted to protein, the nutritional level of the population could be raised; if this could be accomplished with little loss of food energy, the over-all picture of world food production would appear immensely brighter. Most of us prefer to obtain our protein from meat, yet the production of such protein results in huge losses of food energy. For example, 100 lb of beef can be produced by the feeding of 718 lb of shelled corn to beef cattle—a great loss of food energy, since beef is about 50 per cent water, and 718 lb of corn contain the equivalent of about 480 lb of sugar, plus corn proteins and fat. Production of dairy foods also involves the loss of great quantities of food energy; in the production of dairy products about 78 per cent of the food energy fed is lost. Thaysen (1943) has calculated that one acre devoted to the production of carbohydrates could yield 840 lb of protein in the form of food yeast but only 70 lb in the form of meat or milk protein.

It has long been known that enormous quantities of yeast cells can be produced from a cheap sugar source and a few inexpensive mineral salts, but it is only in comparatively recent years that much consideration has been given to the possibility of producing yeast on a large scale for human consumption. Thaysen has pointed out that large quantities of yeast have been produced as a by-product of the brewing industry but that little progress has been made in the use of brewer's yeast either for human food or for stock feeding because of its bitter taste (due to hops) and high cost, despite its known high protein content. Carter and Phillips (1944) also cited dried brewer's yeast as a readily available source of protein, but they state that the annual production of brewer's yeast in the United States amounts to only about 30,000,000 pounds of dried yeast, which represents but a small fraction of the quantity that would be required if yeast were used as a substantial source of protein for human consumption. These workers point out that when brewer's yeast is debittered to render it palatable, some of the vitamin content is lost.

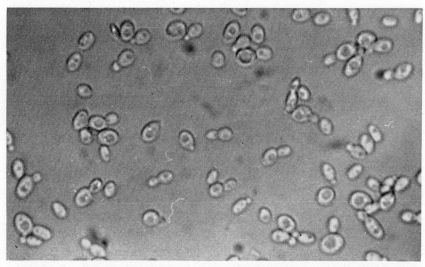

FIG. 41.   *Cells of* Torulopsis utilis (*food yeast*) *highly magnified.* (*Courtesy Charmin Paper Products Division, Green Bay, Wisconsin.*)

Although most of the common yeasts can be readily produced in quantity, much of the recent work on the large-scale production of yeast for food purposes has centered around *Torulopsis utilis* (also referred to as *Torula utilis* and *Candida utilis*). This yeast (Fig. 41) is one of the nonsporulating, or "false," yeasts which has a very acceptable odor and taste. Interest in it probably stems from the work of Hayduck (Thaysen, 1943), who reported that protein could be synthesized, using ammonia as the nitrogen source, with a type of yeast (*Torulopsis?*) which grew well in the absence of organic nitrogen. The work of Hayduck was conducted as a result of conditions created by the blockade of the First World War, which cut off Germany and her allies from their source of protein concentrates for cattle feeding. Thaysen states that large-scale production was not realized in Germany at that time because of a shortage of sugar. Early in the Second World War a renewal of interest in food yeast was noticeable in England and in the United States, as well as in other countries. The same writer has reported on a process for food yeast production worked out in the Chemical Research Laboratory at Teddington, England, in which yields of at least a fifteenfold increase in yeast weight were obtained in nine hours. A yeast variety (*Torulopsis utilis* var. *thermophila*) developed during the course of this work grows at a higher temperature than other varieties of *T. utilis* and was especially recommended for use in tropical countries—in order to eliminate the expensive cooling process required for other yeasts. Weight yields of dried yeast were 60 per cent (based on the weight of sugar utilized), and the yields of crude protein represented almost theoretical conversion from the inorganic nitrogen supplied. In the process described by Thaysen, after the growth period is completed the yeast is washed with water in yeast separators, and the yeast suspension then passed over drying rollers, from which it comes out as thin, straw-colored flakes having a pleasant nutty or meaty taste. These flakes are "food yeast" and contain 45–50 per cent protein and all the known B vitamins.

Gubin (1944) reports that food yeast may be produced in quantity as follows: 125 lb of yeast are placed in a vat with 7000 gal of water containing 3000 lb of molasses and some ammonia. The contents of the vat are then aerated by passing air through the medium at a rate of 1000 cu ft per min. After a 12-hr growth period, the yeast weight is multiplied by a factor of about 16; thus the yield from a relatively small vat is approximately one ton.

In the United States considerable experimental work has been done on the production of food yeast from fruit juices. Using laboratory-scale fermenters of 10-liter capacity, Lewis and others (1944) reported high conversion of sugar in fruit juice media by *Torulopsis utilis.* Average yields of about 55 grams of dry yeast per 100 grams of sugar were obtained. In their experiments air was supplied at a rate of about 1.5 liters per minute per liter of medium, with the sugar concentration maintained at about 0.5 per cent. The propagation period lasted 6–8 hours, during which time a tenfold increase of yeast was obtained; ammonia was added periodically in order to supply nitrogen and also to maintain the reaction of the medium at about pH 4.0–5.0. Their analyses showed that the vitamin content of yeast so produced was roughly comparable to that of baker's and brewer's yeasts; a summary of their data on dry weight yields and vitamin content of *T. utilis* is presented in Table 7.

Table 7.—Vitamin synthesis by Torulopsis utilis

Vitamin	*No. of Runs*	*Average Dry Yeast Produced,* *(g/100 g of sugar)*	*Average Net Vitamin Synthesis,* *(gamma/g of dry yeast produced)*
Thiamin	19	53	22
Riboflavin	21	53	71
Nicotinic acid	22	53	530
Pantothenic acid	21	53	241
Biotin	4	54	1.23
Pyridoxin	4	54	35
p-Aminobenzoic acid	5	54	56

From Lewis and others (1944).

Stubbs and his co-workers (1944) called attention to the fact that thousands of tons of cull fruits and other waste fruit materials are produced in the United States annually, and that such material may be used as a source of carbohydrates for the production of food yeast. They cultured *T. utilis* in worts prepared from fruit syrups or concentrates of prunes, figs, and raisins and from press juices of apples, pears, and peaches. In laboratory-scale fermenters yields of 42 to 58 grams of dry yeast per 100 grams of sugar were obtained, and in pilot-plant equipment, higher yields were obtained with prune syrup. According to their analyses the yeast had a protein content of 53 to 58 per cent, but since their protein estimates were based on total nitrogen determinations, these values are probably somewhat high. They state that the effectiveness of the process depends on vigorous aeration and the maintenance of sugar concentration at a low level by the addition of nutrient materials only as they are required. Their pilot-plant runs were conducted in a fermenter of 250-gal capacity in which the temperature was maintained at 30 C and to which air was supplied at a rate of 70 cu ft per min; ammonia was added periodically during the 7-hour propagation period. Data from two pilot-plant runs are shown in Table 8.

Table 8.—Pilot-plant fermentations on prune medium

	Run 1	Run 2
In Fermenter at Start		
Tap water	645 l	795 l
$(NH_4)_2SO_4$	500 g	1000 g
K_2SO_4	570 g	570 g
$MgSO_4 \cdot 7H_2O$	430 g	430 g
$(NH_4)_2HPO_4$	300 g	300 g
Prune wort (17% sugar)	34 l	24 l
Seed yeast (4250 g. of yeast, 75% moisture)	76 l	76 l
Yield Data		
Total sugar supplied	20 kg	19.7 kg
N supplied as ammonium salts	297 g	403 g
N supplied as ammonia	1010 g	980 g
Total N supplied	1307 g	1383 g
Final volume of culture	758 l	974 l
Dry wt of yeast in 15 ml	0.256 g	0.191 g
Dry wt of yeast in culture	12910 g	12380 g
Dry wt of seed yeast	980 g	980 g
Dry wt of yeast produced	11930 g	11400 g
N content of dried yeast	9.2 %	9.2 %
N in yeast produced	1098 g	1049 g
Calculated yield	60 %	58 %
Yeast actually recovered	39.4 kg	42 kg
Net yield based on recovery	39 %	42 %

After Stubbs and others (1944).

FIG. 42.   *Dried food yeast. (Courtesy Charmin Paper Products Division, Green Bay, Wisconsin.)*

FIG. 43.   *Fermentation tanks and separators used in the production of food yeast. (Courtesy Charmin Paper Products Division, Green Bay, Wisconsin.)*

Other workers have suggested the use of such materials as waste bananas, waste citrus press juice, wood hydrolyzates, and waste sulfite liquor from paper manufacture as a source of carbohydrate for food yeast production. If clarification processes (to render the end product suitable for human consumption) prove too costly, some of these materials might be more efficiently used in the production of high-protein livestock feeds. Waste sulfite liquor has been used successfully for several years as a raw material for the production of food yeast (Fig. 42) by the Lake States Yeast Corporation, in Rhinelander, Wisconsin, and the Charmin Paper Products Division, in Green Bay, Wisconsin (Fig. 43). Beesch and Shull (1955) estimated that about 20 per cent of the food yeast being produced will be utilized in soups, sausage mixes, and other products; presumably the remainder will be used as a supplement for mixed feeds for livestock and poultry.

USES AND NUTRITIONAL VALUE OF FOOD YEAST. When a new scientific discovery or technological development is first announced, its properties or benefits may be exaggerated by inept publicity. This was true of food yeast during the early revival of interest in it. References to "substitute beefsteak" and other similar exaggerations have implied that food yeast is a substitute for meat protein or that the entire world food problem could be solved with this yeast. But it is extremely doubtful that food yeast will supplant meat as the principal source of protein in the human diet, at least in the near future. In fact, Gubin (1944) has stated that too much yeast taken at any one time may actually be harmful to the human digestive process. The real value of food yeast is as a supplement to, not as a substitute for, other foods. According to Gubin, the addition of 1.5 ounces of food yeast to an ordinary loaf of bread will give the loaf additional food value equivalent to $2\frac{1}{2}$ eggs, $\frac{1}{4}$ pound of beef, or 2 ounces of cheese. Thaysen (1943) states that food yeast can be mixed with flour and baked to produce a loaf of bread which has a nutty or meaty flavor; he also recommends its incorporation into soups, milk, and stews.

Yeast proteins are of high quality, since they contain many of the essential amino acids, but Carter and Phillips (1944) concluded that they may be somewhat inferior to animal proteins in human nutrition. Vitamins are extremely important in the human diet, and in addition to its value as a protein supplement, food yeast would also be a good source of the B vitamins. The possibility of using food yeast as a supplement in the diet of aged persons should be further investigated, since Stephenson, Penton, and Korenchevsky (1941) have reported that when food yeast, plus ascorbic acid (vitamin C), was given to aged people, there were in a few cases improvements in, or disappearance of, some of the pathological features of senility. Other investigators have also attributed certain curative properties to yeast; these are more appropriately discussed in the chapter concerned with the uses of fungi in medicine (Chap. 8).

Literature Cited

Beach, W. C. 1937. Control of mushroom diseases and weed fungi. *Pa. Agr. Exp. Sta. Bull. 351.*

Bechmann, E. 1929. Untersuchungen über die Kulturfähigkeit des Champignons (*Psalliota campestris*). *Zeit. Bot. 22:*289–323.

Beesch, S. C., and Shull, G. M. 1955. Fermentation. *Ind. & Eng. Chem. 47:* 1857–1875.

Brock, T. D. 1951. Studies on the nutrition of *Morchella esculenta*. *Mycologia 43:*402–422.

Carter, H. E., and Phillips, G. E. 1944. The nutritive value of yeast proteins. *Fed. Proc. 3:*123–128.

Costantin, J. 1894. La culture du champignon de couche et ses recents perfectionnements. *Rev. Sci. IV, 1:*423.

———. 1936a. La culture de la morille d'après M. Molliard. *Academie d'Agriculture de France Comptes Rendus 22:*589–592.

———. 1936b. La culture de la morille et sa forme conidienne. *Annales de Science Naturelle X, Botanique 18:*111–140.

——— and Matruchot, L. 1894. Culture de champignon de couche a partir de la spore. *Rev. Mycol. 16:*62–66.

Duggar, B. M. 1905a. The principles of mushroom growing and mushroom spawn making. *U.S.D.A. Bur. Pl. Ind. Bull. 85.*

———. 1905b. *The cultivation of mushrooms. U.S.D.A. Farmers Bull. No. 204.*

———. 1915. *Mushroom growing.* Orange Judd Co., New York.

Falk, R. 1920. Wege zur Kultur der Morchelarten. *Der Pilze—und Kräuterfreund 3:*211–223, 247–255.

Ferguson, M. 1902. A preliminary study of the germination of the spores of *Agaricus campestris* and other Basidiomycetes. *U.S.D.A. Bur. Pl. Ind. Bull. 16:*1–40.

Frear, D., Styer, J. F., and Haley, D. E. 1928. A study of the effect of H-ion concentration on the growth of *Agaricus campestris*. *Plant Physiol. 3:*91–94.

Gilman, J. C. 1940. Illustrations of the fleshy fungi of Iowa: I. The purple-brown spored agarics. *Proc. Iowa Acad. Sci. 47:*83–90.

Gubin, E. K. 1944. Food yeasts. *Hygeia 22:*124–128.

Hebert, A., and Heim, F. 1909. Sur la nutrition mineral du champignon de couche. *Ann. Sci. Agron. France et étrangère II (III)* :1–12.

——. 1911. Nouvelle contribution à l'étude de la nutrition du champignon de couche. Composition des fumiers employés à sa culture. *Ann. Sci. Agron. France et étrangère III (5)* :337–347.

Heim, F. 1936. La culture des morilles. *Rev. Mycol. Suppl. 1:*10–11, 19–25.

Herrick, J. A. 1948. Mushrooms—to eat or not to eat. *School Sci. and Math.,* Dec. 1948; pp. 679–685.

Hutchison, H. B., and Richards, E. H. 1921–23. Artificial farmyard manure. *Jour. Min. Agr. Great Brit. 28:*398–411.

Jenkins, S. H. 1935. Organic manures. *Tech. Com. Imp. Bur. Soil Sci. 33.*

Klebs, G. 1900. Zur Physiologie der Fortpflanzung einiger Pilze III. Allgemeine Betractungen. *Jahrb. wiss. Bot., Bd. 35, Heft 1:*80–203.

Lambert, E. B. 1930. Studies on the relation of temperature to the growth, parasitism, thermal death points and control of *Mycogone perniciosa. Phytopathology 20:*75–83.

——. 1932. *Mushroom growing in the United States. U.S.D.A. Circ. No. 251.*

——. 1933. Effect of excess carbon dioxide on growing mushrooms. *Jour. Agr. Res. 47:*599–608.

——. 1938. Principles and problems of mushroom culture. *Bot. Rev. 4:* 397–426.

Lewis, J. C., Stubbs, J. J., and Noble, W. M. 1944. Vitamin synthesis by Torula yeast. *Arch. Biochem. 4:*389–401.

Ramsbottom, J. 1923. *A handbook of the larger British fungi.* Taylor and Francis, London.

Repin, C. 1897. La culture du champignon de couche. *Rev. Gen. Sci. 8:* 705–717.

Rettew, G. R., and Thompson, F. G. 1948. *Manual of mushroom culture.* Mushroom Supply Co., Toughkenamon, Pa.

Rolfe, R. T., and Rolfe, F. W. 1928. *The romance of the fungus world.* Lippincott, Philadelphia.

Stoller, B. B. 1936. The preparation of composts and some physiological activities of *Agaricus campestris* L. Unpublished Master's thesis, Iowa State Coll. Agr.

Stephenson, W., Penton, C., and Korenchevsky, V. 1941. Some effects of vitamins B and C on senile patients. *Brit. Med. Jour. 2:*839–844.

Stubbs, J. J., Noble, W. M., and Lewis, J. C. 1944. Fruit juices yield food yeast. *Food Ind. 16:*694–696, 751.

Styer, J. F. 1930. Nutrition of the cultivated mushroom. *Am. Jour. Bot. 17:*982–994.

Sugihara, T. F., and Humfeld, H. 1954. Submerged culture of the mycelium of various species of mushroom. *Appl. Microbiol. 2:*170–175.

Szuecs, J. 1954. U.S. Patent 2,693,664.

Thaysen, A. C. 1943. Value of micro-organisms in nutrition (food yeast). *Nature 151:*406–408.

Thomas, C. A. 1931. Mushroom insects; their biology and control. *Pa. State Coll. Bull. 270.*

Waksman, S. A. 1932. On the nutrition of the cultivated mushroom, *Agaricus campestris,* and the chemical changes brought about by this organism in the manure compost. *Am. Jour. Bot. 19:*514–537.

————, and McGrath, J. M. 1931a. Preliminary study of the processes involved in the decomposition of manure by *Agaricus campestris. Am. Jour. Bot. 18:*573–581.

————, and Nissen, W. 1931b. Lignin as a nutrient for the cultivated mushroom, *Agaricus campestris.* Science *74:*271–272.

————, Tenney, G. F., and Diehm, R. A. 1929. Chemical and microbiological principles underlying the transformation of organic matter in the preparation of artificial manures. *Jour. Am. Soc. Agron. 21:*533–546.

Ware, W. M. 1935. Mushroom growing. *Min. Agr. Great Brit. Bull. 34.*

Yin, H. C. 1949. Microbial farming. *Econ. Bot. 3:*184–192.

6 · *Fungi and Food Processing*

CHEESE
FUNGI AND BREAD MAKING

FUNGI, in addition to being used directly as food as described in Chapter 5, are also employed in the processing of certain food products designed for human use. In such applications, regardless of whether the fungus tissue becomes part of the final edible product, it is the agent responsible for the production of some particularly desirable or characteristic odor, flavor, or texture. In Japan and China, fungi of the *Aspergillus flavus-oryzae* group have long been variously used in the processing of a number of food products, but in the Occident fungi have been used as processing agents primarily in the cheese-making and baking industries.

Cheese

Cheese may be defined in general as a solid or semisolid protein food product manufactured from milk. The degree of solidity depends to a large extent upon the amount of curdling or coagulation of the protein, the amount of whey (watery part of the milk) expelled from the curd, and the nature of the ripening process. Cheese provides a means of preserving many of the important nutrients of milk in a consumable form for long periods of time. Before the advent of modern methods of food handling and processing, cheese manufacture constituted the only method of preserving milk. How long cheese will remain edible depends upon its initial composition and its water content. Thus, a cheese of relatively high water content (60–70 per cent), such as cottage cheese, will spoil if not consumed within a few days after it is made.

There are a great variety of different types of cheeses. Doane and Lawson (1918) listed nearly three hundred varieties, a figure increased to over five hundred seven years later by Thom and Fisk (1925). Since the publication of these two papers, newly developed process cheeses have considerably lengthened the list. There are many similarities between differently named varieties, the names having been derived for the most part from the city or region in which the cheeses were first produced. In France the most widely known "blue" cheese, Roquefort, is closely imitated by Pâté Bleu, Fromage Bleu, Gex, Mont Cenis, Septmoncel, and other named varieties.

In spite of the great number of varietal names, cheeses may be classified into a comparatively small number of basic types. Following is a classification of cheeses (similar to that used by Thom and Fisk) which is based upon such factors as degree of ripeness, method of curdling the milk, nature of the ripening agent, etc.:

I. Cheeses with sour milk flavor only—soft cheeses (45 to 75 per cent water). Eaten fresh.
    A. Curdled by souring. Cottage cheese and its allies in America; many related varieties in Europe.
    B. Curdled by souring and rennet—the Neufchâtel group.
        1. Made from skim milk: Skim-milk Neufchâtel.
        2. Made from part skim to whole milk: American or domestic Neufchâtel.
        3. Made with fat added: The cream cheeses of the Neufchâtel group (Both American and European) such as cream, Gervais, Malakoffs, etc.
II. Cheeses ripened.
    A. Soft cheeses (40 to 50 per cent water).
        1. Curdled by souring; heated, then ripened: Hand cheese, Pennsylvania pot cheese, etc.
        2. Curdled by both souring and rennet; ripened: Ripened (French) Neufchâtel.
        3. Curdled primarily by rennet.
            a. Ripened by fungi: Camembert, Brie, and their allies.
            b. Ripened by bacteria.
                * Made from soft or friable curd: d'Isigny, Liederkranz, etc.
                ** Made from firm or tough curds: Limburger and allies.
    B. Semihard cheeses, firm, well-drained (28 to 45 per cent water).
        1. Curd not cooked; ripened by fungi.

a. Made from friable curd: Roquefort and its various imitations.

b. Made from firm or tough curd: Gorgonzola, Stilton, and such French forms as Gex and Septmoncel.

2. Curd cooked; ripened with bacteria: Brick, Munster, Port du Salut.

C. Hard cheeses; cooked and pressed (30 to 40 per cent water).

1. Ripened without gas holes.

a. Dutch: Edam, Gouda.

b. Danish.

c. The Cheddar Group.

* English: Cheddar and related forms known principally in Great Britain.

** American: The factory Cheddar of the United States and Canada.

2. Ripened with the development of gas holes.

a. Holes large: Swiss-Emmenthal, Gruyere, American Swiss.

b. Holes small: Parmesan and related varieties.

From the above outline it is obvious that only two general types of cheeses are made in which fungi are employed as the ripening agents (Figure 44). The first of these is typified by Camembert, a fungus-

FIG. 44. *Examples of some common cheeses.* Left, *wedge of Roquefort (fungus-ripened).* Left foreground, *wedge of Camembert (fungus-ripened).* Right foreground, *wedge of blue cheese (fungus-ripened).* Right, *a cut of Cheddar cheese.* Background, *a cut of natural Swiss cheese.* (*Courtesy of the Kraft Foods Company, Chicago, Ill.*)

ripened soft cheese; the second is a semihard cheese of which Roquefort is a typical example.

CAMEMBERT CHEESE.   This very distinctive variety of soft cheese is said to have originated in the Department of Orne in the northwest part of France. Various other soft cheeses resembling Camembert have also originated in that country: among these are Brie, Thenay, Troyes, and Vendôme. In the manufacture of Camembert cheese, milk is curdled primarily with rennet, and the curd then placed in hoops where it is allowed to drain. After draining, the curd is trimmed, salted, allowed to drain again, and subjected to a special ripening or curing process (Fig. 45). Proper conditions of temperature and humidity must be maintained throughout the ripening process in order to obtain the desired results.

During the three- to four-week ripening period, a variety of changes take place in the cheese. The acid is neutralized or destroyed, the curd softens to a smooth buttery consistency due to the action of proteolytic enzymes on the casein of the milk, and the water content is lowered. Several microorganisms seem to be involved in the ripening process peculiar to this type of cheese. The production of certain characteristic

FIG. 45.   *Camembert cheese in the curing room.* (*Courtesy of the Kraft Foods Company, Chicago, Ill.*)

flavors of Camembert cheese are ascribed by Thom (1909) to the action of lactic acid bacteria, typically present in milk. The transformation of the curd texture is due to the activity of organisms that develop on the outside (rind) of the cheese during the ripening period. Characteristically these organisms are *Penicillium camemberti* or a white form of the same species (*P. camemberti* var. *rogeri*), *Oidium lactis,* and several species of bacteria. According to Thom, inoculation of the curd with *P. camemberti* prior to the ripening period has not been practiced in Camembert factories except when a new factory is being established. Apparently once the proper species has been introduced into a cheese factory it becomes established and there is no further need for inoculation of fresh cheeses. Occasionally other fungi may occur as contaminants on Camembert cheeses: when *P. roqueforti* occurs as a contaminant it imparts a bitter flavor; *P. brevicaule* and related varieties of fungi may produce a strong ammonia odor.

Thom, who made analyses of various Camembert cheeses selected as representing choice examples of texture and flavor, stated that the composition of the best cheeses is within the following limits: water, 47–50 per cent; fat, 25–28 per cent; protein, 18–21 per cent.

ROQUEFORT CHEESE.   One of the most famous of the fungus-ripened cheeses, the Roquefort type originated in the southern part of France, where it has been made for many years (Figs. 46 and 47). Originally made only from sheep's milk, many good imitations of this type of cheese are now prepared from cows' milk. Roquefort may be classed as a blue or blue-veined cheese, such common names being applied to this variety because the ripened cheese has blue streaks running through it, due to the presence of a fungus. Gorgonzola may be considered an Italian counterpart of Roquefort, and Stilton the English counterpart. Many types of cheese that resemble Roquefort are manufactured in France, such as Pâté Bleu, Fromage Bleu, Gex, Mont Cenis, and Septmoncel. Roquefort type cheese has also been successfully made in the United States.

Although the ripening process also involves the growth of a fungus, in Roquefort the mycelium grows throughout the curd (Fig. 48), rather than being restricted to a superficial growth on the rind as in Camembert. The fungus principally involved in the ripening of Roquefort cheese is *Penicillium roqueforti,* which, according to Thom and Currie

(1913), occurs in practically pure cultures in this type of cheese. These investigators also reported that both Gorgonzola and Stilton cheeses likewise contain *P. roqueforti* in fairly pure condition. Since oxygen disappears and carbon dioxide is formed in considerable quantities within the curd during the ripening process, the question naturally arises as to how an organism as highly aerobic as a filamentous fungus is capable of growing in the interior of the curd under conditions of high carbon-dioxide and low oxygen concentration. Tom and Currie provided the answer by demonstrating that *P. roqueforti* has the capacity to grow under conditions of high carbon-dioxide concentration and low oxygen concentration far beyond the capacities of other species of *Penicillium* and *Aspergillus*. These workers tested 22 species of *Penicillium* and *Aspergillus* and found that in an atmosphere contain-

FIG. 46.   *Passageway in a cheese cellar at Roquefort. (From Garard, Minsky, Baker, and Pascale, 1937.)*

F<small>IG</small>. 47. *Cheese salting chamber at Roquefort. (From Garard, Minsky, Baker, and Pascale, 1937.)*

ing 75 per cent carbon dioxide and 25 per cent air, only *P. roqueforti* was able to form fairly strong colonies. Thus it would appear that this species of *Penicillium* is dominant in Roquefort cheese because most other fungi cannot grow under the conditions of low oxygen concentration existing in the open spaces in the cheese. Dattilo-Rubbo (1938), who isolated fungi from all of the blue-veined types of cheese available in London (Stilton, Blue Cheshire, Roquefort, Wensleydale, Danish Roquefort, Gorgonzola, Blue Vinney, and Dolce Verde) reported that with the exception of the fungus isolated from Dolce Verde cheese, all fungi isolated were *P. roqueforti.* He described the Dolce Verde fungus as being related to *Penicillium expansum* (a blue fungus associated with fruit decay) and noted that this fungus, like *P. roqueforti,* can remain in viable condition in the partially anaerobic cavities of the cheese.

In the manufacture of Roquefort cheese the curd is ordinarily inoculated with *P. roqueforti* by mixing it with bread crumbs on which the organism has been cultured. Thom and Currie state that Gorgonzola and Stilton cheeses are usually not inoculated with the organism; Doane and Lawson, however, point out that in the manufacture of Gorgonzola cheese, the layers of the curd are interspersed with moldy bread crumbs as the curd is placed in hoops to drain.

FIG. 48.   *American made Roquefort-type cheese. Note fungus growth (dark areas) in the larger cavities.*

During the ripening of Roquefort, the temperature and humidity must be carefully controlled. Relative humidity should be high, and the temperature should be maintained at about 48F. In spite of its capacity to live under conditions of low oxygen concentration, *P. roqueforti* must have some oxygen or it will not grow; for that reason holes are punched in the curd in order to facilitate the growth of the mycelium throughout the cheese. After the mycelium has grown to the desired extent, the cheese is stored at a lower temperature, where growth is inhibited, but the fungus enzymes are still active.

The characteristically pungent odors and flavors of Roquefort cheese are due to the action of fungus lipase, a fat-digesting enzyme. As a result of this enzymatic action, milk fats are hydrolyzed and organic acids of characteristic odor and flavor (capric, caproic, and capryllic) are liberated.

Fungi and Breadmaking

The fact that man considers his daily bread of vital importance is partly attested to by the second sentence of the Lord's Prayer. Long considered the most basic of all foods, bread has often been termed the staff of life. Paradoxically enough, advances made in the science of breadmaking have closely paralleled and are related to advances in the technology of alcohol fermentation, a process once held to be associated with the black arts. That advances in our knowledge of alcoholic fermentation should have paralleled the art of breadmaking is not at all surprising, since basically the same biochemical activity is involved in both processes—the formation of ethyl alcohol and carbon dioxide from sugar through a process of anaerobic respiration. Which of the two end products (alcohol or carbon dioxide) is desired depends entirely upon whether the fermentation is done by a brewer, a distiller, or a baker. The brewer or distiller is interested primarily in the alcohol, while the baker is interested in the carbon dioxide, but both products are formed in any case. The purpose of promoting alcoholic fermentation in bread dough prior to baking is to provide adequate and uniform aeration of the dough so that a well-risen loaf of desired volume and texture will result.

That the ancient peoples had a considerable knowledge of the process of fermentation has been well established. Apparently the knowledge of breadmaking also dates back to very ancient times. According to Frey (1930), breadmaking was known to the ancient lake dwellers of Switzerland, to the Babylonians, and to the ancient Egyptians. The Egyptians apparently regarded the art of fermentation as a divine gift from the god Osiris. The Hebrews were quite familiar with the yeasting (leavening) process, as is obvious from the Scriptural instructions for the first Passover, where there is a clear distinction between leavened and unleavened bread. The fermentation power of even a small amount of yeast is well stated by Paul in I Corinth. 5:6: "Know ye not that a little leaven leaveneth the whole lump?" In the early days of breadmaking, bakes were probably yeasted by mixing into the fresh dough a small amount of unbaked dough (leaven) from a previous batch. The term "sourdough" applied to pioneer trappers and prospectors probably arose from their habit of saving a lump of yeasted dough from one baking to the next—to avoid the alternative of eating hardtack.

The first important advance in the yeasting process in breadmaking came in the early eighteenth century when it became a general practice to use brewers' yeast for the inoculation of bread dough. The bread-making industry was thus dependent upon the brewing industry for its yeast until a definite organization came into existence for the purpose of culturing breadmaking yeast in large quantities. Although the intro-duction of brewers' yeast in the baking process was unquestionably a marked improvement over the older method of keeping the yeast alive, the bread made at that time was not the uniform product we have to-day, since yeast obtained from the brewery varied greatly in quality, causing a marked variation in the amount of rise of the dough from batch to batch.

The compressed-yeast industry began about 1840 with the develop-ment of the Vienna process, in which yeast was propagated in $15°$ to to $20°$ Balling unaerated grain mash. After 20 to 23 hours the yeast was skimmed off, washed, and separated from undissolved grain par-ticles, then washed again and pressed. Yields of yeast obtained through the Vienna process were about 10 to 14 per cent, depending upon the grain used. The discovery that strong aeration during fermentation in-creased the yeast yields, together with other improvements of the proc-ess, finally resulted in yeast yields of about 40 per cent. According to Frey (*loc. cit.*) the first compressed yeast manufactured in the United States was made by Gaff, Fleischman and Company in Cincinnati, Ohio.

Problems encountered by the early compressed-yeast industry were numerous. The bakers who were accustomed to the use of brewers' yeast had to be educated to the use of compressed yeast; the yeast had to be cultured so as to assure uniform production and a uniform prod-uct; the distribution of compressed yeast before the advent of mechani-cal refrigeration presented many difficulties, and plants had to be built in widely separated localities to assure satisfactory and prompt distri-bution throughout the country. That the industry has overcome all of these difficulties is well exemplified by the fact that by the middle 1930's approximately 230 million lb of compressed yeast were being produced annually in this country.

The next important advance in large-scale yeast production following improvement of the Vienna process was the ammonia-molasses process, developed in Germany early in World War I. The Allied blockade, resulting in scarcity and high cost of grain in Germany, provided strong

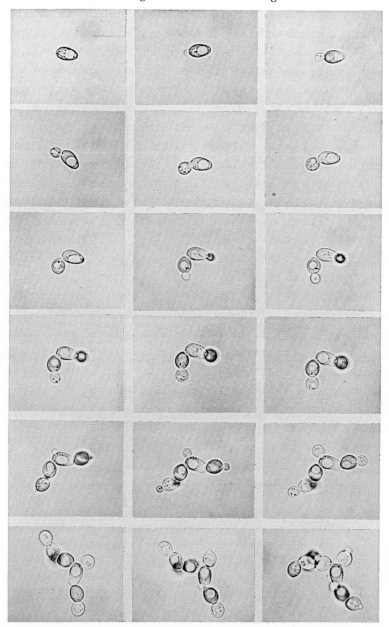

FIG. 49. Saccharomyces cerevisiae, ×1000. *Photomicrographs taken at 15 minute intervals and illustrating the budding process by which this organism multiplies vegetatively. (Courtesy The Fleischmann Laboratories, Standard Brands Incorporated.)*

motivation for intensive research in this area. In the German process, molasses is supplied as the carbon source, and ammonia, which can be synthesized, is used as the nitrogen source. The phosphate content of the molasses can be increased if necessary, but the sugar content of the medium is not as high as in the Vienna process. Careful control of *p*H, temperature, sugar concentration, and aeration is maintained throughout the growth period of the yeast, and the medium in which the yeast is cultured is highly aerated by the passage of large volumes of sterile air into the bottom of the culture tank. After the growing process is completed, the yeast is separated from the spent medium either by filtration or by centrifuging, after which it is washed and pressed. Starch may be added to the yeast before pressing in order to facilitate molding of yeast cakes.

In compressed-yeast manufacture only selected strains of *Saccharomyces cerevisiae* are used (Fig. 49), the strain selected by each yeast manufacturer depending to a large extent upon past experience with the various strains tested. In order to meet the demands of a highly mechanized baking industry in which the various steps are timed and synchronized, the yeast manufacturer must deliver a product with a high degree of uniformity that will produce the same predictable results for the baker in a specified time period day after day.

Pavcek and his co-workers (1938) have compared yields of yeast obtained with different species and strains of yeast on different types of

Table 9.—Yields of dry yeast from various media

Type of Yeast	Grain Medium (%)	Molasses-salts Medium (%)	Glucose-salts Medium (%)
Bakers' Yeast A	24.3	34.6	18.0
Bakers' Yeast B	42.5	33.6	34.3
Brewers' Yeast A	34.6	42.7	29.0
Brewers' Yeast A (autoclaved medium)	32.2		
Saccharomyces logos	33.1	28.0	21.4
Willia anomala	21.4	28.6	11.4
Endomyces vernalis	40.9	33.6	30.5

From Pavcek and others, (1938).

media and have demonstrated that yields vary not only with the type of yeast used but also with the type of medium. The results of their studies are summarized in Table 9.

Many of the details of commercial yeast production are protected by patents, and some are in the category of trade secrets. It can be stated in general, however, that in such processes yeasts are cultured in dilute sugar medium to which an inexpensive nitrogen source (such as ammonia) and mineral salts have been added. The medium in which the yeast is cultivated is vigorously aerated by the passage of sterile air into the culture vessel, and pH, temperature, etc. are closely controlled throughout the growth period. Pavcek and others (1937) have designed an apparatus for the culturing of yeasts; this apparatus is diagrammed in Fig. 50.

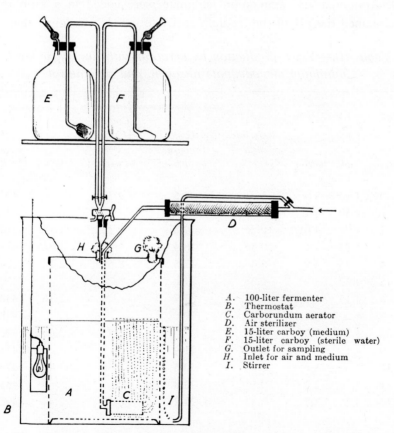

A. 100-liter fermenter
B. Thermostat
C. Carborundum aerator
D. Air sterilizer
E. 15-liter carboy (medium)
F. 15-liter carboy (sterile water)
G. Outlet for sampling
H. Inlet for air and medium
I. Stirrer

FIG. 50. *Diagram of apparatus used for culturing yeast. (From Pavcek, Peterson, and Elvehjem, 1937.)*

A continuous process for the production of pure culture distillers' yeast has been developed and described by Stark and others (1941) for use in distillery fermentations, but such a process might well serve for the large-scale production of yeast for the bakery industry and for other uses. As a culture medium, Stark and his co-workers used a wort prepared from a 40 per cent corn, 30 per cent distillers' barley malt, and 30 per cent long-fibre barley malt sprouts mash adjusted to 10° Balling (approximately 10 per cent sugar). One liter of this medium was inoculated with sufficient yeast to provide an initial cell count of 400 million per ml; this was then aerated at a rate of 0.4 cfm of air per gal. When the sugar concentration of the medium had decreased to 0.3 to 0.5 per cent, fresh wort was supplied at a controlled rate to prevent increase in sugar concentration of the medium in the culture vessel. Ammonia and ammonium sulphate were added in a ratio that maintained the pH of the medium at 4.1 to 4.3. It was found that up

Table 10.—Yeast production by aeration with low sugar level, minimum air, adequate nitrogen, and pH control

Hour	pH	Balling	Reducing sugar (g/100 ml)	Amino nitrogen (mg/100 ml)	Nitrogen Content of Yeast (% by weight)	Alcohol	Cell Count (× 10^6)
0	4.13	5.9	3.73	25.6	9.35		400
1	4.39	4.1	0.43	16.6			470
2	4.01	4.05	0.36	17.8	9.12	1.72	510
3	3.92	4.1	0.36	18.4		1.82	413
4	4.25	3.9	0.36	17.5	8.55	2.12	475
5	4.22	3.9	0.38	27.6			450
6	4.15	4.6	0.67	31.7		2.16	430
7	4.20	3.8	0.47	20.0			488
8	4.15	3.7	0.40		8.75	2.06	506
9	4.16	3.9	0.42	21.9			425
10	4.30	3.8	0.40	20.5	8.88	2.40	470
11	4.26	4.2	0.55	28.8			483
12	4.35	3.7	0.37	24.2	8.19	2.44	492

After Stark and others (1941).

to 30 per cent of the total volume of the unit could be withdrawn every hour and replaced with an equal volume of fresh wort without reducing the cell count or causing an increase in sugar concentration. A summary of their data is presented in Table 10.

Literature Cited

Dattilo-Rubbo, S. 1938. The taxonomy of fungi of blue-veined cheese. *Trans. Brit. Mycol. Soc. 22:*174–180.

Doane, C. F., and Lawson, H. W. 1918. Varieties of cheese: descriptions and analyses. *U.S. Dept. Agr. Bull. 608.*

Frey, C. N. 1930. History and development of the modern yeast industry. *Ind. Eng. Chem. 22:*1154–1162.

Garard, I. D., Minsky, A., Baker, J. H., and Pascale, V. 1937. Identification of Roquefort cheese. *Ind. Eng. Chem. 29:*1167–1171.

Pavcek, P. L., Peterson, W. H., and Elvehjem, C. A. 1937. Effect of growth conditions on yield and vitamin B_1 of yeast. *Ind. Eng. Chem. 29:*536–541.

———. 1938. Factors affecting the vitamin B_1 content of yeast. *Ind. Eng. Chem. 30:*802–805.

Stark, W. H., Scalf, R. E., and Kolachov, P. J. 1942. The development of a continuous process for the production of pure culture distiller's yeast. In: Wilkie, H. F. and Kolachov, P. J. 1942, *Food for thought.* Indiana Farm Bureau, Inc., Indianapolis.

Thom., C. 1909. Camembert cheese problems in the United States. *U.S. Dept. Agr. Bur. Animal Ind. Bull. 115.*

——— and Currie, J. N. 1913. The dominance of Roquefort mold in cheese. *Jour. Biol. Chem. 15:*249–258.

——— and Fisk, W. W. 1925. *The book of cheese.* Macmillan, New York.

7 · *Production of Livestock Feed*

FOR A BALANCED DIET man must have all three of the basic food types: carbohydrates, fats, and proteins. Man's fats and carbohydrates may be derived from quite varied sources, but generally he seems to prefer meat as the source of his protein. Because of his decided preference for this type of protein man must rear and maintain large quantities of livestock, even though the production of animal protein is a highly inefficient process and involves the loss of tremendous quantities of food energy. In countries such as the United States, where there are large acreages of suitable grazing land in addition to ample farm land, the maintenance of such large herds and flocks presents no particular problem. But such land areas are steadily diminishing while the population is increasing at a rapid rate, leading inevitably to the time when such large acreages are not available for grazing purposes or for the production of grain for livestock feeding. One need but drive through any agricultural area today to see what was formerly productive agricultural land now devoted to superhighways, industrial installations, building sites, and the ubiquitous and constantly growing cemeteries. The time is approaching when more efficient means of producing food for livestock must be developed in order that larger areas of grazing land may be devoted to home building and more grain diverted directly into human foodstuffs.

The possibilities of substituting yeast proteins (at least in part) for meat proteins in the human diet have been discussed briefly in Chapter 5. However, even if this substitution may be desirable in regions where the average diet is low in proteins, it is hardly necessary in the United States at the present time, although some steps have been taken in that direction. A partial solution to the problem of supplying meat protein in protein-poor areas would be to process inedible organic materials so as to obtain nutritious, high-protein products suitable for use in feeding livestock. The best possibility seems to be to use micro-organisms for processing such material, since these organisms are known to be capable of synthesizing their amino acids and their proteins from simple chemical compounds.

The production of edible livestock feed from otherwise inedible or nonpalatable material has been conducted commercially only on a limited scale and only in time of national emergency. For example, Pringsheim and Lichtenstein (1920) reported the feeding of processed straw to cattle in Germany as an emergency measure during World War I. As a source of nitrogen for amino acid synthesis, ammonium salts were added to the straw, which was then inoculated with a species of *Aspergillus*. After a suitable incubation period in which the fungus grew and thus synthesized protein, the processed straw was then used for feeding purposes. The resultant material, though scarcely a highly nutritious food, could nevertheless be used, and analyses showed that the protein content of the straw was increased about 9-fold during processing. Complete analyses of straw before and after such treatment are shown in Table 11.

Many filamentous fungi as well as yeasts are capable of growing upon synthetic media containing a carbohydrate, a few mineral salts, and an inorganic nitrogen compound. Their capacity to grow under

Table 11.—*Analysis of straw before and after it had been used to support growth of* Aspergillus sp.

Materials Present	Untreated Straw (%)	"Fungus" Straw (%)
Ash	9.1	14.0
Ash (water soluble)	3.9	4.9
Crude protein	0.9	8.0
Ammonium sulphate	—	0.1
Cellulose	50.3	50.7
Pentosans	26.8	10.2
Lignin	12.9	17.0
Crude fiber	55.0	49.5
Nitrogen free extractables	35.0	28.4

From Pringsheim and Lichtenstein (1920).

such conditions indicates that they are capable of synthesizing all of the protein they need for growth; however, this protein is not necessarily composed of all of the amino acids in the quantities needed by other types of living organisms. For example, Skinner and Muller (1940) cultured several fungi (*Aspergillus nidulans, A. flavus, Geotrichum lactis, Penicillium flavo-glaucum, P. rouqefortii* and two unidentified species of *Penicillium*) on a medium of inorganic salts and sugar, recovered the mycelium, and fed it to weanling rats as a sole source of protein. Growth rate of the rats was slow unless one of the amino acids, methionine or cystine, was added. By adding cystine at a level of 0.25 per cent to the diet these investigators were able to rear rats to maturity using only fungus protein.

The work of Hughes (1956) on Basidiomycete proteins indicates that the constituent amino acids of fungus proteins vary in quantity with the species, hence some such proteins might be less effective in an animal diet than others. The fact that a fungus protein is low in some essential amino acid need not necessarily be a deterring factor to its use as a food, since the work of Skinner and Muller has already shown that a single amino acid may be added to the diet to correct such a deficiency.

One very valuable livestock feed has been produced for a long time as a by-product of one of the fermentation industries. In the production of grain alcohol, whole grain is ground, mixed with water, cooked, the starch converted to fermentable sugar by means of malt enzymes, and the converted grain mash then inoculated with yeast. During the fermentation that follows little is removed from the original grain except the carbohydrate, which is converted to alcohol by the yeast. Hence when the alcohol is removed from the fermented mash by distillation the fats, proteins, minerals, and vitamins of the original grain, plus the yeast cells (which also have considerable nutritive value), remain in the still residues. These residues (previously called "slop" but now more delicately referred to as "stillage") were formerly dumped into the nearest stream except for an occasional tankful given or sold to farmers in the vicinity for livestock food. Because such practices naturally created stream pollution problems, other means had to be found for the disposal of these fermentation wastes. Little of this stillage material is discarded today, since it has been found to contain many nutritious materials that form the basis of several valuable livestock feeds.

As it comes from the still, stillage contains about 7 per cent solids. Many of these solids are large fragments of grain and can be recovered simply by passing the stillage over screens of suitable mesh. The material that collects on the screens contains about 75 per cent water; the water content may then be reduced to about 65 per cent by pressing. The resultant pressed caked is further dehydrated by means of suitable dryers, so that the final product contains about 8–10 per cent moisture. Grain so recovered, usually referred to as Light Distillers' Dried Grain, is sold as livestock feed.

The material passing through the screens on which the larger solid particles are suspended is also high in nutritional value. This material ("thin stillage") contains about 4 per cent solids (smaller grain particles, yeast cells, and many materials in solution). From such thin stillage is prepared the most nutritious of all of the distillery by-products—Distillers' Dried Solubles. Since the water content of thin stillage is quite high, it is first concentrated to a syrup (about 30 per cent solids) in suitable multiple-effect evaporators, and then pumped through small orifices onto the surface of a steam-heated rotating drum dryer. The syrup is dried to a moisture content of about 5–8 per cent. A thin layer of dried solubles is formed which leaves the dryer in a continuous sheet about ⅕₀ in. thick (Fig. 51). The sheet is broken into small flakes

FIG. 51.   *Drum dryer on which evaporator syrup is dried to a thin sheet of distillers' dried solubles. Note continuous sheet of dried solubles coming off the heated drum.*

which are then conveyed to the weighing and bagging room. Distillers' Dried Solubles vary in color from straw to dark brown; they are usually employed as a feed supplement.

In some distilleries Light Distillers' Dried Grain and Distillers' Dried Solubles are not prepared as such, but a single dried product containing all of the materials in the stillage is recovered. The process of screening is conducted as described above and the screened material is subjected to pressing; however, as the press cake is fed to the dryers, evaporator syrup (concentrated thin stillage) is added to the cake, which is dried to a moisture content of 8–10 per cent. Such material is marketed as Dark Distillers' Dried Grain.

Since the alcohol industry is the oldest fermentation industry, the recovery of livestock food by-products is perhaps better developed there than in any other phase of the industry. It is quite probable that wastes of other fermentation industries could be similarly recovered as valuable livestock feeds with little further processing. According to Beesch and Shull (1955), 85 per cent of the potential stillage of the grain distillery industry may now be converted to distillers' dried feeds. Another 14 per cent is being fed wet to animals, so that only 1 per cent is wasted.

Usually only a negligible amount of a product for which there is a heavy and continuously expanding demand can continue to be supplied as a by-product of another industry. A solution to the ever-increasing demands for livestock feed will, accordingly, not be met through other fermentation industries alone, but only through the development of procedures designed solely for the production of such materials. In other words, a primary product—not a secondary one—is needed. There is little choice of raw materials for use in such a process. It was pointed out earlier that many fungi are capable of synthesizing proteins from carbohydrates and inorganic nitrogen compounds. However, the problem is not solved merely by using sugar or starch and ammonia and then reaping a harvest of protein. As the human population increases there is an increasing demand for carbohydrates as well as fats and proteins. It would scarcely be logical, therefore, to use man's edible carbohydrates for the production of his edible proteins, since this would merely be a case of robbing Peter to pay Paul. The only real solution lies in the use of carbon-containing materials, inedible in so far as both man and his livestock are concerned, and yet suitable for the growth of fungi if inorganic nitrogen compounds are added. The choice then must be cellulose, lignin, and some of the organic compounds commonly associated (in lesser amounts) with these abundant compounds. The use of lignin for such purpose is especially desirable, since it would not only provide livestock feed, but would also lessen the problem of lignin disposal as a waste product of paper manufacturing.

We are repeatedly told that if man continues at his present rate of power consumption, the raw materials for running his industrial machine will be exhausted in a relatively short period of time. It has been stated that unless atomic energy is put to widespread use, our continuous industrial expansion must eventually come to a halt. These statements appear to be concerned only with industrial energy. It seems just as logical that as populations increase there may be a dearth of food energy, a problem of more immediate biological importance to man.

Attempts to solve the chemical riddle of photosynthesis have added much to our understanding of how this process occurs in the green plant, but as yet nothing applicable to the solution of the food problem has come out of these extended investigations. It is true that if man could find ways of combining solar energy, soil water, and atmospheric carbon dioxide through artificial photosynthesis in a factory installation, much additional carbohydrate could be produced. Yet this would not be a complete solution to the food problem, since carbohydrates merely provide the energy for running the animal machine; the machine itself must still be built largely of protein.

Literature Cited

Beesch, S. C. and Shull, G. M. 1955. Fermentation. *Ind. Eng. Chem. 47:* 1857–1875.

Hughes, S. B. 1956. Amino acids in acid hydrolysates of some Basidiomycete sporocarps. Ph.D. Dissertation, The Ohio State University (unpublished).

Pringsheim, H. and Lichtenstein, S. 1920. Versuche zur Anreicherung von Kraftstroh mit Pilzeiweiss. *Cellulosechemie 1:*29–39.

Skinner, C. E. and Muller, A. E. 1940. Cystine and methionine deficiency in mold proteins. *Jour. Nutrition 19:*333–344.

8 · *Fungi in Medicine*

ERGOT
ANTIBIOTIC SUBSTANCES
SYNTHESIS OF *l*-EPHEDRINE BY YEAST
MICROBIOLOGICAL TRANSFORMATIONS OF STEROIDS
SYNTHESIS OF VITAMINS BY FUNGI
POSSIBLE THERAPEUTIC USES OF YEAST

THE USE OF FUNGI for medicinal purposes has a rather curious history. In much earlier times various fungi were used extensively for their supposed curative properties, but this use gradually declined. During the past two decades, however, attention has once again been focused on the real and potential applications of fungi and fungus metabolic products in medicine.

The decline in the widespread usage of fungi from earlier times was not unique but more or less paralleled the general decline in usage of botanicals in materia medica. Along with other botanical materials, many fungi were reputedly of great importance in medieval and ancient medical practice, and miraculous curative powers often were ascribed to them. As more exact medical and pharmacological information accumulated, it became apparent that these alleged curative properties could not be verified, and such materials were gradually dropped from professional medical use. The supposed curative properties of plants are still reflected in the common names of such plants as "Heart's ease," "Balm of Gilead," and the like.

Rolfe and Rolfe (1928) have recorded the views of many earlier writers concerning the curative properties of fungi. For example, Hippocrates (5th century B.C.) recommended cauterization with fungi for the cure of certain complaints. Dioscorides, whose writings appeared several centuries later (about 200 A.D.), believed fungi could cure a great many ailments and were an almost universal remedy. Gerard (1597), one of the famous early Herbalists, devoted considerable space to his discussion of the curative properties of "agaricke," stating that it would cure asthma and yellow jaundice, among other complaints. With further development of medicine and the placing of pharmacology upon a more scientific basis, only a few species of fungi are now used medicinally except perhaps in some of the less advanced areas of the world. Rolfe and Rolfe state that in 1928 the only fungous material listed in the British Pharmacopeia was *Claviceps purpurea,* the ergot fungus.

Ergot

Claviceps purpurea, the causal organism of the plant disease, ergot of rye, has long been used as a drug for obstetric purposes to induce uterine contractions in cases of delayed childbirth. Although earlier obstetricians and midwives were undoubtedly familiar with the use of ergot, it was not officially admitted into the London College of Physicians Pharmacopeia until 1836. According to Barger (1931) the U.S. Pharmacopeia was the first official publication to admit ergot (1820); however, this drug was included among "such substances as were deemed of secondary or doubtful efficiency."

The ergot fungus is a member of the Ascomycetes, which ordinarily parasitizes rye but may affect other grasses. Since *Claviceps purpurea* forms its asci in perithecia, it is further classified in the series Pyrenomycetes of the subclass Euascomycetes. The organism forms hard, compact, black masses of fungus tissue called *sclerotia,* each of which replaces a kernel of the infected rye plant (Fig. 52). Preparations used for medicinal purposes are derived from the sclerotia. As a disease of rye, ergot is as a rule relatively unimportant in the United States, although in other countries yield reductions due to infections by *C. purpurea* may be quite large. For example, Chester (1942) points out that losses as high as 20 per cent have been suffered in Russia.

Initial infection of rye (or other grasses) occurs in the spring when the plant is in flower, the time when the ascospores of the fungus are forcibly discharged from the perithecia. These wind-disseminated spores germinate on contact with the flowers, the germ tube entering the

FIG. 52. *Heads of rye infected with the ergot fungus,* Claviceps purpurea. *Note the replacement of rye kernels by the dark fungus sclerotia.*

young ovulary. The first noticeable effect of the fungus on rye is that the ovularies of young flowers are covered with white filaments (hyphae). From these filaments short conidiophores bearing minute conidia develop. Insects visit the infected flowers, since the conidia are mixed with a sweet, sticky liquid ("honey dew") which is attractive to insects; the conidia may then be carried to other flowers where they germinate and thus establish other infections. Each infected ovulary gradually becomes replaced by a mass of fungus tissue which becomes hard in texture, purple to black in color, and which may be several times the size of a mature rye kernel. These structures (sclerotia) are found protruding from the head of rye in place of "healthy" kernels. The number of sclerotia occurring in a single head of rye is dependent upon the number of infected ovularies. In the very early spring several spherical, stalked stromata may develop from each sclerotium. The perithecia, containing asci and ascospores, are imbedded in the stromata.

Ergot is the source of a very valuable medicine, which like almost any other drug can be quite harmful (or fatal) if taken too frequently or in excessive quantity. Ergot not only induces uterine contractions but causes contraction of the blood capillaries, and hence is also useful in controlling hemorrage during childbirth. However, the repeated ingestion of ergot through the continued eating of bread or other products made from ergot-containing flour may lead to a serious condition known as *ergotism,* characterized by severe convulsions (*convulsive ergotism*) or by a gangrenous condition (*gangrenous ergotism*) that may result in loss of limbs and death.

Prior to improvements in grain cleaning and milling processes, sclerotia were not separated from the kernels but harvested and milled with rye. Hence ergot was responsible for a great many fatalities in areas where rye bread was entensively consumed. Thus, 8000 people are reported to have died of gangrenous ergotism during an epidemic in the Sologne district of France in 1777 (Barger, 1931). Similar earlier epidemics in various other European countries are recorded; however, there are few recent instances of ergotism reaching epidemic proportions, although an extensive epidemic was reported in Russia in 1926–27, and Alexopoulos (1952) cites reports that a large number of people in the French village of Pont-St. Esprit died from ergotism in 1951. Attempts to induce abortion through the use of ergot may result in an occasional fatality, since ergot, like other powerful drugs, is dangerous except when used under the direction of a competent physician.

ACTIVE INGREDIENTS OF ERGOT.   Many attempts have been made to isolate the active principles of ergot. Tanret (1875) isolated an alkaloidal substance which he called *ergotinine* and which he regarded as the pure active principle. Later workers have isolated several substances which have been variously named: *ergotinic acid, cornutine, spacelotoxin, ergobasine, ergostetrine, ergometrine, ergotocin.* Differences of opinion concerning the identity of these substances obviously exist since Kharasch and others (1936) investigated ergobasine, ergostetrine, ergometrine, and ergotocin and concluded that these four compounds are the same substance. Considerable work must still be done in order to establish the number and chemical nature of the ergot alkaloids. For more detailed information concerning the chemistry of ergot, consult the monograph of Barger.

SOURCE OF ERGOT. Much of the ergot used in this country has been in the past obtained from Spain, Portugal, Russia, and Poland. Wolf and Wolf (1947) state that the alkaloid content of Spanish and Portugese ergot is higher than that of Russian or Polish ergot (0.05 to 0.30 per cent as compared with 0.02 to 0.10 per cent). Ergot sclerotia can be separated from uninfected rye kernels by placing "ergoty" rye in a 20 per cent sodium chloride solution; the sclerotia, having a lower specific gravity than rye kernels, float to the top and may be skimmed off. Use of a 32 per cent solution of potassium chloride solution for flotation separation was advocated by Nobbe (1904), since potassium chloride does not damage the seed.

CULTIVATION OF ERGOT. For many years the world's supply of ergot has been obtained from sclerotia of *C. purpurea,* separated from naturally infected rye. With improvements in agriculture, the advent of more efficient grain-cleaning processes, and the accumulation of more extensive knowledge concerning the parasitism of rye by *C. purpurea,* there has been a gradual reduction in the amount of infection by this organism with corresponding decrease in the amount of material available for medicinal purposes. In addition to the reduction in ergot supply due to the factors just mentioned, political developments in the principal ergot-producing countries (Spain and Russia) have also contributed to the reduction of the supply of ergot available to this country.

In view of the great pharmaceutical importance of ergot, some attention has logically been directed toward attempts to obtain this material from sources other than sclerotia obtained from naturally infected rye. Two general approaches have been made to the problem: (1) cultivating *C. purpurea* in pure culture on suitable media, and (2) artificial infection of rye in the field. Apparently the greatest difficulty associated with the production of ergot by a pure-culture method is that no one thus far has discovered the particular set of conditions under which the organism will develop sclerotia in culture; it is in the sclerotia that the active principles are concentrated. Thus, Bonns (1922) cultured *C. purpurea* on rye meal and sclerotia-like material formed in his cultures, but the material contained no trace of alkaloid. McCrea (1931) also attempted to obtain sclerotia in pure cultures and was unable to do so; however, in her cultures pseudo-parenchymatous mycelia were compacted in knotlike structures. She obtained good mycelial growth upon the following medium:

calcium nitrate	1.0 g
monobasic potassium phosphate	1.25 g
magnesium sulphate	0.625 g
sugar	30.0 g
water	1000 ml

This same investigator also reported that as a carbon source maltose sugar yielded better results than dextrose, levulose, or sucrose, and that a 3 per cent sugar concentration in the medium was adequate, since increasing the concentration had no effect upon the yield of mycelium. McCrea (1936) was issued a patent covering the commercial production of ergot fungus, but it is doubtful if ergot has been produced commercially by this method.

Kreitmair and Küssner (1931) cultured *C. purpurea,* harvested the mycelium, and prepared extracts whose alkaloid content they then determined. Their tests showed that the alkaloid content of the mycelium was up to 75 per cent of the U.S.P. Standard preparation.

More promising results have been obtained by infecting rye in the field than by attempting to produce the drug through the use of pure-culture methods. Production of ergot by this method can be accomplished only if the production "operators" are thoroughly familiar with the life cycle of *C. purpurea,* especially with regard to the manner in which the parasitic relationship is established. As was noted earlier, and as may be seen in the life cycle diagram (Fig. 53), *C. purpurea* forms two types of spores, either of which may lead to infection of the rye plant. While naturally occurring initial infection of the rye plant in the spring occurs by means of germinating ascospores, the greatest amount of infection undoubtedly occurs as a result of the conidia, which are formed in enormous numbers in the so-called *Spacelia* stage during which the ovulary becomes invested with fungus hyphae.

For the artificial infection of rye the use of conidia is obviously more logical than the use of ascospores, since the asexual spores may easily be obtained in quantity by pure-culture means or by diluting honey dew with water. Hecke (*cf.* Barger) sprayed newly opened rye flowers

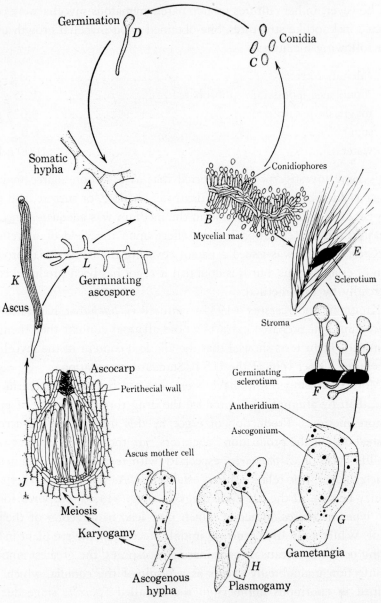

FIG. 53. *Diagrammatic life cycle of the ergot fungus,* Claviceps purpurea.
(From Alexopoulos, 1952.)

with a dilute suspension of conidia through an atomizer and on summer rye obtained a yield of 490 lb of ergot per acre. Hecke's experiments involved much hand labor, since he had to induce opening of the flowers artificially by shaking the rye heads or pulling them between the fingers. As Barger points out, the principal deterrent to the use of Hecke's method is that a large amount of trained labor would be required during one particular week of the year. McCrea also attempted artificial inoculation of rye in the field as a means of obtaining ergot on a large scale, but concluded that the method is impractical in Michigan because of the high cost of labor.

Although the cultivation of ergot by artificial inoculation of rye in the field does not seem to be commercially feasible or necessary at present, continued improvements in agriculture or changes in the world political situation may result in a scarcity of ergot, making it necessary eventually to produce the drug in this manner. On the other hand, such scarcity would very probably give impetus to efforts to obtain ergot through pure-culture methods, and with more intensified efforts along these lines it is altogether possible that the problem might be solved.

Antibiotic Substances

With the exception of such recent developments as nuclear fission and nuclear fusion, or the successful placing of a man-made satellite in orbit, no scientific advance in modern times has so stirred the interest and imagination as the discovery that penicillin, the metabolic product of a common green "mold," could be used to cure a variety of infections which yield slowly or not at all to treatment by other means. Sufficient evidence is now at hand to demonstrate adequately that the discovery of penicillin and its subsequent large-scale production is one of the major medical advances of all time. In the earlier stages of the investigation, penicillin received some unfavorable publicity in that miraculous powers were often ascribed to it, owing more to the overenthusiasm of some popular writers than to any desire to misconstrue the truth. Though not a cure-all, penicillin can be employed successfully in the treatment of pneumonia, gas gangrene, gonorrhea, bacteremias, and other diseases. Furthermore, response to penicillin therapy has been so spectacular in many instances that calling it a "miracle drug" is a pardonable generalization.

The development of the penicillin industry was an outstanding scientific and technological triumph, since in less than two decades a large industry has grown from a casual laboratory observation. The large-scale production of penicillin illustrates what can be accomplished in the development of a mold fermentation, and the rapid strides that can often be made in the solution of a scientific problem—provided adequate financial backing and technically trained personnel are available.

Table 12.—Some antibiotics from filamentous fungi

Antibiotic	Fungus
Aspergillic acid	*Aspergillus flavus*
Chaetomin	*Chaetomium cochliodes*
Citrinin	*Penicillium citrinum*
*Clavicin	*Aspergillus clavatus*
*Clavatin	" "
*Claviformin	*Penicillium claviforme*
†*E. coli* factor	*Penicillium notatum*
‡Flavicin	*Aspergillus flavus*
Fumagacin	*Aspergillus fumigatus*
¶Fumigatin	" "
‡Gigantic acid	*Aspergillus giganteus*
Gliotoxin	*Trichoderma sp.*
¶Helvolic acid	*Aspergillus fumigatus*
Kojic acid	*Aspergillus oryzae*
†Notatin	*Penicillium notatum*
‡Parasiticin	*Aspergillus parasiticus*
*Patulin	*Penicillium patulum*
†Penatin	*Penicillium notatum*
Penicidin	*Penicillium sp.*
Penicillic acid	*Penicillium puberulum*
Penicillin	*Penicillium notatum*
Penicillin	*Penicillium chrysogenum*
‡Penicillin B	*Penicillium notatum*
Puberulic acid	*Penicillium puberulum*
Spinulosin	*Aspergillus spinulosum*

* Identical symbols denote that the terms so marked are synonyms.
(From Waksman, 1945.)

Penicillin is a member of the class of substances known as *antibiotics,* or chemical substances synthesized by living organisms which have the capacity to inhibit the growth or metabolic activities of other living organisms. Obviously, the antibiotics we are primarily interested in are those that are effective against human pathogenic organisms. While more has probably been written about penicillin than most other antibiotics synthesized by microorganisms, it was not the first substance of this type discovered; *pyocyanin* and *gramicidin*—both bacteria-synthesized antibiotics—were discovered and tested before penicillin. A variety of organisms have been demonstrated to be capable of synthesizing antibiotics, and in Table 12 are listed some of the antibiotics of filamentous fungus origin.

Several very useful antibiotics (in addition to a great many which have no practical application at present) have been developed since the discovery of penicillin, their large-scale production facilitated by the experiences gained during the establishment of the penicillin industry. Since the study of antibiotics had its real basis in the development of the penicillin industry, the present discussion will be confined largely to a consideration of that industry. Some of the more widely used antibiotics are synthesized by Actinomycetes; however, because of their uncertain position, this group of organisms will be omitted from this discussion.

DISCOVERY OF AND EARLY STUDIES ON PENICILLIN. Penicillin was discovered quite accidently at St. Mary's Hospital in London by Dr. Alexander Fleming, who reported his findings in 1929. This discovery, which was one of the most remarkable cases of serendipity in science, was made when a culture of a pathogenic bacterium, *Staphylococcus aureus,* became contaminated with a fungus, a spore of which had lodged by chance in the petri dish. It soon became apparent that the fungus colony was inhibiting the growth of the bacterium, and Fleming named the unknown inhibitory substance *penicillin* since the contaminating organism was a species of the genus *Penicillium.* Fleming called the organism *P. rubrum,* but Dr. Charles Thom placed it close to *P. notatum.* Fleming studied the material further and suggested that penicillin might have clinical value if it could be produced on a large scale.

Penicillin was next investigated by Clutterbuck and others, who considered it from the standpoint both of its chemical structure and of its large-scale production. The yield they obtained was quite small, and after publishing their results in 1932 they turned to other studies. Work on penicillin was not resumed until seven years later, when a group at Oxford University under the leadership of Dr. Florey and including Drs. Abraham, Chain, and Heatley again started an investigation of this substance.

At this time a manpower shortage existed in England and the country was being bombed extensively; under such conditions England did not seem to be the most suitable place for the quick attainment of results. Accordingly the Rockefeller Foundation brought Florey and Heatley to this country (Coghill, 1944), and they were eventually sent to the Northern Regional Research Laboratory at Peoria, Illinois. In the meanwhile Dr. A. J. Moyer at the Peoria laboratory had discovered that the addition of corn steeping liquor (a by-product of corn products manufacture) to the fermentation medium increased penicillin yields from 2 Oxford Units (O.U. $= 0.6$ micrograms of penicillin) per ml up to 40 units; this discovery was the greatest single factor in making feasible the large-scale production of penicillin.

As dramatic as its discovery is the fact that penicillin arrived on the medical scene at such a comparatively recent date, since it was almost inevitable that antibiotic substances would be shown to exist. Waksman (1945) stated that during the latter part of the nineteenth century fear was expressed that soil might eventually become a serious source of infections and epidemics, since pathogenic bacteria are being continuously introduced into it. A careful study of the survival of pathogenic organisms in the soil revealed that the majority of such bacteria rapidly die out, due, it was suggested, to the activities of the naturally occurring soil microorganisms. Antibiotics were thus anticipated long ago, but apparently nothing of a specific nature was done to isolate them and attempt to use them in the control of bacterial infections. It is noteworthy that Waksman and others have gone to the soil in their attempts to isolate microorganisms which synthesize antibiotics of possible clinical value.

PRODUCTION METHODS. In the early phases of the development of the industry, penicillin was produced only by methods in which the fungus developed as a mat on the surface of shallow layers of culture medium. However, it was impossible to use large trays as culture vessels, since contaminants had to be excluded. Certain very common bacteria have the capacity to form *penicillinase,* an enzyme that quickly destroys penicillin; hence the earliest large-scale production of penicillin was accomplished in bottle or flask cultures. Such a method of production is quite expensive because of the great amount of hand labor involved, but it was the only method available until strains of *Penicillium* were found which were capable of forming penicillin in quantity in submerged cultures in large tanks. In addition to surface- and submerged-culture methods using liquid medium, Coghill (*loc. cit.*) mentions a third method by which penicillin was produced on a moist bran substrate. The sterile bran was spread in thin layers in trays or placed in slowly revolving rotary drums and inoculated with *P. notatum.* After a period of growth the penicillin was removed from the substrate by percolation with a suitable solvent. All of the penicillin which is produced commercially today is produced in submerged cultures in large tanks through which sterilized air is continuously passed (Fig. 54).

OPTIMUM CONDITIONS FOR PENICILLIN PRODUCTION. As noted earlier, when the English workers (Florey and Heatley) first came to the United States in connection with the penicillin problem the yield of penicillin was quite low, using Fleming's original strain of *P. notatum.* The first efforts were devoted to attempts to increase penicillin yields by establishing a set of conditions more favorable for the synthesis of this particular substance. It was early discovered that lactose is the best carbon source; this with Moyer's discovery of the beneficial effect of corn steeping liquor upon penicillin yield and various other improvements made upon the fermentation medium aided materially in enhancing yields during the first phases of the development work. Foster (1949) lists the following as components of a typical commercial production medium:

	per cent
Corn steep liquor solids	2–4
Lactose	2–4
$CaCO_3$	0.5–1
Precursor	0.1–0.5

The enhancing effect of corn steep liquor upon penicillin yields is apparently due to the presence of minerals (Knight and Frazier, 1945),

Fig. 54.   *Fermentation tanks (50,000 gallon capacity) used for the pro-*
duction of penicillin. (Courtesy of Commercial Solvents Corporation.)

amino acids (White and others, 1945), and penicillin precursors (Foster, p. 580). For further details of media used in penicillin production
the reader is referred to the works of Raper and Alexander (1945),
Pratt and Hok (1946), and Foster (*loc. cit.*).

Optimum temperature for penicillin synthesis is about 23–25 C, and
optimum *p*H for penicillin synthesis is between 7.5 and 8.0.

Since filamentous fungi are strongly aerobic, any process involving
their culture as submerged, discrete colonies in deep tanks must be so
designed to permit adequate aeration of the fermentation medium. In

the commercial production of penicillin this is accomplished by mechanical agitation with stirrers and by sparging sterilized air into the fermentation medium. Stefaniak and others (1946) report that in pilot plant fermenters an air flow of 0.25 to 1.0 volume per minute per volume of culture medium gives maximum penicillin yields, depending upon the efficiency of the mechanical agitation. Obviously, no general statement can be made concerning rate of air flow that will apply in all instances, since this optimum rate will vary with size and shape of the fermenter, volume of liquid medium, type of sparging system, rate of stirring, etc.

Koffler and others (1945, 1946) have reported that if certain substances other than corn steep liquor and precursors are added to the fermentation medium increased yields of penicillin will result. Using several penicillin-forming strains, they obtained increased yields (in some instances over 100 per cent) when boric acid or sodium citrate was added.

SELECTION OF HIGHER-YIELDING STRAINS. In the very early stages of the penicillin investigation, when there was some question as to whether or not large-scale production was at all feasible, anything that increased the yield, even if by only a few percentage points, was of value. For that reason the value of the early investigations relative to the establishment of optimum environmental conditions should not be underrated. Nevertheless the really large increases in penicillin yield were attained not by that approach, but rather by systematic attempts to obtain better-yielding fungus strains. Through selection and testing of monospore cultures derived from Fleming's original strain, culture NRRL 1249B.21 was derived. This high-yielding strain was used in the production on a commercial scale of the major portion of penicillin by the bottle-culture method. The history of this strain as well as the other strains used in the bottle-culture production of penicillin is outlined in Fig. 55.

Because the production of penicillin by the bottle-culture method is an expensive and unwieldy process, efforts were made early in the program to produce penicillin by submerged culture in large tanks. None of the cultures derived from the original Fleming strain gave satisfactory yields in submerged culture, so other strains were examined with regard to their capacities in this respect. The first culture to give satisfactory yields under submerged-culture conditions was NRRL 832, a member of the *Penicillium notatum-chrysogenum* group. Another culture, NRRL 1950, isolated at the Peoria Laboratory from moldy cheese, pro-

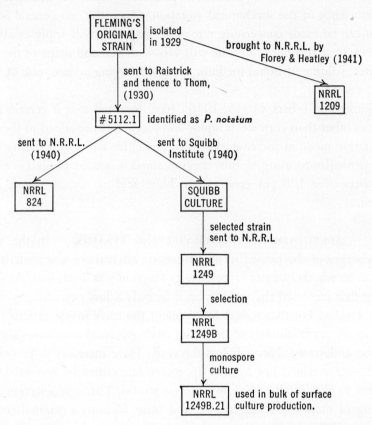

FIG. 55. *History of cultures of* P. notatum *used in the development of penicillin production by the bottle-culture method. (After Raper and Alexander, 1945.)*

duced higher yields than NRRL 832 (68 Oxford Units per milliliter as compared with 50); from this culture an ultraviolet-induced mutant was derived from which yields were obtained averaging 50–80 per cent higher than those obtained with NRRL 1950. Still another culture (NRRL 1951) was obtained which yielded penicillin of the order of 80–90 units per milliliter; this strain was isolated from a cantaloupe. By selections of X-ray and ultraviolet-induced mutants of NRRL 1951, a strain producing nearly 1000 units per ml was obtained (Fig. 56). The results obtained in attempts to develop high-yielding strains of penicil-lin-synthesizing organisms are of considerable significance to anyone interested in industrial fungus fermentations, since they point the way in which yields can be increased. While the determination and maintenance of optimum environmental conditions are important, more spectacular yield increases can be expected to be derived through selection of strains or by developing higher-yielding mutants.

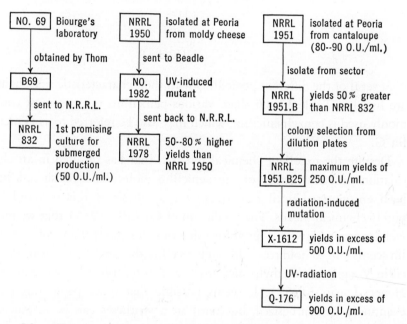

FIG. 56. *History of strains of the* Penicillium notatum-chrysogenum *group used in the development of penicillin production by the submerged-culture method. (After Raper, 1946.)*

CHEMISTRY OF PENICILLIN. Shortly after the great therapeutic value of penicillin became apparent, one line of investigation was devoted entirely to attempts to determine the molecular structure with the view of ultimately synthesizing this valuable drug. It was found that there are several penicillins, but that the basic structural formula is the same for each type, the principal difference being in the character of the side chain. According to Chain (1948) the structural formula of the penicillin molecule which is generally accepted is:

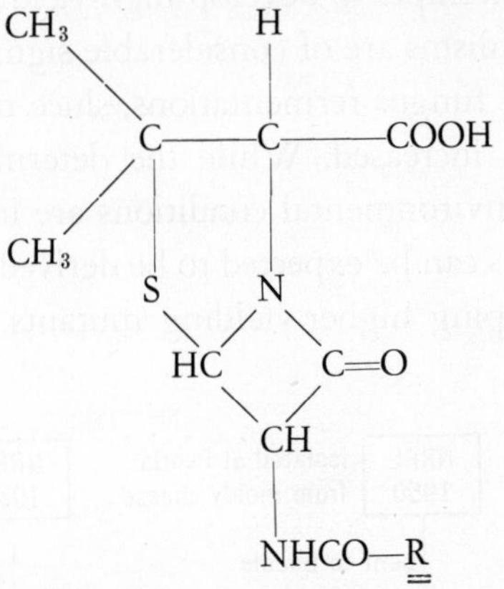

Several of the different penicillins with their characteristic side chains are listed in Table 13. Of these various penicillins the one most commonly used is benzylpenicillin, which may also be referred to as Penicillin G.

Despite the excellent chemical research that has resulted in an elucidation of the structure of the penicillin molecule, little success has been encountered until recently in the synthesis of this material by purely chemical means. The prediction of Coghill (1944) that we may well be dependent upon fungi for some time for the synthesis of penicillin seems still to hold true, although recently the total synthesis of Penicillin V (phenoxymethylpenicillin) was accomplished by Sheehan and Henery-Logan (1957). It seems possible that other penicillins may eventually be synthesized, but until such syntheses can be conducted

Table 13.—Types of penicillin

Name of Penicillin	Side Chain (R)	Empirical Formula
Δ^2-Pentenylpenicillin	$CH_3 \cdot CH_2 \cdot CH:CH \cdot CH_2-$	$C_{14}H_{20}O_4N_2S$
Δ^3-Pentenylpenicillin	$CH_3 \cdot CH:CH \cdot CH_2CH_2-$	$C_{14}H_{20}O_4N_2S$
n-Amylpenicillin	$CH_3 \cdot CH_2 \cdot CH_2 \cdot CH_2 \cdot CH_2-$	$C_{14}H_{22}O_4N_2S$
n-Heptylpenicillin	$CH_3 \cdot (CH_2)_5 \cdot CH_2-$	$C_{16}H_{26}O_4N_2S$
Benzylpenicillin	$C_6H_5 \cdot CH_2-$	$C_{16}H_{18}O_4N_2S$
p-Hydroxybenzylpenicillin	$HO \cdot C_6H_4 \cdot CH_2-$	$C_{16}H_{18}O_5N_2S$

economically we will still be dependent upon fungi for these antibiotics. Rather great possibilities seem to exist for the synthesis of new penicillins by using fungus-synthesized penicillin as the starting compound and preparing various derivatives of this material.

It has been found that if certain materials (in addition to lactose, $CaCO_3$, and corn steep liquor) are added to the fermentation medium, increased penicillin yields are obtained. Thus the addition of phenylacetic acid results in increased yields of benzylpenicillin (Moyer and Coghill, 1947). It is now known that phenylacetic acid is a precursor of benzylpenicillin. According to Foster (*loc. cit.*) it has been established that tyramine and *p*-hydroxyphenylacetic acid are precursors of *p*-hydroxybenzylpenicillin.

ANTIBIOTICS AND THE FUTURE. Although several volumes have already been written on the subject (Waksman, 1945; Duggar and others, 1948; Florey and others, 1949), the antibiotics industry and the study of antibiotics are both in their infancy. Table 14 however, shows the industry to be an extremely healthy one.

The account above has dealt primarily with penicillin, but since the spectacular development of the penicillin industry, several other antibiotics have come into prominence. Thus, *aureomycin, streptomycin, terramycin,* and others (all metabolic products of species of Actinomycetes: "ray fungi" or bacterialike organisms whose exact position in a system of classification is at present not known) have been isolated and have been shown to have great clinical value. A great many other antibiotic substances have been investigated and many fungi are being systematically tested for capacity to synthesize antibiotics (e.g., Robbins, 1946).

The search for new antibiotics must continue, since in no sense can we consider penicillin, aureomycin, or streptomycin to have furnished all the answers to the problem of the control of human diseases. As Waksman (1945) has pointed out, one of the principal problems is concerned with the increasing resistance of certain strains of bacteria to specific antibiotics after prolonged contact. Thus individuals of a penicillin-resistant strain of streptococcus might develop in numbers sufficient to render penicillin virtually valueless in the treatment of infections by this particular strain, and a search would have to be made for a new, more effective antibiotic. Intriguing possibilities also exist with respect to the discovery and isolation of antibiotics effective against diseases that are scarcely affected at all by the now known antibiotics.

The antibiotic story has not been entirely devoid of mishaps. Living in the human gastrointestinal tract as a normal part of the microflora are several yeastlike organisms which are usually harmless to the individual.

Table 14.—U.S. production, sales, and dollar value of some antibiotic substances

Antibiotic	Year	Production (lb)	Sales (lb)	Dollar Value
Penicillin, including salts	1951	625,000	487,000	137,517,000
	1952	671,000	588,000	82,655,000
	1953	753,000	708,000	57,752,000
	1954	861,000	NA	NA
Streptomycin	1951	39,000	36,000	6,051,000
	1952	50,000	51,000	4,876,000
	1953	125,000	104,000	10,785,000
	1954	137,000	NA	NA
Dihydrostreptomycin	1951	315,000	264,000	40,703,000
	1952	337,000	301,000	34,213,000
	1953	305,000	297,000	24,547,000
	1954	359,000	NA	NA
Bacitracin	1951	NA	NA	NA
	1952	4,000	NA	NA
	1953	6,000	4,000	1,520,000
	1954	NA	NA	NA
All others, including broad-spectrum antibiotics	1951	307,000	268,000	132,787,000
	1952	425,000	391,000	144,829,000
	1953	441,000	354,000	136,880,000
	1954	NA	NA	NA
Antibiotics for feed supplements	1951	236,000	196,000	17,532,000
	1952	258,000	172,000	16,962,000
	1953	434,000	391,000	19,423,000
	1954	NA	NA	NA
Total antibiotics for human or veterinary use	1951	1,286,000	1,055,000	317,058,000
	1952	1,487,000	1,321,000	266,574,000
	1953	1,630,000	1,467,000	231,484,000
	1954	NA	NA	NA

NA: not available. Data from Beesch and Shull (1955).

When certain antibiotics are administered orally, the bacteria of the gastrointestinal tract are killed or inhibited and only the yeastlike organisms remain. When the competitive organisms (bacteria) are removed in this manner the fungi may become pathogenic and cause a disease more serious than the one that was being treated. Fortunately in the past several years there has been considerable effort directed toward the search for antibiotics that are antifungal in their activity so that fungus infections following oral administration of antibacterial antibiotics may be controlled in this manner.

Synthesis of l-*Ephedrine by Yeast*

The use of the alkaloid *l*-ephedrine apparently has been quite common in Oriental countries since ancient times, but its introduction into the United States has occurred only recently. Formerly this drug was obtained primarily from two species of flowering plants of the genus *Ephedra* (*E. equisetina* and *E. sinica*) which occur in China. From this crude drug-containing plant material, known as *ma huang*, *l*-ephedrine can be obtained by an extraction process followed by recrystallization. Natural ephedrine is levorotary, the structural formula being

$$C_6H_5 \cdot CHOH \cdot CH \cdot NH \cdot CH_3$$
$$\underset{\displaystyle CH_3}{\overset{\displaystyle |}{}}$$

A dextrorotary isomer is usually found with *l*-ephedrine, but the isomer apparently is of little pharmacological importance. For the treatment of asthma and as a nasal astringent, *l*-ephedrine has had wide usage. Kamlet (1941) states that the domestic production of this drug in 1939 was valued at over half a million dollars, while the value of ephedrine-containing nose-drops, inhalants, and sprays was many times greater.

With a compound as valuable as ephedrine it was inevitable that its synthesis would be attempted. Although several investigators have been able to accomplish this synthesis, all such processes yield optically inactive ephedrine (*i.e.*, *dl*-1-phenyl-2-methylaminopropanol). The separation of the optical isomers is a difficult and expensive process, and such racemic mixtures, though used for medicinal purposes, cannot be sold under the name ephedrine, since this name is reserved for *l*-ephedrine only.

Neuberg and his co-workers (1921, 1922) found that if benzaldehyde was added slowly and with continuous stirring to a heavily inoculated (1000 g of yeast per 25 l of glucose solution) fermentation, a mixture of *l*-acetylphenylcarbinol, benzyl alcohol, and benzoic acid, was produced. These compounds were separated by ether extraction of the spent fermentation medium, and upon evaporation of the ether an oily substance ("Neuberg's oil") remained. From 100 g of benzaldehyde, 91 g of oil was obtained; of this, 25 g was *l*-acetylphenylcarbinol which was formed by a dismutation reaction between the added benzaldehyde and acetaldehyde, which is an intermediate compound in the biosynthesis of ethyl alcohol. Similar mixed dismutation reactions are known, but according to Tauber (1949) this particular reaction cannot be carried out by chemical means. The mixed dismutation of acetaldehyde and benzaldehyde is catalyzed by a yeast enzyme which Neuberg named *carboligase.*

Hildebrant and Klavehn (1934) have developed and patented a process for synthesizing *l*-ephedrine using *l*-acetylphenylcarbinol from "Neuberg's oil" as the starting compound for the synthesis. Their method involves the formation of a condensation product of *l*-acetylphenylcarbinol with methylamine, followed by reduction of the condensation product to *l*-ephedrine. An alternate method is to conduct the condensation and reduction reactions simultaneously so that the condensation product is reduced as soon as it is formed. The reaction involved in the synthesis of *l*-acetylphenylcarbinol and the further reactions leading to the formation of *l*-ephedrine may be written as follows:

$$C_6H_5 \cdot CHO \quad + \quad CH_3 \cdot CHO \xrightarrow{\text{carboligase}} C_6H_5 \cdot CHOH \cdot CO \cdot CH_3$$

benzaldehyde   acetaldehyde   carboligase   *l*-acetylphenylcarbinol

$$C_6H_5 \cdot CHOH \cdot CO \cdot CH_3 + CH_3NH_2 \longrightarrow C_6H_5 \cdot CHOH \cdot C:N \cdot CH_3$$

methylamine

$$CH_3$$

$$C_6H_5 \cdot CHOH \cdot C:N \cdot CH_3 \quad + \quad 2H \xrightarrow{\text{catalyst}} C_6H_5 \cdot CHOH \cdot CH \cdot NH \cdot CH_3$$

$$CH_3 \qquad\qquad\qquad\qquad\qquad\qquad\qquad CH_3$$

l-ephedrine

Hildebrant and Klavehn claim yields of 25–45 g of *l*-ephedrine hydrochloride from 120 g of Neuberg's oil. For catalysis of the reduction, they recommend the use of activated aluminum or colloidal platinum. In their patent claim it is pointed out that the advantage of direct synthesis of the levorotary form is that the costly separation of the two isomers is avoided. Kamlet stated in 1941 that a major American chemical company was producing *l*-ephedrine by this process, and predicted that *l*-ephedrine so produced might completely replace the natural product.

Microbiological Transformations of Steroids

In comparatively recent years a development has arisen in medicine which has already yielded compounds of great importance and eventually may lead to the synthesis of other new and extremely valu-

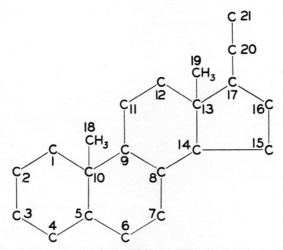

FIG. 57. *Basic structure of the steroid nucleus, showing the system used in numbering the various carbon atoms.*

able medicinals. This development had its beginning with the work of Hench and others (1949) who found that both *cortisone* and *ACTH* (adrenocorticotropic hormone) could be used with striking results in the treatment of patients with severe rheumatoid arthritis. Their work, made possible by the synthesis of cortisone by Sarett (1946), has stimulated the development of new syntheses of *steroid* compounds.

The steroids are a group of organic compounds which are biologically quite important; all compounds of this class possess the *cyclopentanoperhydrophenanthrene* nucleus. Since the isolation of the first steroid hormone, the structure of the steroid nucleus has been established, and four endocrine glands (testis, ovary, adrenal cortex, and placenta of pregnancy) have been shown to form steroid hormones. The basic molecular structure of carbon-21 steroids is shown in Fig. 57, as well as the system used to number the various carbon atoms in the molecule. Nineteen-carbon steroids are also known, in which the carbon atoms numbered 20 and 21 are missing. The rings may all be saturated or may be unsaturated at a number of positions. Figure 58 illustrates the

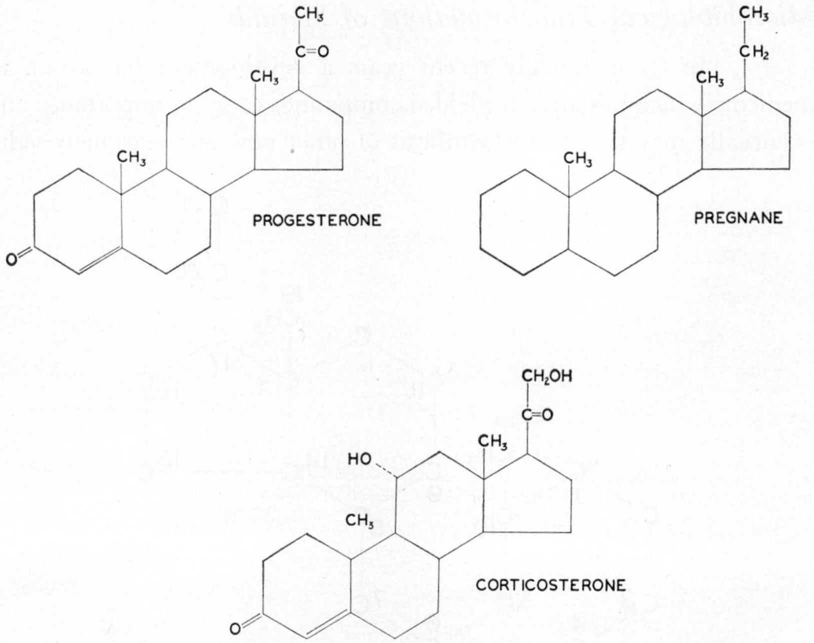

FIG. 58. *Molecular structures of three steroids: progesterone, pregnane, and corticosterone, showing their basic similarity of structure.*

structure of three steroids and demonstrates the basic similarity of their structure. Because all steroids do not have the same physiological activity, it is important that the steroid chemist be able to alter the molecule in a variety of ways in order to obtain the desired compound.

Several groups of investigators have accomplished the complete synthesis of the steroid nucleus (Barkley and others, 1953; Cardwell and others, 1951; Sarett and others, 1952), but according to Fried and his co-workers (1955) all of the corticoids now produced on a commercial scale are derived from naturally occurring steroids. Even starting with the latter there were a great many difficult chemical steps involved in the synthesis of cortisone, resulting in a high price for this compound during the early days of its use. One of the major difficulties of the chemist was the hydroxylation of carbon-11, although hydroxylations in positions 17 and 21 were also quite important. Although Mamoli and Vercellone (1937) had demonstrated that steroidal substrates could be modified by microorganisms, the first investigators to report hydroxylation on the 11-position were Peterson and Murray (1952). Using the Phycomycete, *Rhizopus arrhizus,* they accomplished the oxygenation of progesterone in the 11-position (Fig. 59) and obtained a yield of

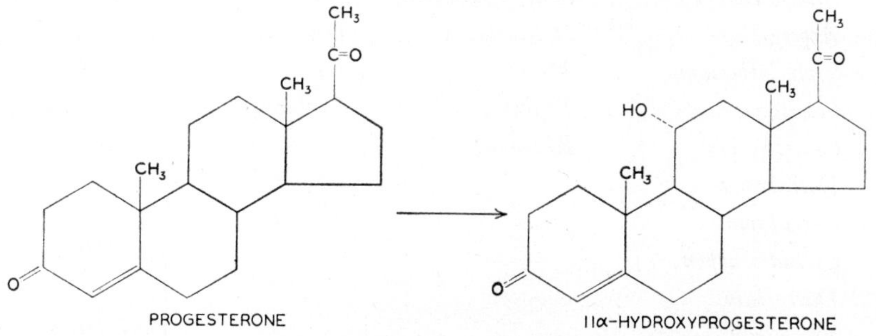

PROGESTERONE   11α-HYDROXYPROGESTERONE

FIG. 59.   *Hydroxylation of progesterone in 11-position by* Rhizopus arrhizus.

about 10 per cent. Shortly after this, Fried and others (1952) accomplished the same reaction with *Aspergillus niger,* as did Mancera and others (1952) and Kahnt and others (1952) using unidentified species of *Rhizopus;* all of these workers obtained yields of about 35 per cent. Peterson and others (1952) next used *Rhizopus nigricans,* the black mold known to all general botany students, and obtained yields of 85–95 per cent of 11*a*-hydroxyprogesterone. Several important syntheses of cortisone and hydrocortisone from this now-abundant starting material are known, and in all of them the availability of this 11-hydroxylated starting material makes possible the syntheses of these medically valuable compounds more economically and with many fewer chemical steps.

FUNGI WHICH TRANSFORM STEROIDS.   The capacity to transform steroids is not restricted to filamentous fungi, since bacteria, actinomycetes, and yeast may also accomplish certain transformations. However, Shull (1956) states that as a group the fungi have yielded

the most diverse assortment of transformation products, and new transformations accomplished through the use of different fungi are frequently reported. Steroid-transforming fungi have thus far been reported for all of the major groups exclusive of the Myxomycetes. The
genera of fungi capable of accomplishing steroid transformations are

Table 15.—Genera of steroid-transforming fungi

Fungi Imperfecti	Phycomycetes	Ascomycetes	Basidiomycetes
Alternaria	Cunninghamella	Calonectria	Lenzites
Aspergillus	Helicostylum	Didymella	Agaricus
Cephalothecium	Mucor	Eurotium	Armillaria
Colletotrichum	Phycomyces	Gibberella	Cantharellus
Coniothyrium	Rhizopus	Neurospora	Hebeloma
Dothichiza		Ophiobolus	Lepiota
Curvularia		Peziza	Lycoperdon
Cylindrocarpon			Morchella
Dactylium			Pleurotus
Epicoccum			Tricholoma
Fusarium			
Gliocladium			
Hormodendrum			
Penicillium			
Pestalotia			
Pycnosporium			
Rhodoseptoria			
Spicaria			
Trichoderma			
Trichothecium			
Wojnowicia			

From Shull (1956).

listed in Table 15; this list should not be considered final since further
investigation will undoubtedly demonstrate that many other fungi have
similar capacities.

TYPES OF FUNGUS TRANSFORMATIONS OF STEROIDS.   Al-
though from the practical standpoint of the synthesis of adrenocortical
hormones, hydroxylations in the 11-, 17-, and 21-positions have been

very important, other transformations of steroids by fungi are also possible, and as still other transformation products are discovered and studied more intensively they may prove to be very valuable compounds.
Aside from practical considerations, all of these transformations are of
theoretical importance to the steroid chemist. The general categories of

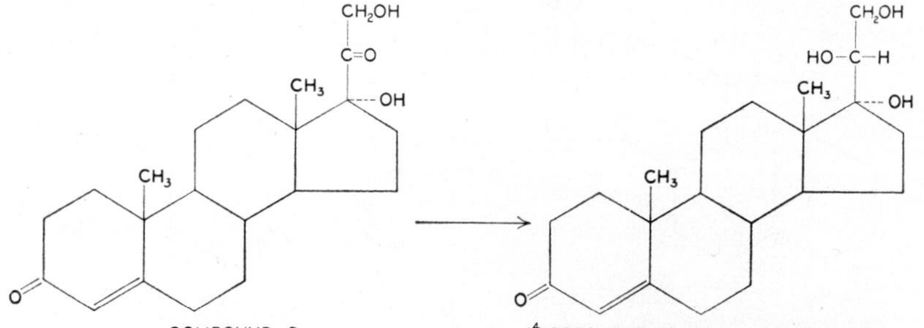

COMPOUND S Δ^4-PREGNENE-17α,20β,21-TRIOL-3-ONE

FIG. 60. *Hydrogenation of a steroid (compound S)*
by Epicoccum oryzae.

such transformations which can be accomplished by fungi are hydrogenation, dehydrogenation, hydroxylation, epoxidation, side-chain
cleavage, and an unusual transformation in which the five-membered
ring of the steroid nucleus is expanded to a six-membered ring.

CORTISONE   PREDNISONE

FIG. 61. *Dehydrogenation of cortisone in the 1,2-position by* Fusarium
solani *with the resultant formation of prednisone.*

Several examples of hydrogenation of steroids by fungi have been
described: reduction of double bonds in the 4,5- and 16,17-positions,
and the reduction of a 20-ketone group. An example of this latter reaction is shown in Fig. 60—a reaction reported by Shull (1956) as being
accomplished by *Epicoccum oryzae.*

Certain fungi are capable of carrying out the dehydrogenation of steroids in the 1,2-position. Vischer and others (1955) have described an example of this in the synthesis of prednisone from cortisone (Fig. 61) by *Fusarium solani.*

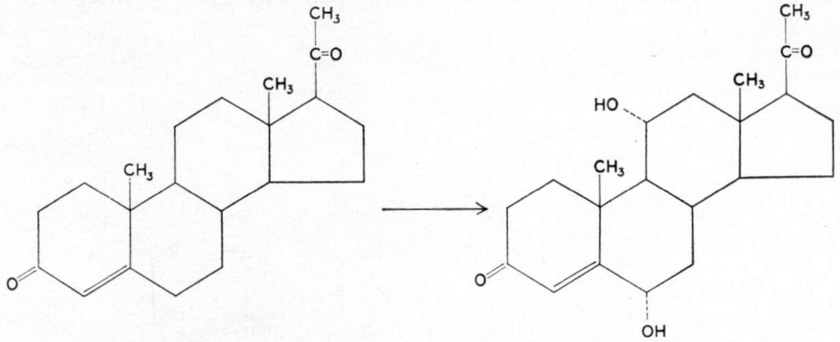

PROGESTERONE   6β,11α-DIHYDROXYPROGESTERONE

FIG. 62.   *Hydroxylation of progesterone in both the 6- and 11-positions by* Rhizopus arrhizus.

Fungus hydroxylations of steroids have received the greatest amount of attention of investigators because of the importance of 11-, 17-, and 21-position hydroxylations in the synthesis of cortisone; however, fungi can also accomplish hydroxylations in the 6-, 7-, 8-, 9-, 10-, 14-, 15-, and

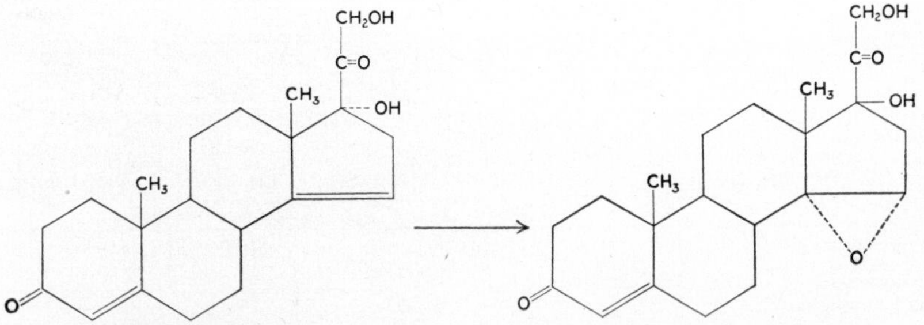

Δ^{14}-DEHYDRO-COMPOUND S   14α,15α-EPOXIDO-COMPOUND S

FIG. 63.   *The epoxidation of a steroid, accomplished through the use of* Curvularia lunata *and several other species of fungi.*

16-positions. Sometimes hydroxylations may occur at two positions, as demonstrated by Peterson and others (1952) in obtaining 6β, 11α-dihydroxyprogesterone when progesterone was fermented with *Rhizopus arrhizus* (Fig. 62).

The steroid transformation known as epoxidation apparently occurs

only in steroids containing an isolated double bond. Several such transformations have been reported. Fig. 63 illustrates the reaction described
by Bloom and Shull (1955), which is accomplished by *Curvularia lunata, Cunninghamella blakesleeana, Helicostylum piriforme, Mucor
griseocyanus,* and *M. parasiticus.*

In 1953 the microbiological cleavage of the 2-carbon side chains
from C-21 steroids was reported by three groups working independently. This type of transformation, which was described by Peterson

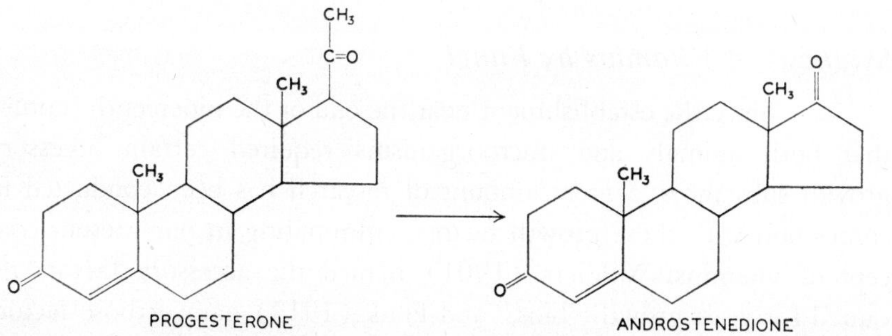

PROGESTERONE   ANDROSTENEDIONE

FIG. 64. *Formation of androstenedione by cleavage of the 2-carbon side
chain from progesterone. This reaction is accomplished by* Gliocladium
catenulatum *and other fungi.*

and others (1953) as being accomplished by the use of *Gliocladium
catenulatum, Penicillium lilacinum,* and *Aspergillus flavus,* is illustrated
in Fig. 64.

The most unusual steroid transformation reported thus far is the one
described by Fried and his co-workers (1952), in which the 5-mem-
bered ring of the steroid is expanded to a 6-membered ring (Fig. 65).

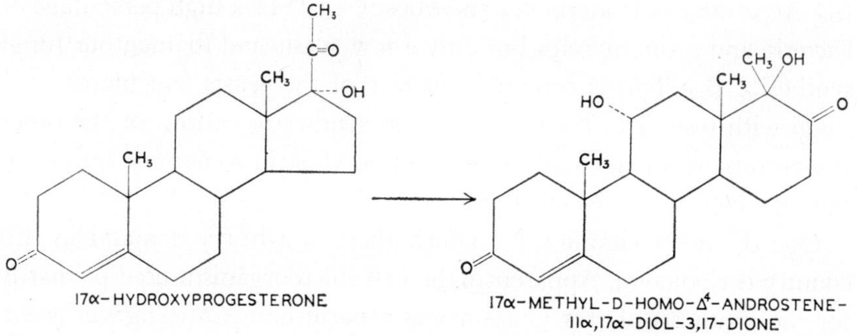

17α–HYDROXYPROGESTERONE   17α–METHYL–D–HOMO–Δ⁴–ANDROSTENE–
                                 11α,17α–DIOL–3,17–DIONE

FIG. 65. *Expansion of the 5-membered ring of 17α-hydroxysterone by*
Aspergillus niger.

From the above examples and discussion it is obvious that an entirely new branch of chemistry has been opened up by the discovery that fungi and other microorganisms can transform steroids in a variety of ways. The practical significance of this discovery cannot at present be evaluated, but judging from what has been accomplished with cortisone, and on the basis of our knowledge of the physiological importance of the steroid hormones, the synthesis and testing of new compounds of this general category may lead to important applications in medicine.

Synthesis of Vitamins by Fungi

Since the establishment near the end of the nineteenth century that both animals and microorganisms required certain accessory growth substances, a great amount of research has been conducted in connection with these growth factors, culminating in our present concept of vitamins. Wildiers (1901) named the accessory factors required for yeast growth "bios," and Funk (1912) named those factors required by animals "vitamines"; Funk's terminology, of course, is retained today. Subsequent work by a great number of investigators has revealed that there are some microorganisms that cannot grow unless supplied with certain vitamins, while others synthesize all their own vitamins, some in considerable quantity.

Much of the vitamin work in relation to microorganisms has been connected with determining the B-complex vitamin deficiencies of certain species (see Chapter 19) or the screening of a large variety of microorganisms for their capacities to synthesize certain of these vitamins. In recent years much of this work has been directed toward vitamin B_{12}. According to Underkofler and Hickey (1954) a high percentage of bacteria and actinomycetes but only a few yeasts and filamentous fungi synthesize B_{12}. This is certainly not true of the yeasts and filamentous fungi with respect to their capacities to synthesize various of the other B vitamins, as is evidenced by the data on vitamin content of fermentation residues presented in Table 16.

One of the B vitamins for which there is a heavy demand in this country is riboflavin. Apparently the first microorganism used primarily for the synthesis of this vitamin was a bacterium, *Closteridium acetobutylicum;* it has been found, however, that a number of organisms can synthesize riboflavin, and two Ascomycetes, *Ashbya gossypii* and *Eremo-*

Table 16.—*Vitamin content of fermentation residues*

(μg/g, dry basis)

Fermentation Process	Material Fermented	Type of Residue	Thiamine	Riboflavin	Pantothenic Acid	Niacin	Pyridoxine	Biotin	Choline
Ethanol	Corn malt	Distillers' dried solubles	6–9	15–20	29–36	104–160	8–10	0.3–0.7	6000–7000
Ethanol	Corn malt	Distillers' dark grains	3–4	7–10	12–15	70–90	4–6	0.2–0.3	4000–5000
Ethanol	Molasses	Condensed solubles	—	5–7	5–25	40	25	1.0–1.5	—
Penicillin	Corn steep lactose	Mycelium	3–7	20–48	88–212	107–180	21–25	0.6–1.5	3000–4000
Penicillin	Corn steep	Mycelium-free	—	7–29	592–805	232–333	82–114	0.6–0.8	—

After Underkofler and Hickey (1954).

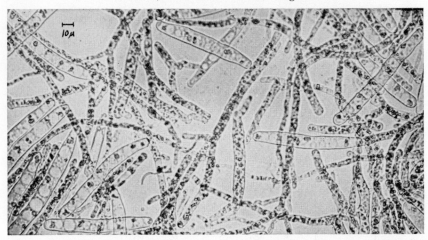

FIG. 66. *Photomicrograph of* Eremothecium ashbyii, *an Ascomycete used for the large scale production of riboflavin. (Courtesy of Commercial Solvents Corporation.)*

thecium ashbyii (Fig. 66), synthesize it in large quantities either in nutrient medium or in residues from other fermentations such as the alcoholic fermentation. Some concept of the magnitude of the riboflavin fermentation industry can be gained from the size of the plant shown in Fig. 67. According to Pridham and Raper (1950), *A. gossypii* forms sufficient riboflavin to permit the fermented medium to be dried down to yield riboflavin concentrates containing 25,000 to 30,000 µg per

FIG. 67. *Plant used for the production of riboflavin and antibiotics. (Courtesy of Commercial Solvents Corporation.)*

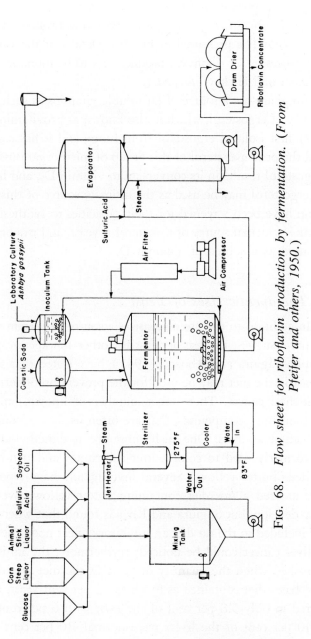

FIG. 68. *Flow sheet for riboflavin production by fermentation.* (*From Pfeifer and others, 1950.*)

gram. Such concentrates can be used directly as feed supplements or can be recovered and purified for human usage. A flow diagram for ribo-flavin production by an *A. gossypii* fermentation as proposed by Pfeifer and others (1950) is presented in Fig. 68. Details of the various fermentation processes for riboflavin production will be found in the work of Underkofler and Hickey (*loc. cit.*).

While fungi are not a source of fat-soluble vitamins as such, they are a good source of ergosterol, which is also known as provitamin D. Tanret (1889) first isolated ergosterol from fungi, and it has come to be considered the principal sterol of this group of microorganisms. Irradiation of ergosterol results in its conversion to vitamin D_2, and hence any source of ergosterol may be used as the ultimate source of this vitamin. Many fungi have been screened for their capacities to synthesize ergosterol, but the principal source of this sterol is yeast, and irradiated yeast is widely used as a source of Vitamin D.

Possible Therapeutic Uses of Yeast

In addition to the use of yeast as a source of certain vitamins, several reports suggest the use of yeast for other therapeutic purposes. For example, Sugiura and Rhoads (1941) have stated that the inclusion of yeast in the diet may be used for the prevention of certain types of experimental cancer. There are a number of known carcinogenic (cancer-producing) compounds, that are often used to produce cancer in experimental animals. One such substance is dimethyl-amino-azo-benzene, formerly used to color butter substitutes and hence is commonly called "butter yellow." Several investigators have reported that when rats are fed a rice diet containing butter yellow, liver cancers commonly develop, but Sugiura and Rhoads found that when brewer's yeast was included in the rat diet an inhibitory effect upon the development of liver cancer could be noticed; furthermore, the inhibitory effect diminished when the quantity of yeast in the diet was decreased. When the basal diet contained as much as 15 per cent yeast, liver cancer occurred in only 5.8 per cent of the rats; with 6 per cent yeast in the diet 40 per cent of the livers were normal, 30 per cent were cirrhotic, and 30 per cent had a few small tumor nodules; of the rats fed with rations containing only 3 per cent yeast, 30 per cent had normal livers and 70 per cent had livers with many cancer nodules. Use of a diet containing 0.6 g of butter yellow per 1000 g of ground, unpolished rice resulted in cancerous livers in 100 per cent of the rats fed. Kensler and others (1941) presented evidence that seemed to indicate the lack of at least two factors in a basal diet of brown rice and carrots which render rats susceptible to the carcinogenic effect of butter yellow. One of these factors they found to be riboflavin, the other to be present in "vitamin-free" alcohol-extracted casein. From the work of Sugiura and Rhoads it is evident that both protective factors are present in brewer's yeast.

McLeod and Ravenel (1938) injected extracts of *Saccharomyces cerevisiae* and *Aspergillus niger* into about 150 cases of advanced malignancy regarded as hopeless. Nearly all patients showed decided improvement, and in many instances there was marked shrinkage of tumor masses. Size reductions took place very rapidly, and pain was greatly relieved. Degeneration and necrosis of tumor cells accompanied other changes. Cures were not obtained and relief from pain was not permanent, since the patients failed to respond further after a number of injections were administered.

From time to time various investigators have attempted to show that different substances cause or cure cancer, so considerable caution should be exercised in the acceptance of reports such as those above. However, in view of the spectactular medical results obtained with penicllin and cortisone, and the fact that the cause and cure of cancer are not completely known, further investigations should be conducted along the lines suggested by Sugiura and Rhoads and McLeod and Ravenel.

The work of Nasset, Pierce, and Murlin (1931) is of interest since it points to the possibility of using yeast in the treatment of diabetes. These investigators studied the influence of yeast on protein metabolism of normal and diabetic dogs (a condition induced experimentally by removal of the pancreas), and obtained some evidence that the inclusion of yeast in the diet of depancreatized dogs alleviated in part the diabetic condition. As a result of feeding yeast there was a prompt decrease in the proportion of ingested nitrogen eliminated in the urine, the dextrose-nitrogen ratio in depancreatized dogs was reduced slightly, and there was evidence that yeast aided in prolonging the lives of diabetic dogs not receiving insulin. In the light of reports of earlier workers that yeast contains an insulin-like substance and that insulin can be absorbed from the alimentary tract, further investigation of this problem should be made to determine the feasibility of using yeast in the treatment of diabetes.

Literature Cited

Alexopoulos, C. J. 1952. *Introductory mycology.* Wiley, New York.

Barkley, L. B., Farrar, M. W., Knowles, W. S., and Raffelson, H. 1953. A synthesis of *dl*-cortisone acetate. *J. Am. Chem. Soc. 75:*4110–4111.

Barger, G. 1931. *Ergot and ergotism.* Gurney and Jackson. London.

Beesch, S. C., and Shull, G. M. 1955. Fermentation. *Ind. Eng. Chem. 47:*1857–1875.

Bloom, B. M., and Shull, G. M. 1955. Epoxidation of unsaturated steroids by microorganisms. *J. Am. Chem. Soc. 77:*5767–5778.

Bonns, W. W. 1922. A preliminary study of *Claviceps purpurea* in culture. *Amer. Jour. Bot. 9:*339–354.

Cardwell, H. M. E., Cornforth, J. W., Duff, S. R., Haltermann, H., and Robinson, R. 1951. Total synthesis of androgenic hormones. *Chem. & Ind.* 389–390.

Chain, E. 1948. Chemical properties and structure of the penicillins. *Endeavour 7:*83–91.

Chester, K. S. 1942. *The nature and prevention of plant disease.* Blakiston, Philadelphia.

Clutterbuck, P. W., Lovell, R., and Raistrick, H. 1932. CCXXVII. Studies in the biochemistry of microorganisms. XXVI. The formation from glucose by members of the *Penicillium chrysogenum* series of a pigment, an alkali-soluble protein and penicillin—the antibacterial substance of Fleming. *Biochem. Jour. 26:*1907–1918.

Coghill, R. G. 1944. Penicillin—Science's Cinderella. *Chem. and Eng. News 22:*588–593.

Duggar, B. M. and others. 1948. Aureomycin—a new antibiotic. Ann. *N. Y. Acad. Sci.,* Vol. 51, Art. 2, Nov. 3, 1948.

Fleming, A. 1929. On the antibacterial action of cultures of a Penicillium, with special reference to their use in the isolation of *B. influenzae. Brit. Jour. Exp. Path. 10:*226–236.

Florey, H. W., and others. 1949. *Antibiotics. A survey of penicillin, streptomycin, and other antimicrobial substances from fungi, actinomycetes, bacteria and plants.* 2 vols. Oxford, London.

Foster. J. W. 1949. *Chemical activities of fungi.* Academic Press, New York.

Fried, J., Thoma, R. W., Gerke, J. R., Herz, J. E., Donin, M. N., and Perlman, D.

1952. Oxidation of steroids by microorganisms. II. Hydroxylation in position 11 and synthesis of cortisone from Reichstein's Compound S. *J. Am. Chem. Soc. 74:*3962–3963.

Fried, J., Thoma, R. W., Perlman, D., Herz, J. E., and Borman, A. 1955. *The use of microorganisms in the synthesis of steroid hormones and hormone analogues. Recent Progress in Hormone Research, Vol. XI,* 149–177. Academic Press, New York.

Funk, C. 1912. The etiology of deficiency diseases. *J. State Med. 20:*341–368.

Gerard, J. 1597. The Herball or general historie of plants. (see Woodward, M., 1927; *Gerard's Herball: The essence thereof.* Houghton Mifflin, Boston.)

Hench, P. S., Kendall, E. C., Slocumb, C. H., and Polley, H. F. 1949. The effect of a hormone of the adrenal cortex (17-hydroxy-11-dehydrocorticosterone: compound E) and of pituitary adrenocorticotropic hormone on rheumatoid arthritis. *Proc. Staff Meetings Mayo Clinic 24:*181–197.

Hildebrandt, G., and Klavehn, W. 1934. Manufacture of laevo-1-phenyl-2-methylaminopropanol-1. U.S. Patent 1,956,950.

Kamlet, J. 1941. Optically active chemical produced by yeast aids synthesis of 1-ephedrine. *Drug Trade News 16:*27, 33, 35.

Kahnt, F. W., Meystre, C., Neher, R., Vischer, E., and Wettstein, A. 1952. Biologische Hydroxylierungen von Steroiden. *Experientia 8:*422–424.

Kensler, C. J., Sugiura, K., Young, N. F., Halter, C. R., and Rhoads, C. P. 1941. Partial protection of rats by riboflavin and casein against liver cancer caused by dimethylaminobenzene. *Science 93:*308–311.

Kharasch, M. S., and Legault, R. R. 1935. Ergotocin. *Science 81:*388.

Knight, S. G., and Frazier, W. C. 1945. The effect of corn steep liquor ash on penicillin production. *Science 102:*617–618.

Koffler, H., Knight, S. G., Emerson, R. L., and Burris, R. H. 1945. The effect of certain chemicals on penicillin production and mold metabolism in shake flask fermentations. *Jour. Bact. 50:*549–559.

Koffler, H., Knight, S. G., Frazier, W. C., and Burris, R. H. 1946. Metabolic changes in submerged penicillin fermentations on synthetic media. *Jour. Bact. 51:*385–392.

Kreitmair, H., and Küssner, W. 1931. Über den Alkaloidgehalt von *Claviceps purpurea* bei Kultivierung auf künstlichen Nährboden. *Biochem. Zeit. 239:*189–192.

Mamoli, L., and Vercellone, A. 1937. Über die biochemische Hydrierung des Dehydro-androsteron. *Z. physiol. Chem. 245:*93–95.

Mancera, O., Zaffaroni, A., Rubin, B. A., Sondheimer, F., Rosenkranz, G., and Djerassi, C. 1952. Steroids. XXXVII. A ten-step conversion of progesterone to cortisone. *J. Am. Chem. Soc. 74:*3711–3712.

McCrea, A. 1931. The reactions of *Claviceps purpurea* to variations of environment. *Amer. Jour. Bot. 18:*50–78.

McCrea, A. 1936. Ergot preparation and process of obtaining same. U.S. Patent 2,056,360. Oct. 6, 1936.

McLeod, J. C., and Ravenel, L. J. 1938. Studies relating to the causes of cancer and therapeutic applications based upon them. *Jour. S. Carolina Med. Assoc.* 34:37–47.

Moyer, A. J., and Coghill, R. D. 1947. Penicillin. X: The effect of phenylacetic acid on penicillin production. *Jour. Bact.* 53:329–341.

Nasset, E. S., Pierce, H. B., and Murlin, J. R. 1931. The influence of yeast on protein metabolism in normal and depancreatized dogs. *Jour. Lab. Clin. Med.* 16:1151–1168.

Neuberg, C., and Hirsch, J. 1921. Uber ein Kohlenstoffketten knupfendes Ferment (Carboligase). *Biochem. Zeit.* 115:282–310.

Neuberg, C., and Ohle, H. 1922. Zur Kenntnis der Carboligase. Weitere Festellungen uber biosynthetische Kohlenstoffkettenverknupfung beim Garungsvorgange. *Biochem. Zeit.* 128:610–618.

Nobbe, F. 1904. Über Alexander Müller's Verfahren zur Reinigung des Saatroggens von Mutterkorn durch Sedimentation. *Landwirt. Versuchstat.* 60:315–319.

Peterson, D. H., and Murray, H. C. 1952. Microbiological oxygenation of steroids at carbon 11. *J. Am. Chem. Soc.* 74:1871–1872.

Peterson, D. H., Murray, H. C., Eppstein, S. H., Reinecke, L. M., Weintraub, A., Meister, P. D., and Leigh, H. M. 1952. Microbiological transformations of steroids. I. Introduction of oxygen at carbon-11 of progesterone. *J. Am. Chem. Soc.* 74:5933–5936.

Peterson, D. H., Eppstein, S. H., Meister, P. D., Murray, H. C., Leigh, H. M., Weintraub, A. and Reinecke, L. M. 1953. Microbiological transformations of steroids. IX. Degradation of C_{21} steroids to C_{19} ketones and testololactone. *J. Am. Chem. Soc.* 75:5768–5769.

Pfeifer, V. F., Tanner, F. W., Vojnovich, C., and Traufler, D. H. 1950. Riboflavin fermentation with *Ashbya gossypii*. *Ind. Eng. Chem.* 42:1776–1781.

Pratt, R., and Hok, K. A. 1946. Influence of the proportions of KH_2PO_4, $MgSO_4$ and $NaNO_3$ in the nutrient solution on the production of penicillin in submerged cultures. *Amer. Jour. Bot.* 33:149–156.

Pridham, T. G., and Raper, K. B. 1950. *Ashbya gossypii*—its significance in nature and in the laboratory. *Mycologia* 42:603–623.

Raper, K. B. 1946. The development of improved penicillin-producing molds. *Ann. N. Y. Acad. Sci.* 48:41–52.

Raper, K. B., and Alexander, D. F. 1945. Penicillin. V: Mycological aspects of penicillin production. *Jour. Elisha Mitchell Sci. Soc.* 61:74–113.

Robbins, W. J., Kavanagh, F., and Hervey, A. 1946. Production of antibiotic substances by Basidiomycetes. *Ann. N. Y. Acad. Sci.* 48:67–72.

Rolfe, R. T., and Rolfe, F. W. 1928. *The romance of the fungus world.* Lippincott, Philadelphia.

Saratt, L. H. 1946. The structure of some derivatives of $3(a)$-hydroxy-Δ^{9-11}-cholenic acid. *Jour. Biol. Chem. 162:*591–600.

Saratt, L. H., Arth, G. E., Lukes, R. M., Beyler, R. E., Poos, G. I., Johns, W. F., and Constantin, J. M. 1952. Stereospecific total synthesis of cortisone. *J. Am. Chem. Soc. 74:*4974–4976.

Sheehan, J. C., and Henery-Logan, K. P. 1957. The total synthesis of Penicillin V. *J. Am. Chem. Soc. 79:*1262–1263.

Shull, G. M. 1957. Transformation of steroids by molds. *Trans. N. Y. Acad. Sci. Ser. II, 19:*147–172.

Stefaniak, J. J., Gailey, F. B., Brown, C. S., and Johnson, M. J. 1946. Pilot plant equipment for submerged production of penicillin. *Ind. Eng. Chem. 38:* 666–671.

Sugiura, K., and Rhoads, C. P. 1941. Experimental liver cancer in rats and its inhibition by rice-bran extract, yeast and yeast extract. *Cancer Research 1:* 3–16.

Tanret, C. 1875. Sur la presence d'un nouvel alcaloide, l'ergotinine, dans le seigle ergote. *Comp. Rend. Acad. Sci. 81:*896–897.

————. 1889. Sur un nouveau principe immediat de l'ergot de seigle, l'ergosterine. *Comp. Rend. Acad. Sci. 108:*98–100.

Tauber, H. 1949. *The chemistry and technology of enzymes.* Wiley, New York.

Underkofler, L. A., and Hickey, R. J. 1954. *Industrial fermentations.* Chem. Pub. Co. New York.

Vischer, E., Meystre, C., and Wettstein, A. 1955. Microbiologische Herstellung von 1-Dehydro-Steroiden. *Helv. Chim. Acta 38:*835–840.

Waksman, S. A. 1945. *Microbial antagonisms and antibiotic substances.* The Commonwealth Fund, New York.

Wildiers, E. 1901. Nouvelle substance indispensable au developpement de la levure. *La Cellule 18:*313–331.

Wolf, F. A., and Wolf, F. T. 1947. *The fungi.* Vol. II. Wiley, New York.

White, A. G. C., Krampitz, L. O., and Werkman, C. H. 1945. On a synthetic medium for the production of penicillin. *Arch. Biochem. 8:*303–310.

9 · *The Alcoholic Fermentation*

EARLY BEGINNINGS OF THE ALCOHOL INDUSTRY
ORGANISMS EMPLOYED IN THE ALCOHOLIC FERMENTATION
RAW MATERIALS AND YIELD CALCULATIONS
MECHANISM OF ALCOHOL SYNTHESIS
COMMERCIAL PRODUCTION OF ALCOHOL
POWER ALCOHOL

OF THE HUNDREDS of known metabolic products of fungi, ethyl alcohol is perhaps most widely used by man and is most important in industry. No other product of fungal origin has been produced under man's control in greater quantity or put to a greater variety of uses. Only a small fraction of the total alcohol produced annually is used as a beverage, the major portion being employed in a great variety of industrial processes. Ethyl alcohol is one of the most widely known of the common chemical compounds, and to attempt to enumerate and describe its various applications would require several large volumes. Ethyl alcohol also serves both as a solvent for hundreds of different materials and as the raw material from which hundreds of other compounds are synthesized. As a solvent it is employed in the manufacture of such widely diverse materials as dyes, drugs, soaps, plastics, resins, and polishes; as a raw material in the synthesis of other compounds, alcohol is used in the manufacture of ether, various esters, acetic acid, hypnotics, synthetic rubber, and many other valuable substances. For further applications, the student should consult the chart prepared by the U.S. Industrial Alcohol Company, a copy of which is reproduced in Prescott and Dunn (1940). In addition to its industrial importance, alcohol is also widely used in one form or another as a beverage. The widespread demand for such beverages has led to the development of huge distilling, brewing, and wine industries, which provide a very considerable source of revenue for the state and federal governments. In some areas the entire economy of a community may be geared to an alcoholic beverage industry.

The production of alcohol through the fermentation of sugar by fungi is the oldest of the industrial fermentation processes. A great number of references to the making of wine in Biblical times, together with certain other ancient references, lead us to believe that then as now the overindulgence in alcoholic beverages by a few may have served to place the fermentation industry beyond the pale of respectability. Such a viewpoint is unduly severe and obviously unjustified, but at times has led to attempts to legislate certain parts of the industry out of existence. Prohibition, the one major attempt in this direction, actually resulted in a dismal failure in this country, making lawbreakers of otherwise law-abiding citizens and ushering in the period of gangsterism. Such attempts to legislate the beverage alcohol industry out of existence are probably always doomed to fail. In those individual instances where alcohol is a real problem, a more rational approach than either the moral or the legislative might be made to the problem.

While alcohol is obviously the immediate cause of alcoholism, the underlying causes have never been satisfactorily explained, and are perhaps to be sought by the psychiatrist, the sociologist, and the medical research worker, and through group therapy, such as that practiced by Alcoholics Anonymous.

Early Beginnings of the Alcohol Industry

Because of the great numbers and widespread distribution of yeasts—the fungi generally responsible for the synthesis of alcohol from sugar—the practical details of the alcoholic fermentation have had many independent discoverers. The preparation of alcoholic beverages was commonly practiced in many widely separated regions (although crudely by present standards) long before the microscope was developed and before the role of microorganisms in the fermentation was established. Most peoples from ancient times have discovered and and developed some process for manufacturing beverage alcohol, notable exceptions being the North American Indian and the Eskimo. For the production of such beverages, the inhabitants of various regions used as the carbohydrate source whatever suitable raw materials were locally available. Thus, in South Africa the Negro prepared his beer (*pombé*) from millet, while the Japanese version of beer, *saké,* was prepared from rice. In regions where grapes grew in abundance, such as the Mediterranean region, some type of wine was usually prepared; in the Central American region the native relied on corn as the source of carbohydrate for the alcoholic fermentation.

The first alcoholic beverages prepared intentionally by man very probably had a relatively low alcoholic content. With the advent of the still, however, it was possible to prepare drinks with high alcohol concentration—whiskey, rum, brandy, gin, and vodka. The development and subsequent improvement of the still also made possible the preparation of highly rectified alcohol and thus paved the way for the manufacture of the many products now synthesized from alcohol. The origins of distillation are lost in antiquity, the process being known to the ancient Egyptians and contemporary cultures.

Organisms Employed in the Alcoholic Fermentation

Although a great variety of fungi are now known to have the capacity of synthesizing ethyl alcohol from sugars (Perlman, 1950; Foster, 1949), those commonly used in the preparation of either industrial or beverage alcohol are members of the group of Ascomycetes known as "true yeasts," of which various strains of *Saccharomyces cerevisiae* are usually employed.

The yeasts are undoubtedly best suited for use in the large-scale production of alcohol for several reasons: (1) they multiply vegetatively at a very rapid rate if proper environmental conditions are maintained, and hence abundant quantities of inoculum consisting of highly active cells can be obtained in a relatively short period of time; (2) they ferment most of the common sugars very rapidly; (3) when conditions are favorable they soon establish a set of environmental conditions in which many other microorganisms are unable to grow (thus minimizing the problems arising from contamination); and (4) many excellent commercial yeast strains are available whose suitabilities for various processes have been demonstrated over many years of plant practice.

A good commercial yeast strain is usually a very stable organism, probably because it is diploid; mutations do not become apparent since it is typically propagated vegetatively as the diploid, and recombinations of characters following meiosis and fertilization are usually prevented. From the standpoint of their unicellular nature, the yeasts are the most admirably suited of all fungi to commercial fermentation processes, since the inoculum problems that may arise in connection with the use

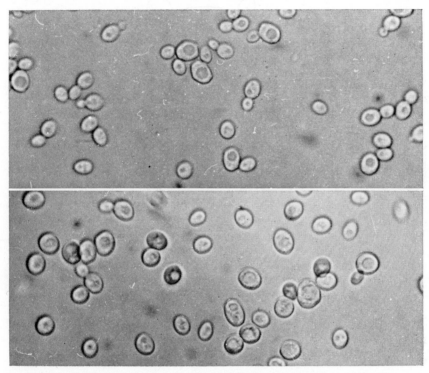

FIG. 69.   *Photomicrographs of* Saccharomyces cerevisiae. *Above, actively growing stage; below, mature stage. (Courtesy of Red Star Yeast and Products Co., Milwaukee, Wis.)*

of filamentous fungi are never encountered in fermentation processes involving yeast.

The many species of yeast capable of forming alcohol do not do so with equal efficiency. As pointed out above, strains of *S. cerevisiae* (Fig. 69) are usually employed industrially. Over a long period of industrial usage and strain testing a number of very efficient, commercially valuable strains of yeast have been selected, primarily on the basis of results obtained under plant conditions. Further selection may possibly reveal still better strains. As Lindegren and Lindegren (1943) have pointed out, yeast-breeding programs can be instituted with the objective of developing yeast hybrids that possess a complement of particularly desirable characteristics. Design of an intelligent yeast-breeding program would of necessity have to be preceded by an accumulation of informa-

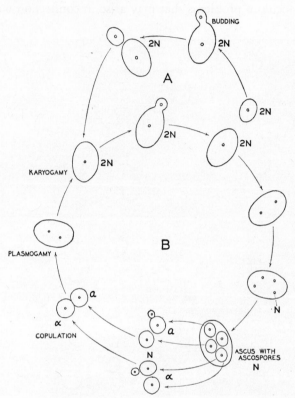

FIG. 70.   *Diagrammatic life cycle of a typical diploid yeast.*

tion concerning the physiological and biochemical characteristics of many known species and strains of yeast.

An examination of a typical yeast life cycle (Fig. 70) reveals the feasibility of a yeast-breeding program. When placed under the proper set of conditions, a diploid vegetative yeast cell will undergo meiotic division, and four haploid ascospores (Fig. 71) are formed. Typically there is a 1 : 1 segregation for mating type, two of the ascospores of a single ascus being of one mating type (a), while the remaining two are of the opposite mating type (α). On germination a spore gives rise to a haploid cell, which may fuse immediately with another haploid cell of opposite mating type, or may bud and give rise to similar haploid cells, resembling the diploid cells but usually smaller and more weakly fermentative. When two cells of opposite mating type fuse, a zygote is formed which by budding forms the typical diploid vegetative cells.

Although strains of *S. cerevisiae* are commonly employed in industrial alcoholic fermentations, it is sometimes necessary to identify other

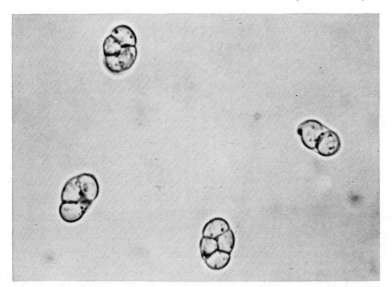

FIG. 71. *Sporulating yeast cells with ascospores. The second division has not occurred in the cell at the extreme right and at this stage there appear to be but two spores. (Courtesy of Fleischmann Laboratories, Standard Brands Inc.)*

yeast species. For such identifications the work of Guilliermond and Tanner (1920) or the more recent monograph of Stelling-Dekker (1931) may be used.

Raw Materials and Yield Calculations

Any material containing glucose, fructose, maltose, or sucrose, or any substances easily hydrolyzed to any of these common sugars, may be used as a source of carbohydrate for the alcoholic fermentation. Thus potatoes and the various cereal grains contain starch which can be hydrolyzed to fermentable sugar either by means of suitable enzymes or acid hydrolysis, and hence both of these materials can be used as a source of carbohydrate. Similarly, Jerusalem artichokes, which contain inulin, a polysaccharide easily hydrolyzed to fructose by the enzyme inulase, are also a source. Although cereal grains and other materials may be employed, the carbohydrate source used in greatest quantity in the United States for the production of industrial alcohol is blackstrap molasses, a by-product of the sugar industry that is cheap, easily handled, and available in quantity.

For the production of distilled alcoholic beverages, corn, rye, wheat, and barley are the most common carbohydrate sources in this country, since the national taste seems to prefer distilled, malted grain drinks (whiskies) rather than distilled or fermented, wines or fruit juices (brandies, cordials or liqueurs) as are preferred in many other areas of the world.

The law requires that the starch used in the preparation of beverage alcohol be enzymatically digested with *malt* (ground, dried, germinated barley kernels rich in starch-digesting enzymes), although for the production of nonbeverage alcohol it is legally permissible to acid-hydrolyze the starch or to hydrolyze it with enzyme preparations of filamentous fungus origin (mold amylases). Actually, it makes little difference in so far as the end product is concerned whether the starch is digested with enzymes or with acid if the product is to be distilled; however, for the production of beer the use of mold enzymes or acid hydrolysis would probably not be satisfactory because of undesirable taste that might be imparted to the beer. Certain groups of Central American Indians, having neither malt nor facilities for acid-hydrolysis (a process with which they are probably unfamiliar), accomplish the digestion of corn starch by means of salivary starch-digesting enzymes simply by chewing each corn kernel before adding it to the fermentation vessel. Although to us this may seem to be a somewhat repugnant way of making beer, it does serve to illustrate the extremes to which people will often go to prepare alcoholic beverages.

The synthesis of alcohol by yeasts or other organisms is accomplished by means of an anaerobic respiration process, to which the term fermentation was originally applied by Pasteur. The over-all equation for the reaction can be written as follows:

$$\underset{\text{glucose}}{C_6H_{12}O_6} \rightarrow \underset{\text{ethyl alcohol}}{2CH_3CH_2OH} + \underset{\text{carbon dioxide}}{2CO_2}$$

Such an equation, although it gives no information concerning the sequence of chemical reactions involved in the transformation, is of value to the commercial alcohol producer because it enables him to determine how efficiently the process is being conducted in his plant. From the equation it is obvious that two molecules of alcohol may be derived from one molecule of glucose; hence, since the molecular weight of glucose is 180 and that of ethyl alcohol is 46, the maximum weight of alcohol that can be derived from a given weight of sugar can be determined as follows:

$$\frac{46 \times 2}{180} \times \text{weight of sugar} = 0.511 \times \text{weight of sugar}$$

Thus the maximum theoretical amount of ethyl alcohol that can be derived from a given weight of a 6-carbon sugar is determined by multiplying the weight of the sugar by the conversion factor 0.511. The efficiency of a fermentation can then be calculated according to the following equation:

$$\text{F.E. (fermentation efficiency)} = \frac{\text{actual weight yield of alcohol}}{\text{wt. of 6-carbon sugar utilized} \times 0.511}$$

Since the fermentation efficiency (which is usually expressed as a percentage) reveals only how efficiently the sugar that was utilized was converted to alcohol, in industrial practice it is customary to state efficiency as plant efficiency:

$$\text{P.E.} = \frac{\text{actual weight yield of alcohol}}{\text{wt. of 6-carbon sugar supplied} \times 0.511}$$

Sometimes fermentation efficiency may be very high but plant efficiency quite low, thus indicating that while the sugar which is utilized is efficiently converted to alcohol, much of the sugar supplied is not fermented at all. For example, if 200 g of sugar is supplied, 51.1 g of alcohol produced, but only 100 g of sugar is utilized, the fermentation efficiency is 100 per cent while the plant efficiency is only 50 per cent. Actually, neither the fermentation nor plant efficiencies can be as high as 100 per cent in a fermentation using living cells, since part of the sugar is utilized in the various other metabolic processes which occur in the cell.

Mechanism of Alcohol Synthesis

The chemical reactions occurring in the biological synthesis of alcohol from sugar have received the attention of many different investigators, and several fermentation schemes have been proposed to explain the various steps which are involved. The most widely accepted scheme, the so-called Embden-Meyerhof-Parnas scheme (Meyerhof: 1942, 1943) represents the sequence of chemical reactions as follows:

1. glucose + ATP^a → glucose-6-phosphate + ADP^b
2. glucose-6-phosphate $\rightleftharpoons$ fructose-6-phosphate
3. fructose-6-phosphate + ATP $\rightleftharpoons$ fructose-1:6-diphosphate + ADP
4. fructose-1:6-diphosphate $\rightleftharpoons$ (dihydroxyacetone phosphate
   $\rightleftharpoons$ 3-glyceraldehyde phosphate)
5. 3-glyceraldehyde phosphate $\underset{\pm \text{ KH}_2\text{PO}_4}{\overset{?}{=\!=\!=\!=}}$ 1:3-diphosphoglyceraldehyde
6. 1:3-diphosphoglyceraldehyde + DPN^c $\rightleftharpoons$ 1:3-diphosphoglyceric acid + H$_2$DPN^d
7. 1:3-diphosphoglyceric acid + ADP $\rightleftharpoons$ 3-phosphoglyceric acid + ADP
8. 3-phosphoglyceric acid $\rightleftharpoons$ 2-phosphoglyceric acid
9. 2-phosphoglyceric acid $\overset{\pm \text{ H}_2\text{O}}{=\!=\!=}$ phosphopyruvic acid
10. phosphopyruvic acid + ADP $\rightleftharpoons$ pyruvic acid + ATP
11. pyruvic acid $\overset{\text{DPT}^e}{\longrightarrow}$ acetaldehyde + CO$_2$
12. acetaldehyde + H$_2$DPN $\rightleftharpoons$ ethyl alcohol + DPN

[a] adenosine triphosphate; [b] adenosine diphosphate; [c] diphosphopyridine nucleotide; [d] reduced diphosphopyridine nucleotide; [e] diphosphothiamin.

The above series of reactions are enzyme-catalyzed. In many instances the enzyme that catalyzes a particular step has been isolated in relatively pure form and subjected to considerable study. For example, Reaction 1 is catalyzed by the enzyme *hexokinase,* which can be isolated from yeast, purified, crystallized, and used to catalyze the transfer of a phosphate group from adenosine triphosphate to glucose. In addition to the enzymes involved in the alcoholic fermentation there are certain compounds (adenosine di- and triphosphate, diphosphothiamin, diphosphopyridine nucleotide) without which certain of the enzymes cannot act. The essential features of the scheme are: (1) the phosphorylation and dephosphorylation reactions in which adenosine triphosphate and adenosine diphosphate are phosphate donor and acceptor respectively, (2) the splitting reaction in which the phosphorylated 6-carbon molecule is cleaved and two phosphorylated 3-carbon molecules ("trioses") are formed, (3) the oxidation-reduction reactions in which diphos-phopyridine nucleotide and reduced diphosphopyridine nucleotide are hydrogen acceptor and donor, and (4) the decarboxylation reaction in which the enzyme carboxylase, with the aid of diphosphothiamin

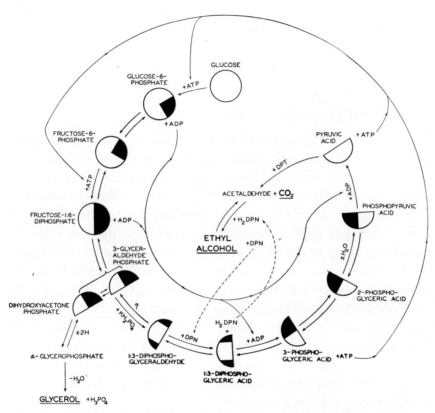

FIG. 72. *Diagrammatic representation of the sequence of chemical reactions occurring in the alcoholic fermentation. The reactions begin at the top with the entry of glucose into the system. A 6-carbon molecule is represented by a circle, a 3-carbon molecule by a half-circle, and phosphorylated molecules are partly shaded.*

(DPT) decarboxylates pyruvic acid with the formation of acetaldehyde and carbon dioxide.

During the course of the alcoholic fermentation, two "shuttling" actions occur: one involving the movement of phosphate groups between adenosine triphosphate and adenosine diphosphate, the other involving the movement of hydrogen between diphosphopyridine nucleotide and reduced diphosphopyridine nucleotide. These "shuttling" actions become more obvious if the course of the fermentation is presented diagramatically as in Fig. 72. Also explained in this figure is the mechanism by which glycerol may be formed during the course of the fermentation, a mechanism which is discussed in greater detail in Chapter 16. For further details concerning the mechanism of this fermentation, and the evidence that is used in support of the scheme outlined, consult the works of Porter (1946) and Prescott and Dunn (1940).

Commercial Production of Alcohol

For the production of beverage alcohol in this country, the principal sources of carbohydrate are the various cereal grains; however, both cereal grains and blackstrap molasses are used for the production of industrial alcohol. In the manufacture of beer the fermentation process is basically the same as that used in the manufacture of alcohol for such distilled beverages as whiskey or gin, the principal differences being in the additives used in beer making and the length of the fermentation time, as well as the temperature at which the fermentation is conducted. The process of wine making is also basically the same, differing only with respect to type of raw materials used and the conditions maintained during fermentation. Since there are a greater number of unit processes in a distillery (in which alcohol is made from grain rather than from blackstrap molasses) than in a brewery or winery, the present discussion of plant procedure will be confined to grain distilleries.

Upon arrival at the distillery, grain is first sampled for analysis and then transported to storage bins by means of bucket-, screw-, or air-conveyor systems. Although the grain arriving at a distillery has usually been cleaned previously at an elevator, it may still contain trash such as sticks, cobs, or small pieces of iron; it may also contain weed seeds, ergot (see Chapter 8), or garlic, all of which must be removed. Grain is usually cleaned by passage through a series of separator screens, at which point trash and dust are extracted. Prior to milling the grain, "tramp" iron is removed by means of magnetic separators, since small pieces of iron passing through mill rolls would not only cause damage to the rolls but might also create sparks, resulting in a dust explosion. In some distilleries grain is ground and then stored in bins; a preferable method is to synchronize the various operations so that the grain is used as soon as it is ground, thus eliminating the need for storage. Roller mills, hammer mills, and attrition mills have all been used for grinding grain in distilleries; Willkie and Prochaska (1943) have listed the advantages and disadvantages of the various types of mills.

COOKING AND MASHING. Since cereal grains contain starch, a nonfermentable carbohydrate, they must first be processed to hydrolyze the starch to a fermentable sugar, accomplished by cooking the ground grain and digesting the starch with enzymes (usually malt enzymes in the U. S.). A slurry, prepared by mixing proper quantities of ground grain and water, is then cooked batchwise or in a continuous cooker. For batch cooking either an open mash tub or a closed pressure cooker may be used; the latter type of cooker has an advantage over the open type in that the slurry can be heated to a much higher temperature, since in the open cooker temperatures cannot exceed 212F. In a batch pressure cooker, a cooking temperature of about 300–310F is usually employed.

Use of a continuous cooker also permits high cooking temperatures. In this type of process the grain slurry is heated to a relatively high temperature for a short period of time by means of a jet heater. Since the cooking period is quite short in the continuous process, the preparation of the grain-water slurry is usually also on a continuous basis, and may be done by metering water and ground grain in proper amounts into a mixer. In the cooking process the starch becomes gelatinized, and as a result cooked grain is quite viscous and sometimes difficult to pump; for that reason a small amount of malt is often added to the slurry prior to cooking, and partial liquefaction of the starch occurs before the malt enzymes are inactivated by the high cooking temperatures (this procedure is referred to as *premalting*).

CONVERSION. The cooking or mashing of grain has partially solubilized the starch, but before it can be fermented to alcohol by yeast it must be converted to soluble sugar. In a beverage alcohol plant the law requires that this conversion be done with malted grain (usually barley) which contains enzymes (*amylases*) that change starch first into dextrins and then into the disaccharide, maltose. The quantity of malt used varies with the grain, corn usually requiring larger quantities for conversion than the small grains. A common practice is to use malt in an amount equivalent to 10 per cent of the total grain bill.

Like all enzymes, the amylases are destroyed by high temperatures, and hence cooked grain must first be cooled by using water coils, water jackets, or a vacuum. A conversion temperature of 145F is commonly used. Exposure to temperatures higher than 152F results in an appreciable destruction of enzymes; however, since malt is often added in the form of a cold slurry, the enzymes are sometimes momentarily exposed to high temperatures, since the cold malt slurry is used to finish the cooling of the cooked grain to conversion temperature.

In plants where cooking is conducted on a batch basis, conversion is also done batchwise, and may be done in the cooking vessel or another tank. However, in plants where cooking is a continuous process, conversion may also be continuous. The cooked grain is cooled to nearly 145F, malt slurry being pumped at the proper rate into the line through which the cooked grain flows. In a process of this type the "converter" may merely consist of many sections of such pipe. Length of conversion time is controlled by the length of pipe and the rate at which the slurry is pumped.

For the preparation of industrial alcohol, conversion may be accomplished by acid hydrolysis rather than through use of malt enzymes. According to Willkie and Prochaska (*loc. cit.*), 95 per cent conversion of grain starch occurs when grain is cooked under pressure with 0.2 normal sulphuric acid. They recommend a cooking time of three minutes and a cooking temperature of 360F.

Starch may also be converted to fermentable sugar by means of "mold bran," which is acidified wheat or rice bran upon which *Aspergillus oryzae* has grown, but mold bran may not be used for conversion in this country if the alcohol is to be used for beverage purposes. The production and use of mold bran is described in detail in the chapter on fungus enzymes.

FERMENTATION.   After most of the starch is converted to sugar, the mash is further cooled, pumped into fermenters, and inoculated with yeast. Fermenters are open or covered tanks made of wood, tile, or steel; the capacity of fermenters varies with the distillery and may range from small tanks holding a few thousand gallons to huge tanks capable of holding over 200,000 gallons. Metal fermenters are preferable to those constructed of wood or tile, since they may be more easily cleaned, and covered fermenters (Fig. 73) are preferable to open ones since the possibility of contamination during fermentation is reduced, the steaming out of fermenters between fermentations is much facilitated, and carbon dioxide arising from the fermenter may be recovered if it is desirable to do so.

The temperature at which a fermentation is "set"—that is, the initial temperature of the mash when it is inoculated with yeast—is de-

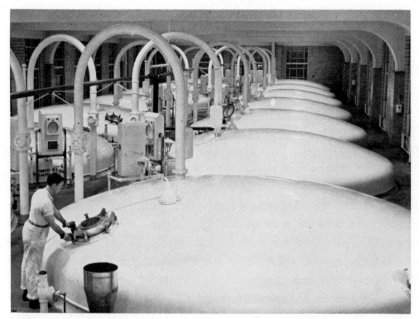

FIG. 73. *View of the upper ends of covered fermenters used for the alcoholic fermentation. Note the large lines through which gaseous products may be recovered.*

pendent upon a number of factors. This is especially true if the fermentation equipment is of the type in which temperature cannot be controlled, in which case initial temperature will be determined by weather conditions (the temperature of the water available for cooling the mash before it is pumped to the fermenter), type of mash, and the amount of time allowed for the fermentation. Usually the initial temperature selected is low enough to prevent the temperature of the fermenting mash from rising above 90F before the fermentation is complete. Higher initial temperatures may be used with fermenters equipped

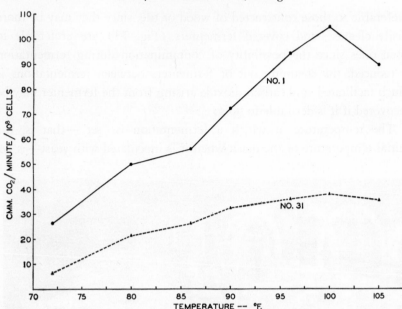

FIG. 74.   *The relation of temperature to initial fermentation rate of two commercial strains of* Saccharomyces cerevisiae.

for circulating the fermenting mash through an external cooler without aeration. Use of external coolers is desirable, since the fermentation rate is increased not only because of the higher temperature but also because of the agitation of the fermenting mash during circulation through the external cooler. The effect of temperature upon fermentation rate is presented graphically in Fig. 74.

From the data presented in Fig. 74 it is evident that both yeast strains have the fastest fermentation rate at approximately 100F. This high temperature should not be maintained throughout the entire course of a fermentation, since it would foster the growth of such contaminants as certain butyric acid bacteria and would have the effect of increasing the inhibitory activity of alcohol on the yeast cells. However, it is definitely advantageous to be able to use a high initial temperature if a faster fermentation is desired. High temperatures during the latter part of the fermentation are undesirable not only because of contaminant growth, but also because they reduce plant efficiency—especially if the initial sugar content is high.

Since the theoretical yield of alcohol which may be derived from a mash increases with sugar content, a high yield of alcohol should be expected from a mash of high sugar content. Furthermore, such a mash set at high temperature should have a relatively high alcohol content in a short period of time. This would definitely be an advantage except that a high alcohol concentration has a markedly inhibitory effect upon the yeast cell, and high temperature increases this effect. The effect of temperature upon the alcohol tolerance of yeast is shown in Fig. 75.

The length of the fermentation period is dependent upon temperature, sugar concentration, pH of the mash, type of yeast used, and similar factors. In plants where for production reasons it is not desirable to keep a fermenter in use too long with a single fermentation, the fermentation may be stopped before it has proceeded to completion. Some fermentable sugar is lost when this is done, but sometimes it is more economical to lose sugar than time.

Although in some plants the entire fermenter may be filled before the yeast inoculum is added, usually the yeast is "dropped" to the fer-

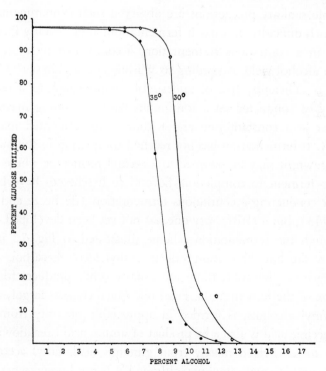

FIG. 75.   *The effect of increasing temperature upon the alcohol tolerance of yeast (DCL Strain No. 1). (From Gray, 1941.)*

menter soon after some of the converted mash is pumped in. This procedure provides a time gain, since with viscous grain mashes (rye,
wheat), the time required to fill a 40,000 gallon fermenter may be in
excess of six hours. Thus, an equivalent amount of time may be saved
if the yeast is introduced into the fermenter in the early stages of the
mash pumping operation.

Although milling, cooking, conversion, and distillation are on a continuous basis in many grain alcohol plants, fermentation is still a batch
process. Obviously it would be quite desirable to operate fermentation
as a continuous process, synchronized with the other processes, but in
a beverage alcohol plant it is almost impossible to ferment continuously
for any extended period of time because of the increase in number of
contaminating organisms introduced with the malt. Since the malt
enzymes would be destroyed if heated to a very high temperature, malt
cannot be heated to the temperatures used in the cooking of other grain,
and as a result the microorganisms in malt are not killed and may
gradually increase in number during the course of a fermentation. If
reasonable sanitary precautions are observed such contaminants rarely
cause much difficulty in a batch fermentation; they steadily increase in
number in a continuous fermentation, accompanied by a steady decrease in alcohol yield. According to Willkie and Prochaska (loc. cit.),
if mash is sufficiently free of undesirable microorganisms a fermentation may be conducted on a continuous basis by adding mash to the
fermenter at a constant rate and withdrawing fermented mash continuously. If fermentation has not reached completion in the mash that
is withdrawn, it may be pumped to a second fermenter where it is allowed to ferment to completion. Several such schemes have been devised for conducting a continuous fermentation (de Becze and Rosenblatt, 1943), but a satisfactory one has not yet been developed.

Although the fermentation scheme illustrated in Fig. 72 indicates
that there are but three end-products (ethyl alcohol, carbon dioxide,
and a trace of glycerol), there are usually other products formed in
the course of the fermentation. Fusel oil, which consists largely of amyl
and isoamyl alcohols, is formed in appreciable quantity from amino
acids. Succinic acid is also a by product of amino acid breakdown and is
believed to be derived mostly from glutamic acid. Ethyl acetate may
also be found in small amounts, although it is not known whether this
compound is formed by yeast or by bacterial contaminants. There is no

evidence that *S. cerevisiae* is capable of synthesizing ethyl acetate; however, it has been demonstrated (Gray, 1949) that a related yeast, *Hansenula anomala,* does synthesize this ester.

YEASTING. Some time before the cooking operation described above was begun, another process was started in order to insure that sufficient yeast inoculum would be ready at the time it was required for inoculating the mash in the fermenter. The process of preparing yeast inoculum is known as yeasting. The early stages of the yeasting process are conducted in the laboratory and consist of gradually building up an inoculum of active yeast cells until a volume sufficient to inoculate a plant starter mash (dona) is obtained. This is accomplished by inoculating a small amount of liquid medium in a test tube from a fresh agar slant culture of the desired yeast. After 18–24 hours the liquid culture is poured into a small flask containing an amount of medium larger than that in the test tube. Successive transfers are made at similar intervals to larger volumes of medium. The yeast that is used directly to inoculate fermenters is cultured in yeast tubs (Fig. 76) which are inoculated from the dona.

FIG. 76. *Yeast tubs showing developing yeast mash. The final stage of the yeasting process occurs in these tanks, since the large fermenters are inoculated directly from yeast tubs such as these.*

During the laboratory stages of yeasting, commercial Diamalt, malt extract, or strained sour yeast mash may be used, but in the dona and yeast tubs sour yeast mash is ordinarily employed. Yeast mash is prepared like other mash but usually has a higher sugar content. Prior to inoculation with yeast the mash is commonly soured by introducing a lactic acid bacterium, *Bacillus delbrücki.* This results in a mash that is acid in reaction, and more favorable for yeast growth though less

Table 17.—*Relation of alcohol concentration to percentage of glucose utilization by aerated and nonaerated cultures of yeast no. 31.*

Culture Method	Initial Alcohol (% by volume)	Final Glucose (g/100 ml)	Glucose Utilized (%)
Aerated	0.0	0.0380	96.61
Nonaerated	0.0	0.0381	96.59
Aerated	8.0	0.0623	94.44
Nonaerated	8.0	0.0575	94.86
Aerated	10.0	0.5040	55.00
Nonaerated	10.0	0.3470	69.01
Aerated	12.0	0.9900	11.61
Nonaerated	12.0	0.9460	15.54

From Gray (1947).

favorable for the growth of bacterial contaminants. During the souring process a temperature of 130F is maintained. When the *p*H of the mash has dropped to 4.0 the souring process is stopped by raising the temperature to 135–140F; the souring process usually requires 3–10 hours. Just before the introduction of yeast from the dona, soured mash is pasteurized, and then cooled to about 75F. Yeast mash should contain about 16 per cent sugar, about 40 per cent of which should still remain when the yeast is dropped to the fermenters.

Since "finished" yeast should be ready at about the same time that the fermenter is ready for inoculum, a breakdown or other delay in milling or cooking operations can cause the yeast inoculum to develop past its optimum state with a high proportion of old cells. Fortunately, since most yeast tubs are equipped with a jacket through which either cold or hot water can be circulated, it is possible either to speed up or slow down yeast development by raising or lowering the temperature in the yeast tub. Yeast development can be accelerated by mechanical agitation of the mash.

In the yeasting process described above, yeast cells are produced under partially anaerobic conditions; however, as Willkie and Prochaska (*loc. cit.*) have pointed out, yeast inoculum may also be prepared under aerobic conditions. These authors state that the aerobic production of inoculum has certain advantages over partially anaerobic methods. Greater numbers of yeast cells can be obtained in shorter periods of time if the culture medium is vigorously aerated, but, it has been demonstrated (Gray, 1947) that the alcohol tolerance of a yeast is decreased by culturing it under highly aerobic conditions (Table 17). For the preparation of inoculum to be used for the fermentation of mashes of high sugar content (with resultant production of alcohol in high concentrations) excessive aeration should therefore be avoided.

DISTILLATION. After a fermentation has reached completion, the fermented mash (beer) is subjected to distillation, the process of separating the alcohol from the fermented mash by evaporation. The alcohol is vaporized by heating the mash and the vapors are collected, condensed, and recovered as a liquid, which may then be redistilled to obtain alcohol of higher percentage.

Distillation may be a continuous or a batch process, the nature of the process varying with the purpose for which the alcohol is being produced. Thus, for the production of highly purified grain alcohol (about 95 per cent alcohol), the distillation process is somewhat more complicated than that involved in the production of whiskey. For a discussion of the principles upon which the process of distillation is based, the reader is referred to the works of Young (1922) and Willkie and Prochaska (1943); in the latter work will also be found discussions of distillation equipment used specifically in the alcohol industry.

RECOVERY OF DRIED GRAIN AND SOLUBLES. After the alcohol has been removed by distillation the fermented mash is known as *stillage.* Although stillage is over 90 per cent water, it contains enough dissolved and suspended materials of value to justify further processing, and two by-products, distiller's dried grain and distiller's solubles, are obtained. Since both of these materials are used as livestock feed, their production is discussed in detail in Chapter 7.

Power Alcohol

The use of ethyl alcohol, either alone or in combination with gasoline or other materials, as a fuel for use in internal combustion engines, has been discussed for many years; however, there apparently has been but one serious attempt to market such a product in the United States. Whether or not this project should receive serious consideration depends upon one's point of view and also upon an accurate estimate of our petroleum reserves, which latter information should determine to a large extent the necessity for developing a substitute for gasoline.

As early as 1906, the U. S. Department of Agriculture started an inquiry concerning the possibility of using alcohol as a complete or partial substitute for gasoline in internal combustion engines. In a preliminary report issued by Lucke and Woodward in 1907, the possibility of using alcohol as a motor fuel was presented in a very favorable light, but the report pointed out that it would probably be some time before alcohol could be produced cheaply enough to compete with gasoline. While the net heat of combustion of alcohol is less than that of gasoline (10,000 Btu per lb as compared with 19,000 Btu per lb), and the latent heat of vaporization is greater than that of gasoline (thus creating engine-starting difficulties), the combustion of alcohol is cleaner; moreover, alcohol can be transported and stored with considerably greater safety than gasoline. Lucke and Woodward's report made the prediction that alcohol engines will eventually replace gasoline engines but only when the cost of fuel for operation is a subordinate consideration. The problems connected with power alcohol are not primarily mechanical (the use of a gasoline-alcohol mixture having been adequately demonstrated in a number of European countries as well as in the United States), but are rather economic in nature.

Two principal factors are of paramount importance in any consideration of the proposed use of alcohol as a motor fuel: (1) the cost of production, and (2) the future availability of the material it is intended to replace. At the present time the cost of production makes alcohol unable to compete on the market with gasoline. The cost of alcohol production by fermentation processes can be reduced only through the use of cheaper raw materials, since many of the industrial yeast strains are capable of synthesizing alcohol in quantities approaching the yield theoretically possible from the fermentable carbohydrate supplied. In addition, the type of distillery equipment available today is of very efficient design. The disadvantage of current alcohol production practice is that much edible carbohydrate is used as a source of raw material, so that the raw material costs are high. There seem to be gross differences of opinion concerning the size of our petroleum reserves. Some oil geologists and conservationists state that our petroleum reserves are practically inexhaustible; if this is true it would seem a waste, from the standpoint of carbohydrate economy, to advocate the conversion of edible carbohydrate to motor fuel in the face of increasing world population and decreasing arable land acreage. On the other hand, if our petroleum reserves are likely to be exhausted in the forseeable future (another mechanized world conflict would undoubtedly aid materially in exhaustion of such reserves), we should squarely face the fact that some day we must quickly develop a substitute for gasoline. The attitude that petroleum reserves are inexhaustible is extremely short sighted, especially in view of well-documented instances of mineral resources being depleted over relatively large areas. An example of the "inexhaustibility" of mineral resources was the almost total depletion of Indiana's known natural gas in a little over a decade. If our society remains as highly mechanized as it is today, we may someday be faced with the problem of choosing between eating our carbohydrates or powering our engines with alcohol derived from carbohydrates. Alcohol can, of course, be easily obtained by fermenting the carbohydrate of many edible foodstuffs (Table 5, Chapter 4); competition between the food and fuel industries, however, should never arise, since diversion of food into such channels could never result in a solution of the fuel problem. If the annual world's production of sugar cane was used solely for the production of alcohol, the resultant alcohol would not be of nearly sufficient quantity to supply the demand for motor fuel.

If alcohol is to become a potent factor in the field of motor fuel, it must be made through the utilization of the most abundant carbohydrate in the world—cellulose. The development of efficient, economical methods for the almost quantitative conversion of cellulose to fermentable sugars would result in providing the raw materials for production of tremendous quantities of cheap alcohol. Several methods for the acid hydrolysis of cellulose to glucose have been proposed and patented, but these methods leave much to be desired if alcohol is to be sold competitively with gasoline as a motor fuel. Attempts to prepare and isolate cellulose-hydrolyzing enzymes should be pursued vigorously, although at present such a method for digesting cellulose does not seem such as immediate a possibility as acid hydrolysis.

Willkie and Kolachov (1942) have strongly advocated the use of alcohol as a power fuel, but are primarily seeking its use as a fuel for farm power. They envision small distillery units scattered through farming country, each distillery serving a relatively small area. On the surface this seems like a feasible plan, since it would enable the farmer to obtain fuel from his surplus farm crops, and would avoid costly long-distance transportation of either raw material or finished product. These authors also recommend the return of the distillery residues to the land on which the crops were produced. Yet, if alcohol is ever to become a factor in power fuel supply, planning will have to be done on a much larger scale, in terms of continents rather than small rural areas. Furthermore, edible carbohydrates must of necessity be ruled out as a source of any sizeable amount of raw material. A power alcohol program must eventually rest upon the utilization of presently non-edible carbohydrates if the alcohol is to be produced by microbiological means.

Leslie (1923) states that the development of an alcohol industry on a scale comparable in any sense with the petroleum industry is contingent upon the use of wood as a raw material. Shortleaf pine has a commercial range of over 150 million acres in the southern part of the United States, and would be an excellent type of tree to use for conversion to alcohol. A 25-year rotation yields a wood production of 208 cu ft per acre per year. Allowing a yield of 20 gal of 95 per cent alcohol per ton of wood, the annual yield per acre would be over 62 gal, and the cost of raw wood laid down at the plant was estimated at 7 cents per gallon of alcohol. (The price estimate would have to be adjusted upward in keeping with present day higher prices.) For the annual production of one million gallons of alcohol, to be maintained indefinitely, 16,129 acres of land would be necessary: approximately 645 acres would be clear cut annually—each acre yielding 5,220 cu ft of wood, which would yield 1,556 gal of alcohol.

It is a truism that in times of plenty most individuals do not heed words of caution. Times of plenty have constituted most of the early history of the United States, but it is unrealistic to believe that any resource is inexhaustible, and some of our research and development programs should be pointed toward discovering substitutes for materials which may soon be exhausted.

Literature Cited

de Becze, G., and Rosenblatt, M. 1943. Continuous fermentation. *Amer. Brewer,* February, 1943.

Foster, J. W. 1949. *Chemical activities of fungi.* Academic Press, New York.

Gray, W. D. 1941. Studies on the alcohol tolerance of yeasts. *Jour. Bact. 42:* 561–574.

————. 1947. Further studies on the alcohol tolerance of yeasts: its relationship to cell storage products. *Jour. Bact. 55:53–59.*

————. 1949. Initial studies on the metabolism of *Hansenula anomala* (Hansen) Sydow. *Amer. Jour. Bot. 36:475–480.*

Guilliermond, A., and Tanner, F. W. 1920. *The yeasts.* New York.

Leslie, E. H. 1923. *Motor fuels. Their production and technology.* Chemical Catalog Co., New York.

Lindegren, C. C. and Lindegren, G. 1943. Selecting, inbreeding, recombining, and hybridizing commercial yeasts. *Jour. Bact. 46:405–419.*

Meyerhof, O. 1942. Intermediate reactions of fermentation. *Wallerstein Labs. Commun. 5:181–186.*

————. 1943. New chemical and physical tools for investigating the intermediary metabolism of carbohydrate. *Wallerstein Labs. Commun. 6:19–25.*

Perlman, D. 1950. Observations on the production of ethanol by fungi and yeasts. *Amer. Jour. Bot. 37:237–241.*

Porter, J. R. 1946. *Bacterial chemistry and physiology.* Wiley, New York.

Prescott, S. C., and Dunn, C. G. 1940. *Industrial microbiology.* McGraw-Hill, New York.

Stelling-Dekker, N. M. 1931. *Die Sporogenen Hefen.* Koninklifke Academie von Wetenschappen. Amsterdam.

Willkie, H. F., and Kolachov, P. J. 1942. *Food for thought.* Indiana Farm Bureau. Indianapolis.

Willkie, H. F., and Prochaska, J. A. 1943. *Fundamentals of distillery practice.* Seagram and Sons, Louisville.

Young, S. 1922. *Distillation principles and processes.* Macmillan, London.

10 · *Synthesis of Gallic Acid*

ALTHOUGH THE ALCOHOLIC FERMENTATION was unquestionably the earliest utilized of all of the fungus fermentations (since ancient man undoubtedly was aware of the changes which would take place in fruit juices or diluted honey if they were not used up immediately), the gallic acid fermentation has the distinction of being the first filamentous fungus fermentation to be investigated. Strictly speaking, this process is neither a fermentation nor a synthesis, since (as will be seen later) gallic acid is formed simply by the hydrolytic cleavage of an already existing compound.

The French investigator Van Tieghem (1867a, 1867b) first described the true nature of the process of gallic acid formation and demonstrated that the responsible agents are fungi. In his classic researches on the gallic acid fermentation Van Tieghem was also the first investigator to establish the fact that fungi in the genera *Aspergillus* and *Penicillium* (Fig. 77) are important organisms in the field of biochemical synthesis. In connection with these pioneering researches, Van Tieghem isolated, named, and recognized as new the species *Aspergillus niger*—a fungus which has since become well known to chemists and biologists and is used in a wide variety of biological syntheses. *Aspergillus niger* (Fig. 78) is also a familiar fungus to all who have had any contact with fungus physiology or applied mycology; it has probably been the most investigated of all fungus species with the exception of the common yeast of industry, *Saccharomyces cerevisiae*. Many different strains of *A. niger* are known, and the biosynthetic capacities of one strain quite frequently are very different from those of another. In fungus fermentation work involving this species the investigator accordingly first studies the capacities of a number of different

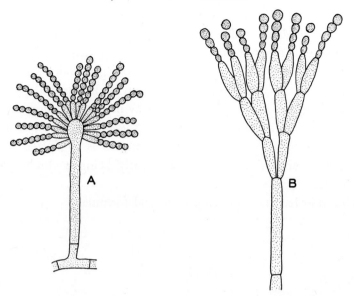

FIG. 77.   *Diagram of the spore-bearing structures of* Aspergillus (*A*) *and* Penicillium (*B*). *Highly magnified.*

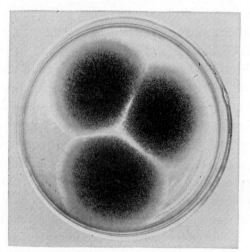

FIG. 78.   *Petri plate culture of* Aspergillus niger.

strains in order to determine the one best suited to a particular process.

Gallic acid is prepared from tannin, a material found in a great variety of plants but especially abundant in oaks and sumacs. The most important source of tannin is *gallnuts,* which are hypertrophied growths formed on sumac and oak as a result of insect injuries. There are apparently several types of tannins, but the one principally concerned in the production of gallic acid is *gallotannin,* a glucoside of gallic acid.

Gallic acid can be prepared from tannin by a chemical process involving the hydrolysis of gallotannin, or by means of a fungus fermentation. Little information is available in the literature concerning the methods by which the gallic acid fermentation is conducted commercially, the details of the process apparently being a closely guarded trade secret.

Gallic acid has the following structural formula:

$$HOOC \overset{OH}{\underset{OH}{\bigcirc}} \overset{OH}{} $$

It has a variety of uses (May and Herrick, 1930). During World War I, when German vat dyes and indigo were not available in this country because of the British blockade of Europe, gallic acid was used in the synthesis of gallocyanin, a blue dye used in American sailors' uniforms of that period. Gallic acid at present is employed in the manufacture of a very fast dyestuff known as alizarin brown. In combination with ferrous sulphate, gallic acid is used in the preparation of permanent black ink, and medicinally as subgallate of bismuth in the treatment of certain skin disorders. This acid is also used as a starting chemical in the synthesis of pyrogallol, an important photographic developer.

Although gallic acid was discovered nearly a century before Van Tieghem's investigations and was known to be formed from gallnuts, some workers believed that it was formed from tannin in the gallnuts simply by an oxidation process, while others held that it resulted from the action of a "ferment" naturally occurring in the gallnuts. Van Tieghem was able to demonstrate that tannin is not transformed through the action of a pre-existing ferment, nor by contact with the air alone. He isolated microorganisms from fermenting gallnuts (probably because of the influence of his mentor, Pasteur) and reported that two fungi appear naturally in the transformation of tannin: *Penicillium glaucum* and a new species which he named *Aspergillus niger.* Of these two, the latter was the dominant organism. The aerobic nature of the fungi was established by Van Tieghem, but he noted that if the mycelial growth was entirely of the surface type, the yield of gallic acid was decreased although the weight of fungus mycelium formed under such conditions was greatly increased.

Chemically the formation of gallic acid from tannin is a simple reaction involving the hydrolytic cleavage of the gallotannin molecule, a fact known to Van Tieghem, who stated that "tannin is split to gallic acid and glucose with fixation of the elements of water." This hydrolytic cleavage is catalyzed by a specific enzyme, *tannase,* which was demonstrated independently by Fernbach and Pottevin in 1900; both of these investigators found that this enzyme was formed by *A. niger.* Knudson (1913b) studied the production of tannase by *A. niger* and found that the enzyme was not formed when the fungus was cultured in a nutrient solution in which there was no tannin. The reaction may be written as follows:

$$\text{Gallotannin} + H_2O \xrightarrow[\text{tannase}]{} \text{Gallic Acid} + \text{Glucose}$$

In the older method of conducting the gallic acid fermentation, gallnuts or other substances containing tannin were heaped up and moistened. Fungi developed through the heap, which was stirred occasionally and maintained at a temperature of about 30C. Gallic acid was then leached from the heap after a fermentation period of about one month (Prescott and Dunn, 1940). Much more efficient methods of conducting a controlled fermentation are now known.

The gallic acid fermentation was studied in some detail by Knudson (1913a), who first tested a large number of fungi in order to determine their suitability for use in this fermentation. These tests involved a determination of the toxicity of tannic acid to the various fungi under investigation, Knudson finding that only *A. niger* and a species of *Penicillium* which he did not name could withstand high enough concentrations of tannic acid to be of possible value in this fermentation. Like Van Tieghem, this later investigator found that of the two organisms, *A. niger* was the best suited. With purified tannic acid as the substrate, 81 per cent was transformed by the tenth day by *A. niger,* whereas in a corresponding time period only 53.3 per cent of the tannic acid was transformed by the *Penicillium.* These same general results were obtained when gallnut extract was used instead of purified tannic acid; however, a more rapid fermentation was obtained with the gallnut extract (8 days required for complete transformation of tannic acid in the extract as compared with 16 days required for complete transformation when purified tannic acid was used).

Since gallic acid is known to be further metabolized by *A. niger,* thus resulting in decreased yields, Knudson attempted to prevent this by adding other nutrients to the fermentation medium. When 5 per cent sugar was added to the medium, there was an increase in growth of *A. niger,* but the gallic acid was not "protected"; the addition of 10 per cent sugar to the fermentation medium resulted in complete protection. It is now known that the disappearance of gallic acid from a fermentation is due to the fact that in addition to the synthesis of tannase, *A. niger* synthesizes another enzyme, *pyrogallase,* which destroys gallic acid (Nicholson *et al.,* 1931). The so-called protection of gallic acid by sugar as described by Knudson is undoubtedly due to the capacity of the fungus to utilize sugar more readily than gallic acid. Knudson also noted that under conditions of decreased aeration, greater yields of gallic acid were obtained; he reported that under such conditions 1 mg of mycelium was sufficient to effect the transformation of 2706 mg of tannic acid in 10 days. On the basis of his findings Knudson recommended two methods as economical ones for the production of gallic acid: (1) conducting the fermentation under aerobic conditions and supplementing the tannic acid with cane sugar, or (2) culturing the organism in medium in which tannic acid is the sole source of carbon but limiting the oxygen supply to a small amount.

Calmette (*cf.* May and Herrick) developed and patented a method for the production of gallic acid by the fermentation of a clear tannin extract. According to this investigator, a specific organism which he called *"Aspergillus gallomyces"* is present in small quantities in all gallnuts. He isolated this fungus and obtained it in pure culture. Calmette's method involves the use of a tank equipped with an agitator and suitable means for introducing sterilized air into the medium. The clear tannin extract is first placed in the tank and steam sterilized. After cooling to 35–42C the tannin extract is inoculated; the fermentation is terminated when all of the tannin has disappeared. An essential part of the process is keeping the organism submerged, a point noted much earlier by Van Tieghem. Calmette claimed that the fermentation was faster and the yields superior when this method was used instead of the older method of allowing the fermentation to occur in a heap of gallnuts. Foster (1949) states that today the fermentation is conducted with clear, aqueous tannin-containing extracts, and that when the tannin content of the substrate is high (10 per cent solution), the gallic acid which is formed crystallizes out in the medium.

Literature Cited

Fernbach, A. 1900. Sur la tannase. *Compt. rend. 131:*1214–1215.

Foster, J. W. 1949. *Chemical activities of fungi.* Academic Press. New York.

Knudson, L. 1913a. Tannic acid fermentation. *I. Jour. Biol. Chem. 14:*159–184.

———. 1913b. Tannic acid fermentation. II. Effect of nutrition on the production of the enzyme tannase. *Jour. Biol. Chem. 14:*185–202.

May, O. E., and Herrick, H. T. 1930. Some minor industrial fermentations. *Ind. Eng. Chem. 22:*1172–1176.

Nicholson, W. N., Nierenstein, M., Pool, J. C., and Price, N. V. 1931. The action of tannase on gallotannin. *Biochem. Jour. 25:*752–755.

Pottevin, H. 1900. La tannase. Diastase dédoublant l'acide gallotannique. *Compt. rend. 131:*1215–1217.

Prescott, S. C., and Dunn, C. G. 1940. *Industrial microbiology.* McGraw-Hill, New York.

Van Tieghem, P. 1867a. Sur la fermentation gallique. *Compt. rend. 65:*1091–1094.

———. 1867b. Fermentation gallique. *Ann. sci. nat. Botan., s. 5, t. 8,* 240.

11 · *Synthesis of Citric Acid*

PROPERTIES AND USES OF CITRIC ACID
BIOSYNTHESIS OF CITRIC ACID
RAW MATERIALS USED IN CITRIC ACID PRODUCTION
PRODUCTION METHODS
MECHANISM OF CITRIC ACID SYNTHESIS

ONE OF THE OUTSTANDING CONTRIBUTIONS of mycology to the fermentation industry was the development of a fermentation process for the production of citric acid. This development has made the United States virtually independent of citric acid or calcium citrate imports since 1927. Cochrane (1948) stated that in 1948 approximately 35 million lb of this acid were manufactured by the fermentation process—far greater than the amount annually imported into this country prior to the development of a process involving the use of a fungus as the biosynthetic agent. Until fairly recently essentially all of the fermentation citric acid production in the United States was handled by a single company; however, in the past few years several other companies have started work in this field (Beesch and Shull, 1955).

Calcium citrate (the raw material used in citric acid manufacture) was formerly produced almost entirely from citrus products. According to Wells and Herrick (1938), 90 per cent of the world supply in 1922 was produced in Italy. After 1922 shipments of calcium citrate and citric acid to the United States began to decline, due (according to Wells and Herrick) to three factors: (1) the Tariff Act of 1922 which greatly increased the import duties on both citric acid and calcium citrate, (2) the large increase in acreage of bearing lemon trees in California, and (3) the large-scale manufacture of citric acid by a fermentation process. The decline in imports of calcium citrate and citric acid is shown in Table 18.

Table 18.—U. S. imports of calcium citrate and citric acid for consumption, 1910–36

Year	Calcium Citrate Duty, per pound	Pounds	Citric Acid Duty, per pound	Pounds
1910[a]	Free	4,114,256	0.07	142,001
1915[a]	0.01	6,242,244	0.05	722,434
1919	0.01	3,865,294	0.05	1,224,591
1920	0.01	12,490,196	0.05	1,317,467
1921	0.01	988,969	0.05	922,737
1922[b]	0.01	16,000,692	0.05	1,325,366
1923	0.07	1,672,604	0.17	757,864
1924	0.07	1,938,647	0.17	673,114
1925	0.07	3,475,964	0.17	288,574
1926	0.07	3,039,319	0.17	284,897
1927	0.07	416,045	0.17	71,291
1928	0.07	—	0.17	1,338
1929	0.07	None	0.17	None
1930	0.07	None	0.17	6,726
1931	0.07	None	0.17	90,850
1932	0.07	704	0.17	134,521
1933	0.07	55,272	0.17	9,784
1934	0.07	None	0.17	5,275
1935	0.07	None	0.17	575
1936	0.07	None	0.17	40

Source: U.S. Bureau of Foreign Commerce and Navigation.

[a] Figures for 1910–15 are for the fiscal year; 1919–36 figures are for the calendar year.

[b] New law went into effect September 22, 1922.

Properties and Uses of Citric Acid

Many years before it was discovered that citric acid could be synthesized by certain fungi, this acid was isolated from lemon juice. Chemically, citric acid is a tribasic acid with the following structural formula:

$$
\begin{array}{c}
\text{H} \\
| \\
\text{H}-\text{C}-\text{COOH} \\
| \\
\text{HO}-\text{C}-\text{COOH} \\
| \\
\text{H}-\text{C}-\text{COOH} \\
| \\
\text{H}
\end{array}
$$

Citric acid crystallizes in large rhombic crystals containing one molecule of water of crystallization, which is lost when the acid is heated to 130C. Its melting point is 153C. When it is heated above 175C it decomposes into aconitic acid, itaconic acid, and several other compounds. Citric acid is used in the manufacture of citrates, flavoring extracts, confectionery, soft drinks, effervescent salts, as an ingredient of the material used for silvering mirrors, as an ink ingredient, in dyeing, and in medicine. According to the United States Department of Commerce (*cf.* Wells and Herrick, 1938), the major portion of the citric acid made in this country is used for medicinal purposes. Ellis (1935) has suggested that citric acid may also be used in the manufacture of edible synthetic resins which might be used as substitutes for chicle in the preparation of chewing gum.

Biosynthesis of Citric Acid

Wehmer (1893) first reported the production of citric acid from sugar by fungi, and proposed the generic name *Citromyces* to include the two species of fungi with which he worked (*C. pfefferianus* and *C. glaber*). These fungi were subsequently found to be members of the genus *Penicillium,* and citric acid was later found among the metabolic products of fungi other than these two species. Thom and Currie (1916) showed that citric acid is synthesized by many strains of *Aspergillus niger* and thus made untenable Wehmer's proposal that citric acid production was characteristic of *Penicillium*-like fungi and oxalic acid production characteristic of members of the genus *Aspergillus.* Great differences in quantities of citric acid synthesized by different strains of *A. niger* have been reported, even a single strain showing great variability in this particular capacity. Thus the maintenance of high yielding, stable strains of fungi that produce uniform results from fermentation to fermentation is one of the most important features of the citric acid industry.

The classic investigation of the citric acid fermentation in this country was the work of Currie (1917), who used only *A. niger* in his studies. He stated that a well-selected culture of this species is far superior to any culture resembling Wehmer's *"Citromyces."* Currie prepared a nutrient medium consisting of sucrose, KH_2PO_4, KCl, $MgSO_4 \cdot 7H_2O$, and a nitrogen source which was $NaNO_3$, $NH_4H_2PO_4$, or asparagine; he then determined the effect of varying the quantities of the several components upon sugar utilization and the synthesis of citric acid, oxalic acid, carbon dioxide, and mycelium. He found that by altering the proportions and quantities of the constituents of the medium, the proportions of the metabolic products could be varied at will. Highest yields of citric acid were obtained after 8 days incubation on a medium of the following composition:

	grams per liter
Sucrose	150.0
NH_4NO_3	2.50
KH_2PO_4	1.00
$MgSO_4 \cdot 7H_2O$	0.25

Using this medium, a yield of 55.28 g of citric acid per 100 g of sugar utilized was obtained. Currie represented the general equation of metabolism as follows:

Carbohydrate → Citric Acid → Oxalic Acid → Carbon Dioxide + Mycelium

He considered citric and oxalic acids to be intermediate products of respiration and assimilation and stated that in general the conditions most favorable for high yield of end products (carbon dioxide and mycelium) are least favorable for high yield of intermediate products (citric acid and oxalic acid).

Wehmer (1905–07), whose attempts to develop a commercial citric acid fermentation process apparently failed, stated that citric acid yields were increased by adding calcium carbonate to the medium, the theory being that if the citric acid reacted with the carbonate it could not be further metabolized by the organism. Currie found that higher yields of citric acid and faster fermentation rates resulted if no calcium carbonate was added. These results were undoubtedly due in part to the higher hydrogen-ion concentration in medium containing no calcium carbonate, and Currie recommended that medium be initially adjusted to *p*H 3.4–3.5 with hydrochloric acid.

Beneficial Activities of Fungi

Further experimentation by Currie led to his recommendation of the following fermentation medium:

		grams per liter
Sucrose	....	125–150
NH_4NO_3	....	2.0–2.5
KH_2PO_4	....	0.75–1.0
$MgSO_4 \cdot 7H_2O$	....	0.20–0.25
HCl to *p*H 3.4–3.5.		

Fermentations could be conducted as successfully in shallow pans as in flasks, and analytical data from one series of pan fermentations are shown in Table 19.

Table 19.—Production of citric acid in shallow-pan fermentations

Pan	Citric Acid By Titration (%)	Calcium Citrate in 25 cc By Precipitation (g)	Calcium Citrate (%)	Citric Acid Calculated from Calcium Citrate (%)	Sugar Remaining in the Liquor (%)
1	11.54	3.8789	15.52	10.35	3.95
2	11.51	3.8209	15.28	10.19	4.69
3	11.00	3.7673	15.07	10.05	5.93

After Currie (1917).

Various publications concerning the citric acid fermentation have appeared since Currie's report. Many of these deal with factors that influence the fermentation or attempt to explain the mechanism of a fermentation in which the branched chain structure of the citric acid molecule is synthesized from sugar molecules which contain no branched chain structure. Only a few of these publications will be discussed here; for further information the bibliographies appearing in the works of Fulmer and Werkman (1930), Prescott and Dunn (1949), or Underkofler and Hickey (1954) should be consulted.

Currie (*loc. cit.*) attempted to determine if iron has an effect on citric acid yield. He stated that *A. niger* grew as well and sporulated as abundantly on iron-free as on iron-containing media, and that when nitrogen was supplied as ammonium salts or asparagine, added iron had no effect upon metabolism. However, when nitrogen was supplied as nitrates the addition of iron resulted in increased mycelial weight and carbon dioxide production. The concept of chemical stimulation of growth was in vogue at the time of Currie's work, but he felt that the action of such "stimulants" resulted in the transformation of greater quantities of sugar into assimilation products of the mycelium and less into waste products, and in accord with this principle stated that the highest yield of fermentation by-products will be obtained when mycelium development is restricted, not stimulated. Porges (1932) reinvestigated the effects of certain metallic salts on citric acid synthesis and arrived at somewhat different conclusions to those expressed by Currie. For example, he demonstrated that the presence of $FeCl_3$ affected acid formation, maximum acid yield as well as maximum mycelial weight being obtained when 0.02 g of $FeCl_3$ was added to each liter of medium. The relation between $FeCl_3$ concentration and mycelium weight and acid production is shown in Table 20.

Table 20.—Influence of $FeCl_3$ upon production of citric acid by Aspergillus niger *in a 20 per cent sugar solution in seven days*

FeCl₃ per Liter (g)	Fungus Growth (g)	Titratable Acidity N/10, (cc)
0.00	0.67	91
0.01	1.74	270
0.02	2.73	370
0.05	2.60	364
0.10	2.53	323
0.20	0.36	48

After Porges (1932).

Porges also investigated the effects of zinc, manganese, nickel, and copper (supplied as sulphates) and found that the addition of the zinc salt up to a concentration of 0.3 g per liter resulted in an increase in acid production, with best yields occurring at a concentration of 0.1 g $ZnSO_4$ per liter. Manganese, nickel, and copper sulphates proved inhibiting at concentrations as low as 0.01 g per liter.

In his investigation of the influence of sugar concentration of the medium upon citric acid formation, Porges found that in the sugar concentration range of 5 to 20 per cent, highest percentage conversion of sugar to citric acid occurred at a sugar concentration of 20 per cent, but that a lower percentage of sugar was utilized at this high sugar concentration. He also found that aeration of the fermentation medium prevented the accumulation of citric acid; that replacing the spent fermentation medium under the mycelial mat with fresh medium did not result in increased yields of citric acid; and that $NaNO_3$ was superior to NH_4NO_3 or $(NH_4)_2SO_4$ as a nitrogen source in citric acid formation.

Doelger and Prescott (1934) conducted a critical study of the various factors affecting the citric acid fermentation and made several valuable contributions. Like Currie, they studied the effects of inorganic salt concentration upon this fermentation and recommended the following medium:

grams per liter

Sucrose	140.00
NH_4NO_3	2.23
K_2HPO_4	1.00
$MgSO_4 \cdot 7H_2O$	0.23

adjust pH to 2.2–1.6 with normal HCl.

They found that larger quantities of salts resulted in increased mycelial growth and spore production accompanied by a decreased citric acid yield. Whereas Currie had recommended that the initial pH of the medium be adjusted to 3.4–3.5, these investigators recommended that the starting pH be somewhat lower (2.2–1.6). Under these more acid

Table 21.—*Effect of incubation temperature on citric acid production*

Temperature of Incubation (°C)	Titratable Acidity (Normality)	Citric Acid Produced per flask fermentation (g)	per 100 g sugar (g)	Evaporation of Medium (%)
20–22	1.0024	3.37	32	24
24	1.0535	3.55	34	27
26	1.1187	3.96	38	26
28	1.1564	3.88	37	30
30–33	1.1045	2.87	27	36

After Doelger and Prescott (1934).

conditions, heat sterilization of the medium resulted in hydrolysis of the sucrose. Since such hydrolysis led to decreased yields, the recommendation was made that the sugar solutions and mineral salt solutions be sterilized separately. Optimum temperature for citric acid formation was found to be 26–28 C, as shown in Table 21.

In their investigation of the effect of varying the ratio of volume of medium to surface area in shallow pan cultures, Doelger and Prescott obtained their highest percentage yield with the lowest volume/surface area ratio (see Table 22). These investigators used aluminum pans as

Table 22.—Effect of varying ratio of volume to surface area of medium on yields of citric acid

Volume-Surface-Area Ratio (cc/sq cm)	Original Volume (cc)	Total 14% Sugar Solution (g/pan)	Final Volume (cc)	Citric Acid (g/100cc)	Total Citric Acid (g/pan)	Yield of Sugar to Citric Acid (%)
2.45	2000	280	1810	6.35	114.9	41.0
2.20	1800	252	1620	7.05	114.2	45.3
2.08	1700	238	1490	7.40	110.3	46.3
1.83	1500	210	1310	7.75	110.2	48.3
1.22	1000	140	780	8.80	68.6	49.0

After Doelger and Prescott (1934).

culture vessels and found that pans constructed from ordinary commercial grade aluminum were badly etched by the relatively high concentrations of citric acid formed during fermentation. Some pans were so badly corroded that they leaked after being used for three fermentations; this difficulty was subsequently avoided by the use of aluminum rated 99.8 or 99.98 per cent pure.

Raw Materials Used in Citric Acid Production

Most investigators working with the citric acid fermentation have found that best yields are obtained using sucrose as the source of carbohydrate (Fig. 79); however, Amelung (1927) has reported that citric acid may also be synthesized from 3-, 4-, 5-, 6-, and 7-carbon compounds. Since a cheap source of raw material is very important to the success of a fermentation process of this type, cane molasses would seem to be admirably suited for the citric acid fermentation, because it is cheap, available in quantity, and contains sucrose, the best carbon source found so far. Karow and Waksman (1947) have found that of the crude molasses which they tested, only "Cuban Invert" and "High Test" could be utilized for the citric acid fermentation, although other molasses could be used if they were purified. Combined treatment

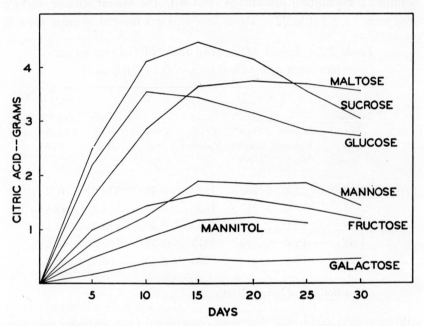

Fig. 79.   *The relation of type of carbon source to yield of citric acid. (Redrawn from Amelung, 1927.)*

with bone char, Suchot CSP, and amberlites (synthetic ion-exchange resins) gave the best results, although the total citric acid produced was slightly less than that produced in the control fermentations using sucrose.

Cahn (1935) proposed a completely new method for producing citric acid, employing a medium composed of a solid material such as cane or beet pulp, impregnated with sugar solutions. The mass is not sterilized prior to inoculation, and the fermentation is said to be complete in four days or less. Cahn reported yields of 55 per cent and 45 per cent, the former on the basis of sucrose supplied, the latter on the basis of total sucrose present in molasses supplied.

Gerhardt (1946) and his co-workers attempted to conduct the citric acid fermentation using beet molasses as the source of carbohydrate, but obtained poor yields from untreated molasses. Their analyses of beet molasses revealed a comparatively high percentage of metals, especially iron; since other investigators had shown that excesses of metals inhibit acid formation, Gerhardt and his colleagues concluded that the poor yields they had obtained were due to the high concentration of iron. When they used either potassium ferrocyanide or potassium ferricyanide as an iron precipitant, yields of citric acid were increased. Potassium ferricyanide precipitation did not result in yields quite so high as those obtained with ferrocyanide precipitation, but the range of optimum level was not as narrow as with ferrocyanide. Using a strain of *A. niger* selected from twenty tested, these workers obtained yields of 45–50 per cent from fermentations conducted in shallow aluminum pans (36 × 25.5 × 7.5 cm) in medium 5 cm deep. Contrary to the reports of other workers who recommended a low initial *p*H, Gerhardt stated that after ferrocyanide treatment best yields were obtained when the medium was adjusted to *p*H 7.0.

DasGupta, Saha, and Guha (1938) reported that citric acid can be produced from solutions of molasses and gur using a species of *Mucor;* however, the yields were lower than those obtained by other investigators who used species of *Aspergillus.*

Details of commercial citric acid fermentation have always been meager, since considerable secrecy has been attached to this process. According to Underkofler and Hickey (1954) no successful surface fermentations using cane molasses as the carbohydrate source have been reported; however, Beesch and Shull (1956) state that "among the field of products that may be profitably produced from blackstrap molasses, citric acid continues to hold a significant position by virtue of its steadily increasing demand and price stability." In view of the reports of various investigators that molasses can be rendered suitable for use in the citric acid fermentation by proper treatment, it seems highly improbable that the commercial producers of this acid have not worked out procedures in which this cheap carbohydrate source may be used.

Production Methods

The details of the methods developed for the large-scale production of citric acid by fermentation are trade secrets and hence have not been published. As May and Herrick (1932) have pointed out, in the early development of the process it very probably consisted of a shallow-pan fermentation of sucrose employing a strain of *A. niger*. The disadvantages of the shallow-pan culture method have long been recognized: it is a costly process and literally hundreds of acres of pans would be necessary to maintain a high level of production. A cursory examination of the patent literature might lead one to believe that there are a great many commercially feasible methods for producing citric acid by fermentation. Nevertheless, it is significant that until recently only one company in this country produced citric acid by a fermentation method, leading one to doubt that there are as many successful procedures as the patent literature would indicate.

In view of the disadvantages of the shallow-pan process, attempts have been made to develop a satisfactory deep-vat process, although in the opinion of Karow and Waksman (1947) such attempts have been largely unsuccessful. These investigators conducted submerged-culture fermentations on a laboratory scale in small flasks which were simultaneously shaken and aerated; their semipilot plant experiments were conducted in 5-liter bottles, the contents of which were aerated during the fermentation period. The organism employed was a strain of *Aspergillus wentii,* which was found to be a better producer of citric acid in submerged culture than *A. niger.* In their semipilot plant equipment they obtained 91.4 per cent sucrose utilization in 10 days; of the sugar utilized, there was a 52.2 per cent conversion to citric acid.

Perlman (1949) has recently reviewed the literature relevant to the submerged-culture production of citric acid and has pointed out that yields of citric acid obtained by this method in laboratory-scale apparatus are now about the same magnitude as those obtained by the older established surface culture method (70 g of acid from 100 g of carbohydrate). An example of yields approaching this magnitude is reported by Steel, Lentz, and Martin (1955), who obtained an average yield of 64 per cent in 51 fermentations in which citric acid was produced in submerged culture from ferrocyanide-treated beet molasses.

Although the details of commercial production methods by a submerged-culture process are not available in the literature, the review of Perlman and the reports of other investigators indicate a strong possibility that a submerged-culture process may become a reality, if indeed, it is not already in operation. Much impetus has been given to the search for a strain of *A. niger* suitable for submerged culture—as well as to attempts to establish sets of optimum conditions for the process—by the experiences gained in the development of the penicillin industry.

Mechanism of Citric Acid Synthesis

Many attempts have been made to ascertain the sequence of chemical reactions which result in the biological synthesis of citric acid. From the results of these attempts have arisen a number of hypotheses purporting to explain this particular biosynthetic mechanism. To be fully acceptable and to fit all of the known experimental results such an hypothesis must explain how citric acid may be synthesized from 2-, 3-, 4-, 5-, 6-, 7-, and 12-carbon molecules, and how a branched-chain molecule may be formed. It must also account for the high yields of citric acid frequently obtained in fermentations. Porges (*loc. cit.*) has pointed out that the various hypotheses may be grouped into four general categories as follows:

1. Citric acid is a product of proteolysis and is a residue of the decomposition of amino acids.
2. Citric acid is formed by an inner aldolization process, a 5-carbon ring being formed, broken, and then oxidized to the acid.
3. Citric acid is formed as a result of the progressive oxidation of sugar to gluconic acid, saccharic acid, adipic acid, and then citric acid, or some similar series of reactions through sugar acid intermediates.
4. Citric acid is formed as the result of a synthetic process, the sugar molecules being broken down to shorter chains of carbon from which the acid is then synthesized. Thus, the units may be acetaldehyde, or oxalic, acetic, and similar acids.

PROTEOLYTIC HYPOTHESIS. This hypothesis was supported by very few workers and is presented here only for historic purposes. Maze (1909) suggested that citric acid was a product of incomplete respiration; Kostychew (1927) apparently believed that the compounds incompletely respired were amino acids and other cleavage products of proteins. The latter worker called attention to the fact that in the formation of amino acids, branched carbon chains are formed from sugar Since the carbon framework of isoleucine is identical with that of citric acid, Kostychew suggested that citric acid might be formed from this amino acid.

$$
\begin{array}{cccc}
& \text{H} & & \text{NH}_2 \\
& | & & | \\
& \text{H—C—COOH} & & \text{H—C—COOH} \\
& | & & | \\
\text{citric acid} & \text{HO—C—COOH} & & \text{H—C—CH}_3 \ \text{isoleucine} \\
& | & & | \\
& \text{H—C—COOH} & & \text{H—C—CH}_3 \\
& | & & | \\
& \text{H} & & \text{H}
\end{array}
$$

There is no experimental evidence to support the proteolytic hypothesis and little if any credence is given to it today.

INNER ALDOLIZATION HYPOTHESIS. This hypothesis, proposed by Butkewitsch (1924), explained citric acid synthesis as occurring by the direct oxidation of glucose to citric acid:

$$C_6H_{12}O_6 + \tfrac{3}{2}O_2 \rightarrow C_6H_8O_7 + 2H_2O$$

Butkewitsch was of the opinion that glucose was oxidized first to gluconic acid, which in turn was converted to glucuronic acid. Glucuronic acid was then supposed to undergo an intramolecular aldol condensation with the formation of a 5-membered ring. Breakage of the ring followed by oxidation resulted in the formation of citric acid. The carbon skeletal structures involved in the latter part of the synthesis may be represented as follows:

$$
\begin{array}{ccccc}
\text{C—C} & & \text{C—C} & & \text{C—C} \\
\diagup \quad | & & \diagup \quad | & & \diagup \\
\text{C—C} \quad | \ \rightarrow \ \text{C—C} & & | \ \rightarrow \ \text{C—C} & & \\
| & & \diagdown & & \diagdown \\
\text{C—C} & & \text{C—C} & & \text{C—C}
\end{array}
$$

Apparently there is little or no experimental evidence to substantiate this hypothesis and few if any investigators have supported Butkewitsch's view.

PROGRESSIVE OXIDATION HYPOTHESIS. Several hypotheses have been advanced that explain citric acid formation as occurring by way of metabolic pathways involving the oxidation of glucose to a sugar acid. In a sense the scheme proposed by Butkewitsch would fit into this general category, although the aldol condensation followed by ring breakage sets it apart from other schemes in which a sugar acid is thought to be an intermediate. Franzen and Schmitt (1925) suggested that citric acid is formed as follows:

Sugar → Saccharic Acid → βγ-Diketoadipic Acid $\xrightarrow[\text{rearrangement}]{\text{by benzilic acid}}$ Citric Acid

The scheme proposed by Raistrick and Clark (1919) also involves the initial oxidation of sugar to saccharic acid. According to these investigators, glucose is oxidized to saccharic acid, which by loss of water is converted to αγ-diketoadipic acid; hydrolytic cleavage of this latter acid results in the formation of oxalacetic acid and acetic acid which then combine and form citric acid. Thus, the last stage of this scheme would also fit in with the hypotheses classified in the fourth category. The reactions involved in the Raistrick and Clark scheme are:

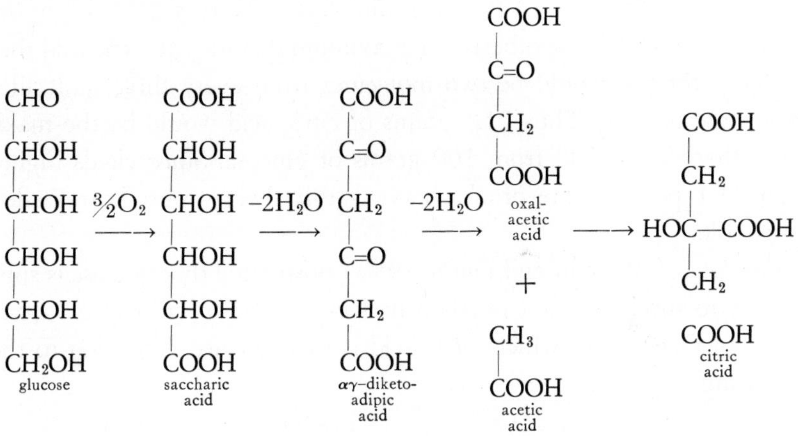

Challenger and others (1927) isolated saccharic acid from an *Aspergillus niger* fermentation of glucose. This result would seem to add weight to the hypotheses which include this dicarboxylic sugar acid as an intermediate compound in the synthesis of citric acid. Any scheme such as the one proposed by Raistrick and Clark which explains the formation of a 6-carbon acid molecule from a single molecule of hexose would allow for the formation of 192 grams of citric acid from 180 grams of hexose (maximum yield of theory: 106.6 per cent), and hence could account for the high yields of citric acid which are frequently obtained in experimental fermentations. From the standpoint of yield alone this would be an acceptable hypothesis; however, with such a scheme it is impossible to account for the synthesis of citric acid from 2-, 3-, 4-, 5-, and 7-carbon molecules unless it is assumed that a hexose sugar is first synthesized.

SYNTHETIC PROCESS HYPOTHESIS.   Fermentation schemes of this general category all explain citric acid formation by a series of reactions in which the sugar molecule is first broken down to molecules of shorter chain length, which then combine and form the 6-carbon, branched-chain molecule of citric acid. Thus it was early suggested by Euler (1909) that acetaldehyde was formed from sugar as in the alcoholic fermentation, and that three molecules were then condensed and the condensation product oxidized to citric acid:

$$\underset{\text{glucose}}{3C_6H_{12}O_6} \rightarrow \underset{\text{acet-aldehyde}}{6CH_3CHO} + 6CO_2$$

$$\underset{\substack{\text{condensation} \\ \text{and oxidation}}}{\big|_____} \rightarrow \underset{\text{citric acid}}{2C_6H_8O_7}$$

On the basis of this hypothesis, the maximum quantity of citric acid that could be formed would be two molecules from every three molecules of glucose utilized. Thus 71.1 grams of citric acid would be the maximum theoretical yield from 100 grams of glucose. Since yields higher than 71.1 per cent are often obtained, this theory must be regarded untenable.

Gudlet (*cf.* Prescott and Dunn, 1949) postulated that glucose is split directly to succinic acid (4-carbon molecule) and acetaldehyde (2-carbon molecule) from which citric acid is then formed according to the following reactions:

$$
C_6H_{12}O_6 + H_2O \rightarrow \left\{
\begin{array}{l}
\underset{\text{succinic acid}}{\begin{array}{c} COOH \\ | \\ CH_2 \\ | \\ CH_2 \\ | \\ COOH \end{array}}
\xrightarrow{}
\underset{\text{malic acid}}{\begin{array}{c} COOH \\ | \\ CH_2 \\ | \\ CHOH \\ | \\ COOH \end{array}} \\[2em]
+ \quad {}^{1\!/_2}O_2 \\
\underset{\text{acetaldehyde}}{CH_3CHO} \xrightarrow{} \underset{\text{acetic acid}}{\begin{array}{c} CH_3 \\ | \\ COOH \end{array}}
\end{array}
\right\}
\underset{-H_2}{\longrightarrow}
\underset{\text{citric acid}}{\begin{array}{c} COOH \\ | \\ CH_2 \\ | \\ HOC\!-\!COOH \\ | \\ CH_2 \\ | \\ COOH \end{array}}
$$

While Gudlet's fermentation scheme will allow high yields of citric acid from glucose, such a scheme could be accepted only if adequate proof of the initial reaction (glucose → succinic acid and acetaldehyde) is supplied.

According to Foster (1949) serious consideration is given today only to those hypotheses that explain the synthesis of citric acid on the basis of initial formation of a 4-carbon dicarboxylic acid molecule and a 2-carbon monocarboxylic acid molecule, from which two molecules the 6-carbon, branched-chain molecule of citric acid is then formed. Thus Chrzaszcz and Tiukow (1930) explain citric acid formation as resulting from the combining of a molecule of malic acid with one of acetic acid, the malic acid molecule having been formed from 2 molecules of acetic acid through succinic and fumaric acid intermediates:

$$
\begin{array}{c}
\text{COOH} \\
| \\
\text{CH}_3 \\
+ \\
\text{CH}_3 \\
| \\
\text{COOH} \\
\text{acetic acid}
\end{array}
\xrightarrow{-\text{H}_2}
\begin{array}{c}
\text{COOH} \\
| \\
\text{CH}_2 \\
| \\
\text{CH}_2 \\
| \\
\text{COOH} \\
\text{succinic acid}
\end{array}
\xrightarrow{-\text{H}_2}
\begin{array}{c}
\text{COOH} \\
| \\
\text{CH} \\
|| \\
\text{CH} \\
| \\
\text{COOH} \\
\text{fumaric acid}
\end{array}
\xrightarrow{+\text{H}_2\text{O}}
\begin{array}{c}
\text{COOH} \\
| \\
\text{CHOH} \\
| \\
\text{CH}_2 \\
| \\
\text{COOH} \\
\text{malic acid}
\end{array}
$$

$$
\begin{array}{c}
\text{COOH} \\
| \\
\text{CHOH} \\
| \\
\text{CH}_2 \\
| \\
\text{COOH} \\
+ \\
\text{COOH} \\
| \\
\text{CH}_3
\end{array}
\xrightarrow{-\text{H}_2}
\begin{array}{c}
\text{COOH} \\
| \\
\text{CH}_2 \\
| \\
\text{HOC–COOH} \\
| \\
\text{CH}_2 \\
| \\
\text{COOH} \\
\text{citric acid}
\end{array}
$$

The scheme presented above seems plausible enough; however, if it is assumed that acetic acid is formed from acetaldehyde (the initial stages being similar to those of the alcoholic fermentation) the high yields of citric acid obtained experimentally would rule out this hypothesis. Bernhauer, Böckl, and Siebenauger (*cf.* Prescott and Dunn, 1940) have suggested that the acids involved are succinic and acetic, while Ciusa and Brüll (1939) have suggested a condensation of malic and glycolic acids. The latter investigators have found that the addition of malic acid to an *A. niger* fermentation increased the yield of citric acid to 332 per cent the sugar utilized, the addition of glycolic acid increased the yield to 132 per cent, and the addition of equimolar quantities of malic and glycolic acids caused the yield to be increased to 928 per cent. These increased yields do not necessarily implicate malic and glycolic acids as the immediate precursors of citric acid, since it is possible that they may have been converted to other acids, which in turn were then converted to citric acid.

Although it seems probable that citric acid is synthesized through a series of reactions ending with the combination of a 2-carbon acid with a 4-carbon acid, it is impossible at this time to state exactly what these reactions are. In view of the investigations of the Krebs Cycle in recent years, there is a strong possibility that the two acids involved are oxalacetic and acetic. In order to explain the high yields of citric acid obtained from sugar, the fermentation mechanism must not be one that involves the loss of very much carbon dioxide from the system through the decarboxylation of pyruvic acid. Perhaps the solution might best be sought by using such techniques as those employed by Foster and others (1941) who showed that when *A. niger* was supplied with carbon dioxide in which the carbon atom was a radioactive isotope, it synthesized citric acid in which the tracer carbon was present in a carboxyl group. In view of this and similar findings, perhaps a significant amount of the citric acid synthesized by a fungus may be formed according to the following general scheme:

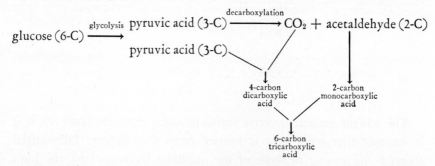

Regardless of the exact mechanism by which citric acid is synthesized by fungi, one point seems fairly obvious: under the conditions under which fungi are routinely cultured, even a high-yielding strain could not be expected to form this acid in quantity. Citric acid formation in the great quantities obtainable with some fungi is unquestionably an example of shunt metabolism, since fungi typically further metabolize citric acid as it is formed, and thus it does not accumulate in cultures except when conditions are so arranged that the major part of the carbon metabolism is shunted into the citric acid pathway from other metabolic pathways. The reports of the various investigators who have concerned themselves with the citric acid fermentation indicate that the conditions most favorable for acid synthesis and accumulation are certainly not those most favorable for growth. The fermentation medium usually employed has a very acid reaction, a relatively high sugar concentration (compared with the concentrations usually employed in the culture of fungi), and is deficient in phosphate and certain essential trace elements—conditions not especially optimal for growth.

The fact that citric acid can be formed by fungi on a commercial scale is an excellent example of how man can adjust the culture conditions in order to change the metabolic pathway of a fungus so that it synthesizes a desired compound. That the metabolism of fungi may be changed very easily by altering the environmental conditions has been demonstrated many times and is one of the most significant features of these organisms, since it provides almost unlimited possibilities for their use as agents of biosynthesis.

Literature Cited

Amelung, H. 1927. Beiträge zur Säurebildung durch Aspergillus niger. *Ztschr. Physiol. Chem. 166:161–209.*

Beesch, S. C., and Shull, G. M. 1956. Fermentation. *Ind. Eng. Chem. 48:1585–1603.*

Butkewitsch, W. 1924. Über die Bildung der Glucon- und Citronensäure in den Pilzkulturen auf Zucker. *Biochem. Zeit. 154:177–190.*

Cahn, F. J. 1935. Citric acid fermentation on solid materials. *Ind. Eng. Chem. 27:201–204.*

Challenger, F., Subramanian, V., and Walker, T. K. 1927. The mechanism of the formation of citric acid and oxalic acid from sugars by *Aspergillus niger.* Part I. *Jour. Chem. Soc. 1927 (I):200–208.*

Chrzaszcz, T. and Tiukow, D. 1930. Biochemische Umbildungen der Essigsäure durch Schimmelpilze und über den Chemismus der Citronensäurebildung. *Biochem. Zeit. 229:343–357.*

Ciusa, R., and Brüll, L. 1939. Sul meccanismo della fermentazione citrica. -1. *Ann. chim. applicata 29:3–11.*

Cochrane, V. W. 1948. Commercial production of acids by fungi. *Econ. Bot. 2:145–157.*

Currie, J. N. 1917. The citric acid fermentation of *Aspergillus niger.* *Jour. Biol. Chem. 31:15–37.*

DasGupta, G. C., Saha, K. C., and Guha, B. C. 1938. The fermentative production of citric and oxalic acids from "gur" and molasses. *Science and Culture 3(7):397–398.*

Doelger, W. P., and Prescott, S. C. 1934. Citric acid fermentation. *Ind. Eng. Chem. 26:*1142–1147.

Ellis, C. 1935. Edible synthetic ester resins. U.S. Patent 2,007,965. July 16, 1935.

Euler, H. 1909. Grundlagen und Ergebnisse der Pflanzenchemie, *Teil 3:182*. Braunschweig.

Foster, J. W. 1949. *Chemical activities of fungi.* Academic Press, New York.

Foster, J. W., Carson, S. F., Ruben, S., and Kamen, M. D. 1941. Radioactivity as an indicator of carbon dioxide utilization. VII. The assimilation of carbon dioxide by moulds. *Proc. Nat. Acad. Sci. 27:*590–596.

Franzen, H. and Schmitt, F. 1925. Die Bildung der Citronensäure aus Ketipin-säure. *Ber. 58:*222–226.

Fulmer, E. I., and Werkman, C. H. 1930. *An index to the chemical action of microorganisms on the nonnitrogenous organic compounds.* Thomas, Springfield, Ill.

Gerhardt, P., Dorrell, W. W., and Baldwin, I. L. 1946. Citric acid fermentation of beet molasses. *Jour. Bact. 52:*555–564.

Karow, E. O., and Waksman, S. A. 1947. Production of citric acid in submerged culture. *Ind. Eng. Chem. 39:*821–825.

Kostychew, S. 1927. *Plant respiration.* Blakiston, Philadelphia.

May, O. E., and Herrick, H. T. 1932. Production of organic acids from carbohydrates by fermentation. U.S.D.A. Circ. 216.

Maze, P. 1909. Note sur la production d'acide citrique par les *Citromyces* (Wehmer). *Ann. Inst. Pasteur 23:*830–833.

Perlman, D. 1949. Mycological production of citric acid—the submerged culture method. *Econ. Bot. 3:*360–374.

Porges, N. 1932. Citric acid production by *Aspergillus niger. Amer. Jour. Bot. 19:*559–567.

Prescott, S. C., and Dunn, C. G. 1940. *Industrial microbiology.* McGraw-Hill, New York.

Steel, R., Lentz, C. P. and Martin, S. M. 1955. Submerged citric acid fermentation of sugar beet molasses. *Canadian Jour. Microbiol. 1:*299–311.

Raistrick, H., and Clark, A. B. 1919. On the mechanism of oxalic acid formation by *Aspergillus niger. Biochem. Jour. 13:*329–344.

Thom, C., and Currie, J. N. 1916. *Aspergillus niger* group. *Jour. Agr. Res. 7:*1–15.

Underkofler, L. A., and Hickey, R. J. 1954. *Industrial fermentations.* Chem. Pub. Co., New York.

Wehmer, C. 1893. Note sur la fermentation citrique. *Bull. soc. chim. de Paris 9:*728–730.

———. 1905–07. In Lafar, *F. Hanb. Technischen Mykologie,* Jena.

Wells, P. A., and Herrick, H. T. 1938. Citric acid industry. *Ind. Eng. Chem. 30:*255–262.

12 · *Synthesis of Gluconic Acid*

CHEMISTRY OF GLUCONIC ACID SYNTHESIS BY FUNGI
PRODUCTION OF GLUCONIC ACID BY FERMENTATION

THE BACTERIAL SYNTHESIS of gluconic acid was reported as early as 1880 by Boutroux, but it was not until 1922 that this sugar acid was discovered among the metabolic products of a fungus. Molliard (1922) found that gluconic acid was synthesized along with citric acid and oxalic acids by *Aspergillus niger,* and in 1924 published studies in which he described some of the optimum conditions for the formation of gluconic acid. Since gluconic acid is an important chemical compound, considerable attention has been given to the development of a high-yielding fermentation process. Especially active in the development of the process were May, Herrick, Moyer, and others of the U.S. Department of Agriculture. As a result of the work of this group and others, methods are now used whereby high yields of gluconic acid can be obtained through a fermentation process in relatively short periods of time.

Because of the high solubility of the calcium salt of gluconic acid, it is an especially valuable compound to use as a means of administering calcium. Calcium gluconate can be injected into tissues without causing necrosis and has been used for injection into cows suffering from milk fever; it has also been employed to increase the calcium content of egg shells of hens suffering from calcium deficiency (Ramsbottom, 1936). Calcium gluconate is used in the manufacture of toothpastes and routinely as a source of calcium during pregnancy.

The investigation of the gluconic acid fermentation and its development (principally by the Department of Agriculture group) serves to illustrate a principle quite different from that illustrated in the history of penicillin development. In the latter instance really startling increases in yield were not obtained until the problem was approached from the standpoint of the development of special strains of fungi by means of ultraviolet or X-radiation. In the case of the gluconic acid fermentation, the process was developed almost entirely by investigation of environmental conditions and different types of culture methods, and the subsequent employment of the conditions under which highest yields and most rapid fermentations resulted. Ramsbottom (*loc. cit.*) has stated that modern man does not remain satisfied with the methods of his ancestors, or even with those of his immediate predecessors; he not only desires to make two blades of grass grow where one grew before, but wants them twice as big at half the cost and twice the speed. There is no better exemplification of this idea in the field of industrial mycology than in the series of investigations dealing with the development of the gluconic acid fermentation.

Chemistry of Gluconic Acid Synthesis

A comparison of the molecular structures of glucose and gluconic acid reveals that these two compounds are quite similar chemically, and that the conversion of glucose to gluconic acid can be accomplished with only a slight molecular alteration:

$$
\begin{array}{cc}
\text{H} & \text{H} \\
| & | \\
\text{H}-\text{C}-\text{OH} & \text{H}-\text{C}-\text{OH} \\
| & | \\
(\text{H}-\text{C}-\text{OH})_4 & (\text{H}-\text{C}-\text{OH})_4 \\
| & | \\
\text{C}=\text{O} & \text{C}=\text{O} \\
| & | \\
\text{H} & \text{OH} \\
\text{glucose} & \text{gluconic acid}
\end{array}
$$

From these structural formulas it is obvious that the conversion of glucose to gluconic acid is chemically simple, involving only the oxidation of the aldehyde group of glucose with the resultant formation of a carboxyl group. The simplified reaction may be written as follows:

$$C_6H_{12}O_6 + \tfrac{1}{2}O_2 \rightarrow C_6H_{12}O_7 \tag{1}$$

From Equation (1) it is apparent that the theoretical weight yield of gluconic acid from glucose is greater than the glucose utilized. Complete conversion of 100 g of glucose would result in 108.8 g of gluconic acid.

In the biological synthesis of gluconic acid the reaction is not quite so simple as is indicated in Equation (1). Actually, one molecule of hydrogen peroxide is formed for each molecule of glucose utilized and the equation should read:

$$C_6H_{12}O_6 + H_2O + O_2 \rightarrow C_6H_{12}O_7 + H_2O_2 \qquad (2)$$

With living cells the hydrogen peroxide is destroyed by the enzyme catalase as soon as it is formed, so for practical purposes Equation (1) is generally used. The enzyme involved in the transformation of glucose to gluconic acid, called glucose-oxidase or more properly *glucose-aero-dehydrogenase,* has been studied by a number of workers; for references to investigations which deal specifically with this enzyme, the work of Foster (1949) should be consulted. It is of interest to note that glucose-aerodehydrogenase has been shown to be identical with an "antibiotic" variously known as penicillin B, notatin, and penatin. Since this enzyme has no antibacterial activity in the presence of the enzyme catalase, it is obvious that such activity is due to the presence of the hydrogen peroxide which is produced.

Production of Gluconic Acid by Fermentation

Shortly after Molliard first reported the synthesis of gluconic acid by a fungus, Butkewitsch (1923) found a strain of *Aspergillus niger* which in the presence of calcium carbonate formed gluconic acid almost to the exclusion of other acids; this strain was later studied by Bernhauer (1924). A few years later May and others (1927) initiated the work of the U.S. Department of Agriculture group in this country by testing 172 different strains of fungi for their capacities to synthesize gluconic acid. The fungi tested belonged to the genera *Aspergillus, Mucor, Penicillium,* and *Monilia.* The culture solutions in which all strains of the *Penicillium luteum-purpurogenum* group were cultured became strongly acid after seven days, and gluconic acid was recovered as the calcium salt from these solutions in amounts sufficient to account for the entire titratable acidity. On the basis of their screening tests, one strain of *P. purpurogenum* var. *rubrisclerotium* was selected for subsequent study. Herrick and May (1928) later determined some of the optimal conditions for acid production by this strain (Thom No. 2670). They conducted 1-liter fermentations in large Erlenmeyer flasks allowing a fermentation period of fourteen days. It was found that a *p*H range of 3.0 to 6.4 was satisfactory for the fermentation, and a temperature of approximately 25 C was found to be nearly optimum. The following mixture of mineral salts was chosen as their standard solution:

$$\textit{grams per liter}$$

MgSO$_4$·7H$_2$O 0.25

KCl 0.05

Na$_2$HPO$_4$·12H$_2$O 0.10

NaNO$_3$ 1.00

Little difference in yield was noted between solutions containing 20 and 25 per cent glucose—the yields obtained with both varying from 51.6 per cent to 56.6 per cent. Ratio of the surface area to volume of the fermentation solution was found to be quite important, as might have been predicted since molecular oxygen is involved in the reaction. Ratios of 0.25 to 0.30 (sq cm of surface/ml of solution) were reported to be best for practical purposes, although the closer the ratio approached unity the higher the yield that was obtained. The impracticality of large-scale production of gluconic acid under conditions where there is one square centimeter of fermentation medium surface for every milliliter of liquid is obvious, since for the sustained production of any large quantity literally acres of surface area would be required. Even under widely varying environmental conditions, no appreciable quantity of acids other than gluconic were formed by the organisms used by Herrick and May.

May and others (1929) reported a semiplant-scale method of producing gluconic acid by a fermentation process. Their method involved the culture of the organism in large aluminum pans similar to those employed in the commercial production of citric acid. Using pans 43 × 43 × 2 in. they obtained yields of more than 57 per cent of theory in an eleven-day fermentation period.

The next advance was the use of submerged, aerated cultures. Shreyer (1928) used an organism he called *Aspergillus fumaricus,* which synthesized mixtures of citric and gluconic acids from glucose. He found that if calcium carbonate was added to the fermentation medium which was then agitated and aerated by passing air into the solution, four- to sixfold increases in gluconic acid yield resulted, with the yield of citric acid unaffected. Thies (1930) also used *A. fumaricus* and bubbled oxygen instead of air through the fermentation medium, obtaining yields of 64 per cent of theory in fifteen days.

Currie, Kane, and Findlay (1933) were issued a patent for a fermentation process for the production of gluconic acid. The essential feature of their method is that the fermentation medium is aerated by agitation with a high-speed stirrer (1000–3000 rpm.). These investigators reported that within 48 to 60 hrs the sugar is converted almost completely to *d*-gluconic acid, and that yields of about 90 per cent of theory are obtained. Temperature optima reported in this patent claim are considerably higher than those reported by Herrick and May.

Moyer, May, and Herrick (1936) reported that the strain of *P. luteum-purpurogenum,* which had been used extensively by the U.S. Department of Agriculture group in their gluconic acid investigations, lacked biochemical and vegetative vigor and that close cultural control was necessary to maintain cultures capable of yielding uniform results. They tested over 50 species of *Penicillium* and found that *P. chrysogenum* (No. 5034.11) had a greater capacity for gluconic acid synthesis than any of the others. Using small culture flasks containing medium of 20–25 per cent glucose concentration and having a surface area/volume ratio of 0.4–0.5, they reported that about 60 per cent of the glucose was oxidized to gluconic acid in eight to ten days. No loss of gluconic acid-producing ability was observed in this organism over a three-year period.

May and others (1934) conducted submerged-culture fermentations with *P. chrysogenum* (Fig. 80) in glass washing bottles equipped with

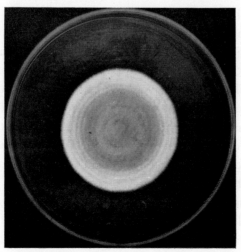

FIG. 80. *Petri plate culture of* Penicillium chrysogenum.

FIG. 81. *Laboratory-scale rotary drum apparatus used in the investigation of the gluconic acid fermentation. (Courtesy of the Agricultural Research Service, Northern Utilization Research and Development Division, U.S. Department of Agriculture.)*

sintered-glass false bottoms and studied the effects of increased air pressure and quantity of calcium carbonate on gluconic acid formation. They reported that at and above a total air pressure of three atmospheres, and with $CaCO_3$ supplied at a ratio of 1 g per 4 g of glucose in the culture solution, yields of gluconic acid of 80–87 per cent (based upon the quantity of sugar supplied) were obtained in a culture period of eight days from the time of inoculation with spores of the organism.

Herrick, Hellbach, and May (1935) attempted to construct a satisfactory large-scale apparatus patterned after the false-bottomed bottles used by May and his co-workers, but satisfactory results were not obtained because of the difficulty of constructing a satisfactory large air-distributing system. They then designed a laboratory-scale rotary drum apparatus in which the fermentation medium could be simultaneously aerated and mechanically agitated (Fig. 81). Using pregerminated spores as inoculum these investigators obtained yields of 80 per cent of theory in 56 hours. Use of this rotary drum apparatus was further studied by Wells and others (1937a), who stated that the three factors which condition oxygen supply (air flow, agitation, and air pressure) have a pronounced effect upon the fermentation rate and determine to a large extent the speed and efficiency of the process. They used *A. niger* (strain No. 67) in their investigation because of its capacity to form spores in larger quantity than *P. chrysogenum,* and found that the optimal values for the three factors listed above are as follows:

rpm of drum 13
Air pressure . . . . 45 lb
Air flow . . . . 1.2 l/min/3200 ml of fermen-
                                      tation medium

Using pregerminated spores of *A. niger* in 15 per cent glucose-containing medium, and operating under optimum conditions of agitation, air pressure, and air flow, yields of gluconic acid in excess of 84 per cent based on glucose supplied were obtained (97 per cent based upon glucose utilized) in eighteen hours from the time of inoculation. Because of the rapidity of the fermentation, these investigators predicted that it might be possible to conduct the fermentation without having to sterilize the fermentation medium—a distinct advantage applicable to few fermentation processes. The stages in the progress made by the U.S.D.A. investigators in the development of a high-yielding, rapid gluconic acid fermentation are listed in Table 23.

Table 23.—Production of gluconic acid using different fungi and different types of fermentation equipment

Type	Organism	Fermentation Vessel	Theoretical Yield of Acid (%)	Fermentation Period (days)
Surface culture	*P. luteum-purpurogenum*	Shallow pan (aluminum)	57.4	11
Submerged (pressure)	*P. chrysogenum*	Glass bottle (sintered glass, false bottom)	80.4	8
" "	*P. chrysogenum*	Rotary drum (aluminum)	80.0	2.2
" "	*A. niger*	Rotary drum (aluminum)	84.0	0.75

After Wells, and others (1937a).

In another report Wells and others (1937b) described a pilot-plant rotary drum apparatus of 420 gal capacity (Fig. 82). Spores of *A. niger* were pregerminated in the small laboratory-scale rotary drum and then used as inoculum for the larger fermentation. These investigators reported that if a 15 per cent glucose solution was used, practically quantitative conversion of glucose to gluconic acid was attained in twenty-four hours by using this apparatus. Gastrock and others (1938) also obtained excellent results with the large-scale rotary drum apparatus, reporting

FIG. 82. *Pilot-plant-scale rotary drum fermenter of 420 gal. capacity. (Courtesy of the Agricultural Research Service, Northern Utilization Research and Development Division, U.S. Department of Agriculture.)*

yields of gluconic acid in excess of 95 per cent (based on sugar present in the medium) in a twenty-four-hour fermentation period.

Porges and his co-workers (1940, 1941) have developed a process for the production of gluconic acid on a semicontinuous basis rather than by the batch process as employed by other investigators. The essential feature of their fermentation process, which was conducted in both the laboratory-scale and pilot-plant rotary drum, is that mycelia are re-used for several fermentations, and thus there is a considerable saving of time, since the lag phase encountered in batch fermentations is eliminated after the first fermentation. In their initial studies they found that the use of the same mycelium through thirteen successive fermentations resulted in no decrease in activity; most fermentations after the first of the series were complete in about nine hours. Best results were obtained with medium in which the glucose concentration was 11.5 per

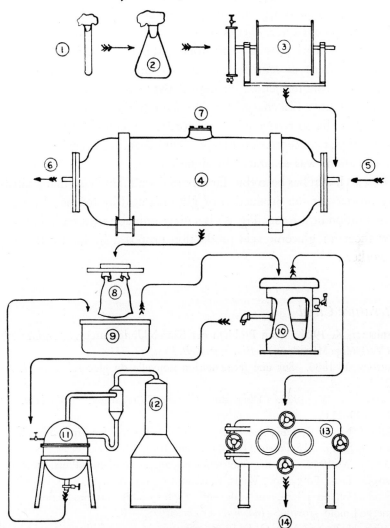

FIG. 83. *Flow sheet for gluconic acid production. 1, tube culture; 2, sporulation flasks; 3, small aluminum germination drums (17-liter volume); 4, large rotating aluminum drums (540-liter capacity); 5, air inlet; water for fermentation solution and inoculum from 3 are also introduced here; 6, air outlet; 7, handhole; commercial dextrose, nutrients, and sterile calcium carbonate are added here; 8, bag filter; 9, aluminum tank for neutralization and crystallization; calcium hydroxide milk is added here; 10, centrifuge (stainless-steel basket, aluminum-lined curb); 11, vacuum evaporator for mother liquors; 12, condenser; 13, vacuum drier; 14, calcium gluconate storage. (From Gastrock and others, 1938.)*

cent when successive transfers of the greater portion of the fungus mycelium (suspended in 20 per cent of the fermented liquors) were made.
In their later work these investigators used both a leaf-type pressure filter and a basket-type centrifuge for more complete separation of the mycelium from the fermented medium between fermentations; they were
thus able to use a full charge of fresh medium in each successive fermentation. Mycelia so recovered satisfactorily fermented a solution of glucose of higher concentration (16 per cent) than had been possible when
the mycelium was separated by flotation.

Research that has been thus far reported would indicate that a satisfactory process for the production of gluconic acid by means of a fungus
fermentation now exists. Fig. 83 is a diagrammatic representation of the
flow sheet for gluconic acid production proposed by Gastrock and his
co-workers.

Literature Cited

Bernhauer, K. 1924. Zum Problem der Säurebildung durch *Aspergillus niger*
(Vorläufige Mitteilung). *Biochem. Zeit. 153:*517–521.

Boutroux, L. 1880. Sur une fermentation nouvelle du glucose. *Compt. rend.
91:*236–238.

Butkewitsch, W. 1923. Über die "Citronensäuregärung." *Biochem. Zeit.
142:*195–211.

Currie, J. N., Kane, J. H., and Finlay, A. 1933. Process for producing gluconic
acid by fungi. U.S. Patent 1,893,819. Jan. 10, 1933.

Foster, J. W. 1949. *Chemical activities of fungi.* Academic Press, New York.

Gastrock, E. A., Porges, N., Wells, P. A., and Moyer, A. J. 1938. Gluconic acid
production on pilot plant scale—effect of variables on production by submerged mold growths. *Ind. Eng. Chem. 30:*782–789.

Herrick, H. T., and May, O. E. 1928. The production of gluconic acid by the
Penicillium luteum-purpurogenum group. II: Some optimal conditions for
acid formation. Jour. Biol. Chem. 77:185–195.

Herrick, H. T., Hellbach, R., and May, O. E. 1935. Apparatus for the application
of submerged mold fermentations under pressure. *Ind. Eng. Chem. 27:*681–
683.

May, O. E., Herrick, H. T., Thom, C., and Church, M. B. 1927. The production
of gluconic acid by the *Penicillium luteum-purpurogenum* group. I. *Jour.
Biol. Chem. 75:*417–422.

May, O. E., Herrick, H. T., Moyer, A. J., and Hellbach, R. 1929. Semiplant scale
production of gluconic acid by mold fermentation. *Ind. Eng. Chem. 21:*1198–
1203.

May, O. E., Herrick, H. T., Moyer, A. J., and Wells, P. A. 1934. Gluconic acid production by submerged mold growths under increased air pressure. *Ind. Eng. Chem. 26:*575–578.

Molliard, M. 1922. Sur une nouvelle fermentation acide produite par le *Sterigmatocystis nigra. Compt. rend. 174:*881–883.

———. 1924. Nouvelles recherches sur la formation d'acides organiques par le *Sterigmatocystis nigra* en milieux desequilibres. *Compt. rend. 178:*41–45.

Moyer, A. J., May, O. E., and Herrick, H. T. 1936. The production of gluconic acid by *Penicillium chrysogenum. Centralbl. Bakt. und Parasitenk. Abt. II. 95:*311–324.

Porges, N., Clark, T. F., and Gastrock, E. A. 1940. Gluconic acid production. Repeated use of submerged *Aspergillus niger* for semicontinuous production. *Ind. Eng. Chem. 32:*107–111.

Porges, N., Clark, T. F., and Aronovsky, S. I. 1941. Gluconic acid production. Repeated recovery and re-use of submerged *Aspergillus niger* by filtration. *Ind. Eng. Chem. 33:*1065–1067.

Ramsbottom, J. 1936. The uses of fungi. *Brit. Assoc. Adv. Sci. Ann. Rept. for 1936,* 189–218.

Schreyer, R. 1928. Säuerungsversuche mit dem Pilze *Aspergillus fumaricus. Biochem. Zeit. 202:*131–156.

Thies, W. 1930. Untersuchungen über den Einfluss der Bedingungen auf die Säurebildung des Schimmelpilzes *Aspergillus fumaricus. Centralbl. Bakt. und Parasitenk. Abt. II. 82:*321–347.

Wells, P. A., Moyer, A. J., Stubbs, J. J., Herrick, H. T., and May, O. E. 1937. Gluconic acid production. Effect of pressure, air flow, and agitation on gluconic acid production by submerged mold growths. *Ind. Eng. Chem. 29:*653–656.

Wells, P. A., Lynch, D. F. J., Herrick, H. T., and May, O. E. 1937. Translating mold fermentation research to pilot plant operation. *Chem. Met. Eng. 44:* 188–190.

13 · *Synthesis of Itaconic Acid*

INTEREST IN THE DEVELOPMENT of a process for the production of itaconic acid by means of a fungus fermentation lies in its high potential of industrial value. Esters of methacrylic acid have long been used in the manufacture of plastics. Since itaconic acid (methylene succinic acid) is a substituted methacrylic acid, it would seem that this acid

$$
\begin{array}{c}
\text{COOH} \\
| \\
\text{CH}_2 \\
| \\
\text{C—COOH} \\
| \\
\text{CH}_2
\end{array}
$$

might also be of some value in the plastics industry. Itaconate esters polymerize readily, and a nonshatterable glass made by using polymerized dialkyl itaconate esters was patented over thirty years ago by Hope (1927). Foster (1949) states that other polymers of itaconate esters have properties that make them particularly suitable for use in the manufacture of lenses, artificial jewelry, and numerous other common objects; he also suggests that such esters may have some application in the field of synthetic detergents.

Itaconic acid can be produced by straight chemical means by the pyrolysis of citric acid, but when prepared in this way it is quite expensive and uneconomical to use in the plastics industry in competition with the more cheaply prepared methycrylic acid esters. For that reason no serious consideration was given to the commercial use of itaconic acid until it was found to be a fungus metabolic product that might, perhaps be produced cheaply by a fermentation method.

Fungi That Synthesize Itaconic Acid

The first investigator to describe itaconic acid as a fungus metabolic product was Kinoshita (1929). The organism accomplishing the synthesis was a species of *Aspergillus,* which Kinoshita had isolated from vinegar made from Japanese sour plums. Because of its unique biochemical activity, its discoverer regarded this fungus a new species and named it *Aspergillus itaconicus.* Thom and Raper (1945) in their *Manual of the Aspergilli* have retained Kinoshita's specific name but regard this species as being identical with *Aspergillus varians.* The only other species of fungus also reported to have the capacity of synthesizing itaconic acid is *Aspergillus terreus* (Fig. 84). The first report of the production of itaconic acid by this latter species was made by Calam, Oxford, and Raistrick (1939). These investigators were studying the metabolic products of six different strains of *A. terreus* and noted that one strain formed itaconic acid along with fumaric, succinic, and oxalic acids.

FIG. 84.   *Petri plate culture of an itaconic acid-forming strain of* Aspergillus terreus.

Chemistry of Itaconic Acid Synthesis

The exact sequence of chemical reactions that occur in the biosynthesis of itaconic acid by fungi has never been definitely established. There are, however, two suggestions as to what these steps may be. Kinoshita (1931) was of the opinion that the synthesis occurred by way of gluconic acid, citric acid, and aconitic acid as intermediates:

$$
\begin{array}{lllll}
\text{CH}_2\text{OH} & \text{CH}_2\text{OH} & & & \\
| & | & \text{COOH} & \text{COOH} & \\
\text{CHOH} & \text{CHOH} & | & | & \text{COOH} \\
| & | & \text{CH}_2 & \text{CH}_2 & | \\
\text{CHOH} & \text{CHOH} & | \quad -\text{H}_2\text{O} & | \quad -\text{CO}_2 & \text{CH}_2 \\
| \;\longrightarrow\; | & \longrightarrow \text{HOC—COOH} \longrightarrow & \text{C—COOH} \longrightarrow & | \\
\text{CHOH} & \text{CHOH} & | & \| & \text{C—COOH} \\
| & | & \text{CH}_2 & \text{CH} & \| \\
\text{CHOH} & \text{CHOH} & | & | & \text{CH}_2 \\
| & | & \text{COOH} & \text{COOH} & \\
\text{CHO} & \text{COOH} & & & \\
\text{glucose} & \text{gluconic} & \text{citric} & \textit{cis}\text{-aconitic} & \text{itaconic} \\
& \text{acid} & \text{acid} & \text{acid} & \text{acid}
\end{array}
$$

Kinoshita found that when *A. itaconicus* was cultured on sucrose or glucose media containing calcium carbonate, appreciable amounts of calcium citrate and calcium gluconate were formed in addition to calcium itaconate, although no aconitic acid was detected in the fermentation medium.

Bernhauer and others (*cf.* Prescott and Dunn, 1940) suggested a fermentation scheme to explain the biosynthesis of citric acid by fungi in which it was also postulated that itaconic acid was formed from aconitic acid, although the earlier steps in the synthesis differed from those proposed by Kinoshita. The sequence of reactions as suggested by these investigators is as illustrated on the next page.

According to Calam and others (*loc. cit.*) there is no evidence to support the view that citric acid is an intermediate compound in the synthesis of itaconic acid from glucose. These investigators reported that with pyruvic acid, acetic acid, or mixtures of malic and acetic acids, no itaconic acid is formed—an observation that serves to cast some doubt on the theory of Bernhauer and his co-workers.

At this time it is impossible to state how itaconic acid is synthesized by fungi; however, it seems likely that once the mode of formation of citric acid is clear, the mechanism of itaconic acid may be explained shortly afterward—if the two syntheses are related as is suggested by the above

$$C_6H_{12}O_6 \xrightarrow[\substack{\text{alcohol} \\ \text{breakdown}}]{} 2CH_3COOH \xrightarrow{-H_2} CH_2COOH \xrightarrow{-H_2} CH\cdot COOH \underset{-H_2O}{\overset{+H_2O}{\rightleftharpoons}} CHOH\cdot COOH$$

$$\underset{\substack{\text{glucose}}}{} \quad \underset{\substack{\text{acetic} \\ \text{acid}}}{} \quad \underset{\substack{\text{succinic} \\ \text{acid}}}{|} \quad \underset{\substack{\text{fumaric} \\ \text{acid}}}{\|} \quad \underset{\substack{\text{malic} \\ \text{acid}}}{|}$$

$$CH_2COOH \qquad\qquad CH\cdot COOH \qquad CH_2\cdot COOH$$

CH_2COOH	$COOH$	$COOH$	$COOH$
$\|$	$\|$	$\|$	$\|$
CH_2COOH	CH_2	CH	CH_2
	$\|$	$\|\|$	$\|$
succinic acid $\xrightarrow{-H_2}$	$HC{-}COOH$ $\xrightarrow{-H_2}$	$C{-}COOH$ $\underset{-H_2O}{\overset{+H_2O}{\rightleftharpoons}}$	$HOC{-}COOH$
$+$	$\|$	$\|$	$\|$
CH_3COOH	CH_2	CH_2	CH_2
acetic acid	$\|$	$\|$	$\|$
	$COOH$	$COOH$	$COOH$
		aconitic acid	citric acid

$$\downarrow -CO_2$$

$$CH_2$$
$$\|$$
$$C{-}COOH$$
$$\|$$
$$CH_2$$
$$\|$$
$$COOH$$
$$\underset{\substack{\text{itaconic} \\ \text{acid}}}{}$$

hypotheses. In making percentage-yield calculations most investigators assume that the maximum theoretical yield is one molecule of itaconic acid from one molecule of glucose. Therefore according to this assumption the maximum weight of itaconic acid that could be derived from 100 g of hexose sugar is 72.2 g. If the assumption is made that itaconic acid is formed by a sequence of reactions in which the initial steps are similar to those involved in the alcoholic fermentation, the maximum weight of itaconic acid that could be produced from 100 g of glucose is 48.1 g. Nelson and others (1952) have reported yields greater than 50 per cent in 20-liter fermentations; Pfeifer and others (1952) have reported yields up to 65 per cent in pilot plant fermentations.

The Itaconic Acid Fermentation

Much of the earlier published work on the itaconic acid fermentation has emanated from the Northern Regional Research Laboratory, Peoria, Illinois, although research has undoubtedly been conducted at other laboratories, since Kane, Finlay, and Amann (1945) have been issued a very broad patent (assigned to Chas. Pfizer and Company,

Inc.) covering the production of itaconic acid by a fermentation process. This patent has aroused considerable interest throughout the fermentation industries because of its broad coverage of organisms, and there is some question as to whether a patent of this type would be upheld in any patent litigation.

When work on this fermentation was initiated at the Peoria Laboratory, Kinoshita's strain of *A. itaconicus* was obtained from Dr. George Smith in England, who had obtained it from the Centrall Bureau voor Schimmelcultures (Moyer and Coghill, 1945). The Peoria investigators found that only traces of itaconic acid were synthesized by this fungus, and concluded that either the strain had lost its capacity to synthesize itaconic acid or else it was not the strain actually used by Kinoshita. In view of these almost negative results obtained with *A. itaconicus,* Moyer and Coghill then turned to another fungus, *A. terreus,* the species used in England earlier by Calam and his co-workers. Thirty strains of *A. terreus* were tested in small flask cultures; only one strain of those tested gave promising yields of itaconic acid. This strain, NRRL 265, was then subjected to detailed investigation in order to determine optimum conditions for acid production. Moyer and Coghill investigated types of nitrogen sources, concentration of nitrogen sources, concentrations of mineral salts, glucose concentration, effects of trace elements and corn steep liquor additions, and temperature. They reported that a near optimum medium is constituted as follows:

	grams
glucose	250
$MgSO_4$	0.25
KCl	0.05
NH_4NO_3	2.00
$ZnSO_4$	0.044

	ml
Corn steep liquor	4.0
0.5N HNO_3	50.0
H_2O to make one liter	

In their investigation of the effects of trace elements Moyer and Coghill prepared the medium with commercial glucose as the carbon source, then treated it with calcium carbonate according to the method of Steinberg (1935) in order to remove most of the trace elements. With medium thus purified, they found that the addition of 44 mg of zinc sulphate and 8 mg of iron tartrate per liter (alone or in combination) resulted in increased growth and acid production, best results being obtained with the iron and zinc salt combination. With unpurified medium prepared with commercial glucose, corn steep liquor, and tap water they found that the addition of trace elements other than zinc is unnecessary.

Optimum temperature was found to be in the range of 30–35 C. One series of cultures incubated at 30 and 35 C yielded results which lead Moyer and Coghill to suggest that cultures be incubated for the first five or six days at 35 C, and then at 30 C for the remainder of the fermentation period. Quite possibly the results obtained using this procedure were due to a lessening of the inhibitory effects of accumulated fermentation products at the lower temperature.

Under optimum conditions, *A. terreus* (NRRL 265) synthesized itaconic acid in quantities of 28 to 29 g per 100 g of glucose utilized during a ten- to twelve-day fermentation period. The acid was recovered by crystallization from the fermentation medium: 85 per cent of the itaconic acid was recovered in two crystallizations, and this value was raised to 90 per cent by two additional crystallizations. Moyer and Coghill stated that the acid was believed to be sufficiently pure to be used directly in the plastics and detergents industries.

Lockwood and Reeves (1945) examined 408 fungus strains to determine their itaconic acid synthesizing capacities. Of these strains, eleven produced yields greater than 45 per cent of theory (assuming that one mole of glucose yields one mole of itaconic acid). The best of these strains (NRRL 1960) was selected for more intensive study. It was found that itaconic acid accumulates in cultures in a *p*H range below 2.3; it is metabolized by the organism at *p*H values above 2.3. Since the optimum *p*H for growth of *A. terreus* is considerably higher than 2.3, it is obvious that the optimum *p*H for acid accumulation is much lower than that for growth. In this respect the itaconic acid fermentation is quite similar to the citric acid fermentation, and it is probable that in the biosynthesis of these acids a similar shunt metabolism is involved.

Optimum temperature was considered to be 30 C. Like Moyer and Coghill, Lockwood and Reeves reported that the addition of iron and zinc salts caused marked increases in acid yield. However, the latter investigators found that these increases occurred only when the *p*H of the medium was quite low (2.0); at *p*H 3.0, the addition of these trace elements resulted in increased growth but not in increased acid accumulation.

On the basis of their findings, Lockwood and Reeves stated that the preferred method for the production of itaconic acid in laboratory equipment involves the cultivation of *A. terreus* (NRRL 1960) at 30 C. for ten days on culture medium of the following composition:

grams

glucose 250
$MgSO_4 \cdot 7H_2O$ 4.5
NH_4NO_3 .... 2.5
NaCl 0.4
$ZnSO_4 \cdot 7H_2O$ 0.0044

ml

HNO_3 (sp.gr. 1.42) 1.6
Concentrated corn steep liquor 4.0
Distilled H_2O to make one liter

Using *A. terreus* (NRRL 1960), Lockwood and Ward (1945) developed a fermentation process for the production of itaconic acid on a semipilot plant scale. Their process involves cultivation of the fungus on the surfaces of shallow layers of medium in large aluminum pans (22 × 36 × 2 in.), arranged in tiers in a special fermentation cabinet described by Ward, Lockwood, May, and Herrick (1935). Each pan contained 12 l of medium. The fermentation was of twelve days duration during which time the temperature was maintained at 30–32 C; sterilized, humidified air was passed through the cabinet at a rate of 5 l per minute. Itaconic acid was recovered from the fermentation liquor by concentrating 12 l to 1 l on a steam bath. Upon such concentration, a slurry of fine crystals of itaconic acid resulted. The slurry was cooled to room temperature and the crystals separated from the liquid in a basket centrifuge. Data obtained from two typical pan fermentations are presented in Table 24.

In the development of the penicillin industry rather spectacular yield increases were obtained with mutant strains of fungi, derived as a result of ultraviolet or X-radiation. In view of these results it is not surprising that similar attempts have been made to derive itaconic acid from high-yielding strains of *A. terreus*. The work of Hollaender and others (1945), Raper and others (1945), and Lockwood and others (1945) indicates that better-yielding mutants have been derived from irradiated conidia of *A. terreus* NRRL 265.

As with other fungus fermentations conducted first in flasks or shallow pans, attempts have been made to supplant the surface type of culture method with a process in which the fungus is completely submerged in liquid medium. In the patent of Kane and others (*loc. cit.*) it is claimed that itaconic acid can be produced in a commercially practicable way by culturing selected fungus strains submerged in nutrient-containing me-

Table 24.—*Production of itaconic acid from glucose by large-pan fermentations*

	Pan 1	Pan 2
Initial glucose (g)	1800	1800
Glucose utilized (g)	1583	1539
Itaconic acid produced (g)	569	602
*Yield of itaconic acid, based on glucose utilized (%)	49.9	54.3
Itaconic acid recovered by crystallization (g)	453	490
Recovery efficiency (%)	79.7	81.4
†Recovery weight yield (%)	25.2	27.2
Mycelial weight (g)	222	114

* Based on the assumption that 1 mole of glucose yields 1 mole of itaconic acid.

† Ratio of grams of itaconic acid recovered to grams of glucose supplied (anhydrous basis).

From Lockwood and Ward (1945).

dium and maintaining aerobic conditions in the fermenter by mechanical agitation of the medium, or by passing air into the fermentation medium.

Lockwood and Nelson (1946) have also investigated the production of itaconic acid by submerged cultures and have established some of the optimum conditions for conducting the fermentation by this method. These investigators used *A. terreus* NRRL 1960 in shaken-flask cultures and found that conditions which were optimum for the production of itaconic acid in submerged cultures were not the same as those previously established for surface cultures. The optimum *p*H was found to be 1.8. In general it was found that the optimal concentrations of the various medium constituents were lower than the optimal concentrations of such constituents in medium for surface-culture fermentations. Optimal concentrations per liter were as follows: corn steep liquor, about 1.5 ml; $MgSO_4 \cdot 7H_2O$, 0.75 g; glucose, about 60 g. The addition of NaCl to the medium resulted in greater mycelial growth accompanied by a sharp reduction in acid yield; the addition of zinc sulphate was not as effective in increasing itaconic acid yield as had been demonstrated with surface cultures.

For inoculum for their fermentations, Lockwood and Nelson used mycelial pellets which had been removed from agitated cultures forty-eight

Table 25.—Effect of various quantities of inoculum on the production of itaconic acid from glucose by Aspergillus terreus *NRRL 1960*

| No. Pellets per Culture | Glucose Utilized (g/culture) | Itaconic Acid Produced (g/culture) | Yield of Itaconic Acid Based on Glucose | | Mycelial Weight (g/culture) |
			Utilized (theory) * (%)	Supplied (weight) † (%)	
1	8.0	2.05	40.4	25.5	1.296
2	8.0	2.05	40.4	25.5	1.144
3	8.0	1.85	32.8	23.0	1.207
4	8.0	1.66	28.6	20.7	1.245
5	8.0	1.17	20.1	14.6	1.477
8	8.0	0.68	11.8	11.7	1.490
10	8.0	0.88	15.1	10.9	1.413
13	7.9	0.98	17.1	12.1	1.545
16	8.0	0.88	15.4	10.9	1.625
20	8.0	0.39	6.8	4.9	1.572
25	8.0	0.78	13.4	9.7	1.622
40	8.0	0.59	10.1	7.5	1.655
70	8.0	0.88	15.4	10.9	1.496
100	8.0	0.78	13.4	9.7	1.480

Incubation period—12 days
* Assuming 1 mole of glucose yields 1 mole of itaconic acid.
† $\frac{\text{g itaconic acid produced}}{\text{g glucose supplied}}$
From Lockwood and Nelson (1946).

hours old. In a series of fermentations designed to determine the effect of inoculum size upon itaconic acid yield, it was found that small inocula were definitely superior to large ones. Agitated cultures (125 ml of medium per flask) were inoculated with varying numbers of mycelial pellets, and best yields were obtained in those flasks which were inoculated with only one or two such pellets. The results of these studies are presented in Table 25.

Itatartaric Acid in the Itaconic Acid Fermentation

Stodala and others (1945) investigated the metabolic products of one of the ultraviolet-induced mutants of *A. terreus* NRRL 265 and found that part of the extra acid synthesized by this mutant was itatartaric acid—an acid previously not known to be a fungus metabolic product. About 5.8 per cent of the total acids synthesized by this organism were shown to be an equilibrium mixture of itatartaric acid and its lactone. Itatartaric acid (see below) apparently exists only in the form of salts or as the lactone and is closely related chemically to itaconic acid:

$$
\begin{array}{ll}
\text{COOH} & \text{COOH} \\
| & | \\
\text{CH}_2 & \text{CH}_2 \\
| & | \\
\text{HOC---CH}_2\text{OH} & \text{C---COOH} \\
| & \| \\
\text{COOH} & \text{CH}_2 \\
\text{itatartaric} & \text{itaconic} \\
\text{acid} & \text{acid}
\end{array}
$$

Although itatartaric acid is at present a relatively unimportant chemical compound (as far as industrial usage is concerned), its production by an ultraviolet-induced mutant suggests similar possibilities that undoubtedly exist in the field of fungus biochemistry. The synthetic capacities of the fungi seem almost unlimited, and yet there is ample evidence that these limits can be further extended by the investigation of mutants derived from existing strains. An interesting point arises in connection with the mutant which synthesizes itatartaric acid, and that is the question of whether it gained a new synthetic mechanism through the mutation or whether it already possessed the capacity to conduct this synthesis but only in such small amounts that the acid remained undetected.

Large-Scale Production of Itaconic Acid

The commercial production of itaconic acid by a fermentation method is a recent development, although for several years it appeared imminent. In 1945 Lockwood and Ward estimated that itaconic acid could be produced and recovered at a raw materials cost of 22 cents per pound, their estimate being based upon the assumption of a 25 per cent recovery yield and a cost of 5.3 cents per pound of glucose (anhydrous basis), 2.5 cents per pound of corn steep liquor, and 0.4 cents for nutrient salts necessary in the production of one pound of itaconic acid. On March 16, 1955, Chas. Pfizer and Company announced in the *Wall Street Journal* that it was prepared to sell itaconic acid in carload lots at a cost of 60 cents per pound. Beesch and Shull (1955) expressed the opinion that the price would come down materially as large scale uses are developed for itaconic acid.

Literature Cited

Beesch, S. C., and Shull, G. M. 1955. Fermentation. *Ind. Eng. Chem. 47:*1857–1875.

Calam, C. T., Oxford, A. E., and Raistrick, H. 1939. Studies in the biochemistry of microorganisms. LXIII. Itaconic acid, a metabolic product of a strain of *Aspergillus terreus* Thom. *Biochem. Jour. 33:*1488–1495.

Foster, J. W. 1949. *Chemical activities of fungi.* Academic Press, New York.

Hollaender, A., Raper, K. B., and Coghill, R. D. 1945. The production and characterization of ultraviolet-induced mutations in *Aspergillus terreus.* I. Production of mutations. *Amer. Jour. Bot. 32:*160–165.

Hope, E. 1927. Manufacture of glass or glasslike objects. U.S. Patent 1,644,131. Oct. 4, 1927.

Kane, J. H., Finlay, A. C., and Amann, P. F. 1945. Production of itaconic acid. U.S. Patent 2,385,283.

Kinoshita, K. 1929. Formation of itaconic acid and mannite by a new filamentous fungus. *Jour. Chem. Soc. Japan 50:*583–593.

———. 1931. Über die Produktion von Itaconsäure und Mannit durch einen neue Schimmelpilz, *Aspergillus itaconicus. Acta Phytochimica (Japan) 5:*271–287.

Lockwood, L. B. and Nelson, G. E. N. 1946. Some factors affecting the production of itaconic acid by *Aspergillus terreus* in agitated cultures. *Arch. Biochem. 10:*365–374.

———, and Reeves, M. D. 1945. Some factors affecting the production of itaconic acid by *Aspergillus terreus. Arch. Biochem. 6:*455–469.

Lockwood, L. B. and Ward, G. E. 1945. Fermentation process for itaconic acid. *Ind. Eng. Chem. 37:*405–406.

———, Raper, K. B., Moyer, A. J., and Coghill, R. D. 1945. The production and characterization of ultraviolet-induced mutations in *Aspergillus terreus.* III: Biochemical characteristics of the mutations. *Amer. Jour. Bot. 32:*214–217.

Moyer, A. J. and Coghill, R. D. 1945. The laboratory-scale production of itaconic acid by *Aspergillus terreus. Arch. Biochem. 7:*167–183.

Nelson, G. E. N., Traufler, D. H., Kelley, S. E., and Lockwood, L. B. 1952. Production of itaconic acid by *Aspergillus terreus* in 20-liter fermenters. *Ind. Eng. Chem. 44:*1166–1168.

Pfeifer, V. F., Vojnovich, C., and Heger, E. N. 1952. Itaconic acid by fermentation with *Aspergillus terreus. Ind. Eng. Chem. 44:*2975–2980.

Prescott, S. C., and Dunn, C. G. 1940. *Industrial microbiology.* McGraw-Hill, New York.

Raper, K. B., Coghill, R. D., and Hollaender, A. 1945. The production and characterization of ultraviolet-induced mutations in *Aspergillus terreus.* II: Cultural and morphological characteristics of the mutations. *Amer. Jour. Bot. 32:*165–176.

Steinberg, R. A. 1935. Nutrient-solution purification for removal of heavy metals in deficiency investigations with *Aspergillus niger. Jour. Agr. Res. 51:*413–424.

Stodala, F. H., Friedkin, M., Moyer, A. J., and Coghill, R. D. 1945. Itatartaric acid, a metabolic product of an ultraviolet-induced mutant of *Aspergillus terreus. Jour. Biol. Chem. 161:*739–742.

Thom, C., and Raper, K. B. 1945. *A Manual of the Aspergilli.* Williams and Wilkins, Baltimore.

Ward, G. E., Lockwood, L. B., May, O. E., and Herrick, H. T. 1935. Production of fat from glucose by molds. Cultivation of *Penicillium javanicum* van Beijma in large-scale laboratory apparatus. *Ind. Eng. Chem. 27:*318–322.

14 · *Synthesis of Kojic Acid*

FUNGI THAT SYNTHESIZE KOJIC ACID; CARBON SOURCES UTILIZED
THE KOJIC ACID FERMENTATION
CHEMISTRY OF KOJIC ACID SYNTHESIS

KOJIC ACID WAS FIRST REPORTED as occurring among the metabolic products of fungi by Saito (1907), who recovered this compound from the fine-ground mycelium of *Aspergillus oryzae* (Fig. 85) which had been cultured on steamed rice. He extracted the fungus preparation with ether, and from the ether extract obtained colorless needle crystals which were then further purified by recrystallization. Saito observed that the aqueous solution of kojic acid gave a red coloration with ferric chloride. His qualitative tests showed that the com-

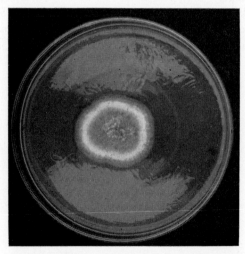

FIG. 85. *Petri plate culture of* Aspergillus oryzae, *a widely used fungus of the Orient.*

pound was not oxalic, succinic, citric, malic, tartaric, or benzoic acid, and he supposed it to be β-resorcyl-carbonic acid.

Shortly after Saito's first account of this new fungus metabolic product, Yabuta (1912) further investigated the compound and named it "kojic" acid. This same investigator (Yabuta, 1924) later established its chemical structure and demonstrated that it was 5-hydroxy-2-hydroxymethyl-γ-pyrone:

$$
\begin{array}{ccc}
 & \text{O} & \\
 & \| & \\
 & \text{C} & \\
 \diagup & & \diagdown \\
\text{H}\cdot\text{C} & & \text{C}\cdot\text{OH} \\
\| & & \| \\
\text{CH}_2\text{OH}\cdot\text{C} & & \text{C}\cdot\text{H} \\
 \diagdown & & \diagup \\
 & \text{O} &
\end{array}
$$

Maurer (1930) synthesized kojic acid and confirmed the molecular structure established earlier by Yabuta.

The physical properties of kojic acid have been listed by Barham and Smits (1934). It crystallizes in the form of prismatic needles which sublime in vacuo without change. Kojic acid is readily soluble in water, ethyl acetate, and acetone and less soluble in ether, alcohol-ether mixtures, chloroform, and pyridine. Melting points as reported by various investigators range from 151 to 154 C.

Although kojic acid can be easily produced by means of a fungus fermentation (this being the only way in which it has been prepared in any quantity) there has been no attempt until recently to manufacture this substance on a large scale. Chas. Pfizer and Company announced in 1955 the large-scale production of kojic acid (Beesch and Shull, 1956). As recently as 1949 Foster suggested that an exaggerated importance had been attached to kojic acid, and at that time the opinion seemed justified, since there were no known uses for the compound in 1949. On the other hand, if a chemical compound can be produced in quantity from cheap raw materials there is a very considerable incentive to find possible uses for the compound. The principal problem with kojic acid has not been obtaining it in quantity but rather with how to use it after it is obtained. Kojic acid was thought to have some application in medicine as an antibiotic (both Saito and Yabuta mentioned its antiseptic power); however, its use as such does not seem possible in view of the work of Friedemann (1934), who demonstrated that it was toxic to dogs and rabbits. This investigator found that the lethal dose of the sodium salt is about 1 g per kg of body weight. Armit and Nolan (1931) attempted to synthesize drugs of the β-eucaine type which have local anesthetic value, using kojic acid as the starting compound, but were unsuccessful; Barham and Smits (*loc. cit.*) are of the opinion that such syntheses are possible. In the announcement emanating from the Pfizer Company (*Chem. and Eng. News 33:2556*, 1955) it was stated that kojic acid is reactive at every position on the ring and that a number of products of value in industrial chemistry can be formed from this compound: metal chelates, pyridones, pyridines, ethers, esters, azo dyes, aldehyde condensation products, halogen derivatives, Mannich bases, and the products of cyanoethylation.

Fungi That Synthesize Kojic Acid; Carbon Sources Utilized

A variety of carbon compounds may be used as carbon sources for the biosynthesis of kojic acid. Traetta-Mosca (1914) found that *Aspergillus glaucus* could synthesize kojic acid from sucrose, glucose, fructose, and glycerol; Challenger, Klein, and Walker (1929) and Barham and Smits (1936) have shown that it may be synthesized from the pentose sugar, xylose, both by *A. oryzae* and *A. flavus*. Prescott and Dunn (1940) state that a large number of carbon compounds can be fermented by fungi with the resultant formation of kojic acid. These investigators list starches, dextrins, sucrose, maltose, glucose, fructose, mannose, galactose, xylose, arabinose, sorbitol, dulcitol, *i*-adonitol, inulin, inositol, glycerol, glycero-β-phosphate, gluconic acid, dihydroxyacetone, tartaric acid, as well as other substances as carbon compounds from which kojic acid can be synthesized by fungi. However, best yields have been obtained from glucose and xylose.

Kojic acid is found among the metabolic products of a number of different fungi, which with one exception are all species of the genus *Aspergillus*. In addition to *A. oryzae*, *A. glaucus*, and *A. flavus* previously mentioned, Tamiya and Hida (1927) showed that *A. gymnosarde*, *A. awamori*, *A. clavatus*, *A. candidus*, *A. fumigatus*, and *A. giganteus* may also synthesize this acid. Prescott and Dunn have expanded this list with the addition of *A. albus*, *A. effusus*, *A. nidulans*, *A. parasiticus*, *A. tamarii*, and *Penicillium daleae*. Birkinshaw and his co-workers

(1931) have claimed that kojic acid production is a biochemical diagnostic for the *flavus-oryzae-tamarii* group of Aspergilli, provided that certain environmental conditions are maintained.

The Kojic Acid Fermentation

The effects of various environmental conditions upon kojic acid yields have been considered by several investigators, most of whom have conducted the fermentation with surface cultures. Kinoshita (1927) obtained a 33 per cent yield of kojic acid by culturing *A. oryzae* upon a fermentation medium in which the carbon source was sucrose and the nitrogen source was cobalt purpureo-chloride (a colbaltamine). Katagiri and Kitahara (1929) tested a large number of carbon compounds in order to determine their suitability as carbon sources for kojic acid synthesis by *A. oryzae*. The medium used by these investigators was as follows:

	per cent
$MgSO_4 \cdot 7H_2O$	0.01
KH_2PO_4	0.10
$(NH_4)SO_4$	0.05
$CaCl_2$	0.01
Carbon compound	5.00

Katagiri and Kitahara used medium which had an initial reaction of *p*H 5.0, but found that an initial *p*H of 2.4 was more favorable for kojic acid synthesis. In a later paper (1933) these same investigators reported yields obtained with a large variety of carbon compounds; the highest yields reported were 40.8 per cent and were obtained with maltose as the source of carbon. Yields were calculated on the basis of sugar supplied.

May and others (1931) studied the production of kojic acid by *Aspergillus flavus* in surface cultures and obtained yields of 45 per cent based upon glucose supplied (55 per cent if based upon glucose utilized) in a ten-day culture period. They found that ammonium nitrate was the best nitrogen source, and that best yields of acid were obtained when glucose was supplied in 20 per cent concentration. Highest yields were obtained when the surface-area/volume ratio was 0.3 to 0.5. A temperature of 30–35 C was found to promote rapid vegetative development with high yields of acid. The medium employed in this work had the following composition:

grams per liter of
glucose solution

$MgSO_4 \cdot 7H_2O$ 0.500

KCl 0.100

H_3PO_4 .... 0.054

NH_4NO_3 .... 1.125

May, Ward, and Herrick (1932) investigated the effects of forty organic compounds on the synthesis of kojic acid from glucose by *A. flavus*. Of these compounds the only one that had an accelerating effect upon the fermentation was ethylene chlorhydrin, which, in a concentration of 100 mg per liter of fermentation medium, brought about a decided increase in acid production in a fermentation period of ten days' duration. Thiourea, sodium thiocyanate, chloracetone, and *o*- and *p*-chloro-phenol exerted inhibitory effects. The effect of ethylene chlorhydrin is apparently not specific with respect to kojic acid synthesis, since the data of May and his co-workers show that sugar is utilized more rapidly and that a greater weight of mycelium is formed in addition to the formation of increased amounts of kojic acid. The acceleratory effect of ethylene chlorhydrin is probably in the same general category as the acceleratory effects that low concentrations of lipid soluble anaesthetics are known to have on cell processes. For example, Gray and Sova (1956) found that the use of below-anaesthetic concentrations of various alcohols and related compounds resulted in slightly more rapid utilization of glucose by *Saccharomyces cerevisiae*.

Kluyver and Perquin (1933) used submerged cultures of *A. flavus* in their research on the kojic acid fermentation and encountered essentially the same findings as those of Lockwood and Nelson (1946) in connection with their investigation of the production of itaconic acid by the submerged culture method. While previous investigators for the most part had recommended initial *p*H values of 2 to 3, Kluyver and Perquin obtained best conversion of sugar to kojic acid in replacement cultures when the initial *p*H of the medium was somewhat lower (*p*H 1.9). At this value conversion was of the order of 78 per cent of theory (based upon the assumption that one mole of glucose yields one mole of kojic acid). When the initial acidity was reduced slightly (to *p*H 2.2), the conversion of sugar to kojic acid was reduced to 49.6 per cent of theory. Apparently in the kojic acid fermentation we are again dealing with a situation in which, by establishing very acid conditions, the metabolism of the fungus is shunted into another pathway—in this instance the pathway that leads to kojic acid synthesis.

Chemistry of Kojic Acid Synthesis

Yabuta, who first established the chemical structure of kojic acid, apparently believed that this compound was formed directly from glucose by a process of oxidation and dehydration—a view shared by Kinoshita (1927) and Haworth (1929). The reaction visualized by Yabuta may be illustrated as follows:

$$
\begin{array}{c}
\overset{\displaystyle CH\cdot OH}{\diagup\quad\diagdown} \\
HO\cdot HC \qquad CH\cdot OH \\
\mid \qquad\qquad \mid \\
HOH_2C\cdot HC \qquad CH\cdot OH \\
\diagdown\quad\diagup \\
O \\
\text{glucose}
\end{array}
\quad
\xrightarrow[-3H_2O]{\tfrac{1}{2}O_2}
\quad
\begin{array}{c}
O \\
\parallel \\
C \\
\diagup\quad\diagdown \\
H\cdot C \qquad C\cdot OH \\
\parallel \qquad\qquad \parallel \\
CH_2OH\cdot C \qquad C\cdot H \\
\diagdown\quad\diagup \\
O \\
\text{kojic acid}
\end{array}
\quad + \ 3H_2O
$$

The above equation works out quite well arithmetically; it fails, however, to explain how kojic acid may be formed from compounds containing less than 6 carbon atoms such as the pentose sugars, xylose and arabinose, or such compounds as glycerol or dihydroxyacetone.

Corbellini and Gregorini (1930) fermented several carbon compounds with *A. flavus* and obtained kojic acid. From their studies they concluded that the pyrone nucleus of kojic acid is synthesized from substances containing a chain of three carbon atoms resulting from the fragmentation of such larger molecules as those of the pentoses or hexoses. According to these investigators the synthesis of kojic acid may be explained by the reactions shown at the top of page 254.

Birkinshaw and others (1931) suggested two possible mechanisms by which kojic acid might be formed from pentose sugars: (1) breakdown of the pentose to acetaldehyde with subsequent condensations resulting in the formation of kojic acid, and (2) formation of a "reserve" material (polysaccharidal, with hexose units?) in the mycelium which is later

$$
\begin{array}{c}
\text{CHO} \\
\diagup \\
\text{CHOH} \\
\mid \quad + \\
\text{C}{=}\text{O} \\
\diagdown \\
\text{H} \quad \text{HO}
\end{array}
\quad
\begin{array}{c}
\text{CHO} \\
\mid \\
\text{HC–CH}_2\text{OH} \rightarrow \\
\diagup
\end{array}
\quad
\begin{array}{c}
\text{COH} \\
\parallel \\
\text{CH} \\
\diagdown \\
\text{OH HO}
\end{array}
\quad
\begin{array}{c}
\text{CHOH} \\
\mid \\
\text{HC–CH}_2\text{OH} \xrightarrow{-2\text{H}_2\text{O}}
\end{array}
$$

$$
\begin{array}{c}
\text{O} \\
\parallel \\
\text{C} \\
\diagup \quad \diagdown \\
\text{HOC} \quad \text{CH} \\
\parallel \quad \parallel \\
\text{HC} \quad \text{C·CH}_2\text{OH} \\
\diagdown \quad \diagup \\
\text{O}
\end{array}
$$

hydrolyzed and its units converted to kojic acid. Challenger, Klein, and Walker (1931) state that it is not necessary to assume hexose formation during the conversion of pentoses to kojic acid, as they obtained more than 30 per cent of the theoretical yield by culturing *A. oryzae* in solutions in which the sole carbon source was dihydroxyacetone (see alcoholic fermentation scheme, Chapter 9). Other investigators had shown that glycerol could be used as a carbon source for the kojic acid fermentation; Challenger and his associates demonstrated that when *A. niger* is cultured on 5 per cent glycerol plus inorganic salts, dihydroxyacetone (or glyceraldehyde) may be recovered as the phenylhydrazone. On the basis of these findings they suggested the following scheme as a possible explanation of kojic acid synthesis:

$$
\begin{array}{c}
\text{OH} \\
\diagup \\
\text{HC} \\
\parallel \\
\text{HO·H}_2\text{C—C} \\
\diagdown \\
\text{OH}
\end{array}
\quad
\begin{array}{c}
\text{HCHOH} \\
\diagdown \\
\text{COH} \quad -3\text{H}_2\text{O} \\
\parallel \quad \xrightarrow{} \\
\text{CH} \quad +\tfrac{1}{2}\text{O}_2 \\
\diagup \\
\text{HO}
\end{array}
\quad
\begin{array}{c}
\text{CO} \\
\diagup \quad \diagdown \\
\text{HC} \quad \text{COH} \\
\parallel \quad \parallel \quad +3\text{H}_2\text{O} \\
\text{HO·H}_2\text{C—C} \quad \text{CH} \\
\diagdown \quad \diagup \\
\text{O}
\end{array}
$$

Gould (1938) tested the two hypotheses advanced by Birkinshaw and his co-workers and was unable to obtain results that would support either hypothesis. Mycelia of *A. tamarii* (Fig. 86) from cultures on media containing hexoses, glycerol, erythritol, xylose, and sucrose were washed, dried, ground to a fine powder and supplied as the carbon source in Czapek-Dox medium. Nine-day-old mycelia were then trans-

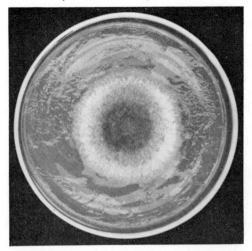

FIG. 86. *Petri plate culture of* Aspergillus tamarii, *one of the several species of fungi capable of synthesizing kojic acid.*

ferred to this medium and incubated at 20 C. No kojic acid could be detected even after ninety days' incubation, which indicates that *A. tamarii* does not contain a reserve polysaccharide or cellular constituent from which kojic acid may be formed. In the presence of an aldehyde-fixing agent such as dimedon (dimethyldihydroresorcinol), kojic acid formation from sugar was not inhibited. When sodium sulphite was used as the fixing agent kojic acid formation was slowed down, but Gould attributed this to the alkaline reaction of the medium rather than to an interference caused by the fixation of acetaldehyde. On the basis of these observations, the hypothesis that kojic acid is formed from acetaldehyde must be regarded as untenable.

In view of the paucity of experimental evidence presented to date, it is impossible to state with certainty the sequence of chemical reactions involved in the synthesis of kojic acid. Hypotheses explaining its formation by the condensation of two 3-carbon intermediates as suggested by Corbellini and Gregorini, and by Challenger and others, seem more feasible than any alternate hypotheses that have been advanced. The mechanism of kojic acid synthesis by fungi is of theoretical importance in fungus biochemistry, since an elucidation of this mechanism might provide a general explanation of the formation of cyclic compounds by ring closures in living cells.

Literature Cited

Armit, J. W., and Nolan, T. J. 1931.   Derivatives of kojic acid.   *Jour. Chem. Soc.:* 3023–3031.

Barham, H. N., and Smits, B. L. 1934.   Kojic acid—a review.   *Trans. Kansas Acad. Sci. 37:*91–113.

————. 1936.   Production of kojic acid from xylose by *Aspergillus flavus. Ind. Eng. Chem. 28:*567–570.

Beesch, S. C., and Shull, G. M. 1956.   Fermentation.   *Ind. Eng. Chem. 48:*1585–1603.

Birkinshaw, J. H., Charles, J. H. V., Lilly, C. H., and Raistrick, H. 1931.   Studies in the biochemistry of micro-organisms.   VII: Kojic acid (5-hydroxy-2-hydroxymethyl-γ-pyrone).   *Trans. Roy. Soc. London, Series B, 220:*127–138.

Challenger, F., Klein, L., and Walker, T. K. 1929.   The production of kojic acid from pentoses by *Aspergillus oryzae. Jour. Chem. Soc. July, 1929:*1498–1505.

————. 1931.   The formation of kojic acid from sugars by *Aspergillus oryzae. Jour. Chem. Soc. (London):*16–23.

Corbellini, A., and Gregorini, B. 1930.   La formazione dell' acido kojico dagli idrati di carbonio per azione dell' "aspergillus flavus." *Gazz. chim. ital. 60:*244–256.

Foster, J. W. 1949.   *Chemical activities of fungi.*   Academic Press, New York.

Friedemann, T. E. 1934.   Chemical and physiological properties of kojic acid. *Science (n.s.) 80:*34.

Gould, B. S. 1938.   The metabolism of *Aspergillus tamarii* Kita.   Kojic acid production.   *Biochem. Jour. 32:*797–802.

Gray, W. D., and Sova, C. 1956.   Relation of molecule size and structure to alcohol inhibition of glucose utilization by yeast.   *Jour. Bact. 72:*349–356.

Haworth, W. H. 1929.   *Constitution of sugars.*   Longmans, Green, New York.

Katagiri, H. and Kitahara, K. 1929.   The formation of kojic acid by *Aspergillus oryzae. Bull. Agr. Chem. Soc. (Japan) 5:*38–47.

————. 1933.   The formation of kojic acid by *Aspergillus oryzae. Mem. Coll. Agr., Kyoto Imp. Univ. No. 26:*1–29.

Kinoshita, K. 1927.   Über die Ernährung der Pilze mit den Kobaltamminkomplexsalzen.   *Acta Phytochim. (Japan) 3:*31–50.

Kluyver, A. J., and Perquin, L. H. C. 1933.   Über die Bedingungen der Kojisäurebildung durch *Aspergillus flavus* Link.   *Biochem. Zeit. 266:*82–95.

Lockwood, L. B., and Nelson, G. E. N. 1946.   Some factors affecting the production of itaconic acid by *Aspergillus terreus* in agitated cultures.   *Arch. Biochem. 10:*365–374.

May, O. E., Moyer, A. J., Wells, P. A., and Herrick, H. T. 1931.   The production of kojic acid by *Aspergillus flavus. Jour. Am. Chem. Soc. 53:*774–782.

May, O. E., Ward, G. E., and Herrick, H. T. 1932.   The effect of organic stimulants upon the production of kojic acid by *Aspergillus flavus. Zentralbl. Bakt., Parasiten., und Infekt. II, 86:*130–134.

Maurer, K. 1930. Überfuhrüng von einfachen Zuckern in γ-Pyron-Derivate und die Darstellung weiterer ungesättiger Anhydro-zucker (III Mitteil.). *Ber. deutsch. chem. Ges. 63:*25–34.

Prescott, S. C., and Dunn, C. G. 1940. *Industrial microbiology.* McGraw-Hill, New York.

Saito, K. 1907. Über die Säurebildung bei *Aspergillus oryzae. Bot. Mag. Tokyo 21:*7–11.

Tamiya, H., and Hida, T. 1929. Vergleichende Studien über die Säurebildung die Atmung, die Oxydasereaktion und das Dehydrierungsvermögen von Aspergillusarten. *Acta Phytochim.* (*Japan*) *4:*343–361.

Traetta-Mosca, F. 1914. La fermentazione di alcuni zuccheri, mediante l'*aspergillus glaucus,* con alcune considerazioni sulla fermentazione alcoolica. *Ann. chim. applicata 1:*477–492.

Yabuta, T. 1912. On kojic acid, a new organic acid formed by *Aspergillus oryzae. Jour. Coll. Agr., Tokyo Imp. Univ. 5:*51–58.

———. 1924. The constitution of kojic acid, a γ-pyrone derivative formed by *Aspergillus oryzae* from carbohydrates. *Jour. Chem. Soc. 125:*575–587.

15 · *Fungus Enzymes*

INVERTASE
STARCH-DIGESTING ENZYME PREPARATIONS
OTHER USES OF FUNGUS ENZYMES

IN VIEW OF the tremendous number of different types of organic compounds that can be utilized or synthesized by fungi, it logically follows that these organisms synthesize a great variety of different enzymes. It is a relatively simple matter to demonstrate that a single species is capable of forming a large number of enzymes, and if the entire group of fungi is considered, the number of different enzymes synthesized is very great indeed. Prescott and Dunn (1940) and Wolf and Wolf (1947) have compiled partial lists; the reader may consult these to determine what enzymes have been reported from fungi as well as the species which synthesize them.

Some species may synthesize an enzyme that other species do not; it is not uncommon to find that two strains of the same species may produce different quantities of the same enzyme or may sometimes differ qualitatively with respect to their respective enzyme complements. An example of this latter condition was reported in the work of Fox and Gray (1950), who found that one mating type of the albino-2 mutant of *Neurospora crassa* (Strain 15,300) formed the enzyme *tyrosinase,* whereas the other mating type did not.

Although the variety of enzymes synthesized by fungi is very great, a relatively small number have been produced in quantity on a commercial scale. With further advances in industry, food technology, and medicine, it might be reasonably expected that additional large-scale usage of fungus enzymes will occur.

Enzymes may be variously classified on the basis of the type of chemical reactions which they catalyze (e.g., *oxidizing, hydrolytic,* etc.) or on the basis of whether or not they may diffuse out of the cells in which they are formed (*exoenzymes* and *endoenzymes*). More recently they have been classified as *particulate* or *nonparticulate* on the basis of whether or not they are associated with definite minute particles in the cell. The two enzymes of fungus origin that probably have been most widely used commercially are both hydrolytic; however, one of these, *invertase,* is an endoenzyme, while the other, *amylase,* is an exoenzyme. The procedures employed in the isolation of exoenzymes are quite different from those used for the isolation of endoenzymes.

Invertase

Invertase specifically catalyzes the reaction in which a molecule of the 12-carbon disaccharide, sucrose (cane sugar), is split to a molecule of glucose and a molecule of fructose through the addition of a molecule of water. This reaction may be represented as follows:

$$\underset{\text{sucrose}}{C_{12}H_{22}O_{11}} + H_2O \xrightarrow{\text{invertase}} \underset{\text{glucose}}{C_6H_{12}O_6} + \underset{\text{fructose}}{C_6H_{12}O_6}$$

When sucrose is so hydrolyzed, the resultant mixture of two hexose sugars is often referred to as invert sugar, hence the name invertase.

Invertase, though known and studied for many years, has been produced on a commercial scale only in comparatively recent years. It is synthesized by many different fungi, but for its commercial production the yeast *Saccharomyces cerevisiae* is commonly used. Since it is an endoenzyme, invertase does not diffuse out of the yeast cell and hence cannot be recovered from the medium in which the yeast was cultured; it is liberated from yeast cells by allowing them to autolyze.

Different strains of *S. cerevisiae* vary in their capacities to synthesize invertase. According to Wallerstein (1939), certain strains have been selected and cultivated primarily because of their capacity to synthesize large quantities of this enzyme, just as other yeast strains have been selected on the basis of their capacity to synthesize large quantities of alcohol. Even with high-yielding strains, however, considerable care must be exercised in the cultivation of the yeast in order to obtain maximum enzyme activity. Cane sugar should be used as the carbohydrate source, the pH of the medium should be controlled, and the culture medium carefully aerated in order to remove alcohol and other metabolic products of yeast. When maximum invertase activity has been attained, the yeast cells are separated from the culture medium and autolyzed in the presence of toluene.

Further steps in the preparation of invertase (Wallerstein, 1933) are precipitation of the enzyme from the autolysate with ethyl alcohol, followed by re-solution of the precipitate in a glycerol solution or other suitable solvent of fairly high concentration; the preparation is then standardized. Wallerstein reports that in addition to liquid preparations, a dry invertase of very high activity is also prepared.

The principal commercial use of invertase is in the preparation of certain confections, a use that arose as the result of a need for a method for producing chocolate-coated candies with a soft cream center in which the sugar would not crystallize. What was desired was a center hard enough and firm enough to be molded and coated with chocolate, yet one that would later soften to a permanent and noncrystallizable cream of desirable consistency. Booker (1919) first offered a solution to this problem by incorporating compressed yeast into the fondant mixture (cream center), depending upon the yeast invertase to hydrolyze the sucrose and thereby yielding a mixture of glucose and fructose. Since a mixture of the invert sugars is more soluble than sucrose, crystallization of the sugar would be prevented, and a creamy consistency would result. Wallerstein points out that Booker's method can give satisfactory results, but that it is difficult to use because of the nonuniformity of yeast, and because undesirable properties may be imparted to the fondant mixture. Paine and Hamilton (1922) proposed and patented a process, in wide use today, in which a standardized invertase preparation is used instead of living yeast cells.

In addition to the preparation of confections, another use for invertase is in the partial hydrolysis of sugar syrups. Invert sugars are sometimes used as plasticizing agents in the manufacture of certain types of paper, and Diehm (1938) has suggested that invertase might be used in the paper mill in the preparation of such agents.

Starch-Digesting Enzyme Preparations

One of the principal uses of a starch-digesting enzyme (amylase, diastase) in this country is in the conversion of starch to fermentable sugars in the alcohol industry. Since the beverage alcohol produced in the United States is made primarily from cereal grains, large quantities of such enzymes are used in place of an acid hydrolysis process, which is prohibited by law in the beverage alcohol industry. Similarly, fungus enzymes have not been used in the preparation of alcoholic beverages in this country, since the law specifies only the use of malt enzymes. In oriental countries such as Japan and China, where such laws do not exist, amylolytic enzymes derived from filamentous fungi have been used on a large scale in the preparation of alcoholic beverages and other materials in the manufacture of which grain starch must be converted to sugar. Waksman (*cf.* Willaman, 1940) has correctly pointed out that the division of the world into Occident and Orient may be made not only upon ethnological, geographical, and other grounds, but also on the basis of the type of diastatic enzymes used in the respective alcoholic fermentations of these regions. What malt diastase is to the Occident, fungus diastase is to the Orient. One alcohol process involving the use of fungus enzymes has been used to a certain extent in Europe, but in the United States the law still prevents the use of enzymes of fungus origin in all phases of the alcohol industry except that where alcohol is produced for nonbeverage purposes.

One of the earliest advocates of the use of fungus amylases in the alcohol industry in this country was Takamine (1913a, 1913b, 1914, 1915, 1918, 1923), whose researches form the basis for the production of such preparations. One fungus, *Aspergillus oryzae,* has been used extensively in Japan for many years in the manufacture of active enzyme preparations. The fungus is cultured on steamed rice, and the moldy resultant preparation is known as *Koji.* Some idea of the extensive use to which this preparation has been put is gained from the work of Atsuki (1929), who reported that about 10 per cent of the total rice production of Japan is converted to the national drink, *sake.* In the preparation of sake, rice starch is converted to fermentable sugar by the enzymes in Koji. In his researches in the United States, Takamine (1914) substituted wheat bran for rice as a substrate for the growth of *A. oryzae* and designated the resultant moldy bran product as *"Taka-Koji."* He recommended the substitution of Taka-Koji for barley malt as the conversion agent used in the alcohol industry and stated that wheat bran could be transformed into an active enzyme preparation in about forty-eight hours.

The production of a crude enzyme preparation (mold bran) which has a high amylolytic activity through the use of a fungus such as *A. ory-zae* involves the culturing of the fungus on wheat bran until the bran is thoroughly permeated with mycelium. The older process, as described by Takamine, was as follows: The bran was first moistened with water * and then steamed. During the steaming process the bran was sterilized, and the small amount of starch remaining on the bran was gelatinized. The steamed bran was then cooled to about 40 C, fungus spores mixed with it, and the mixture spread on a concrete floor in a layer about 1½ in. deep, or placed in wooden or metal trays with false bottoms of fine wire netting. The room in which the inoculated bran was placed was maintained at a temperature of about 30 C by piping live steam directly into the room—a procedure that not only serves to heat the room but also to keep the humidity at a high level. Within sixteen to eighteen hours the fungus grows rapidly, and the temperature of the room rises as a result of the great amount of fungus respiration. By the end of twenty to twenty-four hours the temperature may rise so high that the steam must be turned off and the room cooled by the introduction of cool air. High temperature (40 to 42 C) prevails for eight or ten hours, and then the temperature falls. Maximum diastatic strength is reached in about forty-eight hours under these conditions. When this occurs dry air should be introduced into the room in order to dry the Taka-Koji as rapidly as possible and thus prevent the growth of bacterial contaminants that might destroy the enzyme. The reduction of the moisture content of the mold bran to a value of 10 to 15 per cent renders the product too dry to permit the growth of bacterial contaminants, and the bran may be stored without loss of activity for several months if the moisture content is kept below this value. Takamine recommended the use of antiseptics such as formaldehyde, benzoic acid, or salicylic acid to inhibit the growth of contaminants. Such antiseptics are added before the bran is inoculated, and the fungus should be acclimatized to the particular antiseptic used by culturing it for a number of passages on medium containing this antiseptic. Concentrations recommended by Takamine were 1 part in 2500 for formaldehyde, and 1 part in 300 for benzoic acid or salicylic acid.

The use of concrete floors or trays is subject to the same difficulties as

* More recent investigations at the Iowa State College have shown that better results may be obtained if dilute HCl (0.1 to 0.3 N) is used instead of water for moistening the bran.

the use of shallow pans of liquid medium for fungus fermentations. Takamine attempted to produce mold bran by more economical means involving less hand labor and offering less opportunity for the entrance of contaminating organisms. He first used small revolving drums, but eventually he successfully used a large drum of 4800-lb capacity. The drum was a plain iron cylinder with an inlet on one side and an outlet on the other, so arranged that air could be passed through the drum by means of a suction fan mounted on the outlet side. An iron pipe extended through the center of the drum, and either water or steam could be introduced through this pipe. Preparation of mold bran in the drum was accomplished as follows: Bran was placed in the drum, the proper amount of water added, the steam turned on, and the drum placed in motion. After sufficient steaming to accomplish sterilization, the bran was cooled to 45 C with cool, moist air. Antiseptics were then added, and the wheat bran inoculated with spores of *A. oryzae*. The drum was not turned during the first twelve hours; however, at the end of this time the temperature started to rise, the drum was put in motion (1 rpm) and a slight current of air was passed into the drum. The process was complete about forty-eight hours after inoculation; during the process the temperature was prevented from rising above 38 C by introducing air.

Takamine noted that the fungus mycelium grew primarily on the inner sides of the bran flakes. He stated that the amount of labor expended in connection with the drum process is only one-sixth of that expended in the older tray process. Underkofler and Hickey (1954) note that some industrial enzyme plants currently use drums, but that in others drums have been abandoned for the older tray or cabinet culture methods. These workers point out that during the early stages of growth in the rotating drum the delicate mycelium may be damaged by the rubbing action of the bran particles, but with careful control excellent enzyme production occurs in plants using the drum system.

Owen (1933) has reported on a process for producing industrial alcohol known as the *amylo process*. In this process grain mash (such as corn) is first cooked under pressure, then cooled to about 40 C, and inoculated with *Rhizopus delemar* or *Mucor sp.* (both Phycomycetes). After twenty-four hours the fermenter contents are cooled to 32 C and then inoculated with yeast. The amylo process is reported to have been used both in France and in Belgium. In the *Boulard process,* yeast and fungus are added to the main mash simultaneously, and the process is said to be complete in forty-eight hours.

In more recent years considerable research on fungus amylases has been conducted at the Iowa State College (Underkofler and others, 1939; Hao, 1943). These investigators reported that better alcohol yields were obtained from grain mashes in which fungus enzymes were used than from similar mashes in which the conversion agent was malt amylase. They pointed out that the raw materials used in the production of mold bran are cheaper than those used in the production of barley malt, and that mold bran can be prepared in a much shorter period of time than barley malt. In a later paper (Underkofler and others, 1946) it was stated that a grain bill using 2.5 to 4.0 per cent mold bran gave results equivalent to a grain bill which contained 9 to 10 per cent malt.

During World War II, a government hemp mill at Eagle Grove, Iowa was converted to a mold bran plant (Boyer and Underkofler, 1945), and commercial tonnages of this material were produced under

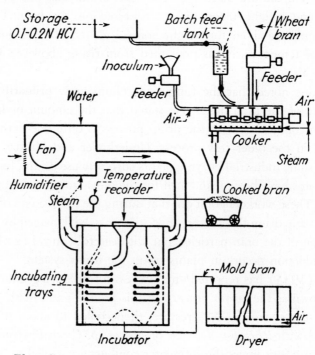

FIG. 87.   *Flow diagram for the production of mold bran at Eagle Grove, Iowa. (From Boyer and Underkofler, 1945; reprinted by permission from* Chemical Engineering.)

the brand name "Eaglezyme." It was reported that at the Omaha plant of the Defense Plant Corporation, 4 lb of mold bran per 100 lb of grain accomplished the same saccharification of starch as the 10 lb of barley malt customarily used. Saccharification and fermentation in the 150,-000 gal fermenters of the Omaha plant was accomplished in about thirty-six hours. The flow diagram for production of mold bran at the Eagle Grove plant is shown in Fig. 87; results of plant-scale tests of mold bran are presented in Table 26.

Table 26.—Results of plant-scale tests of mold bran

Number of Fermenters	Saccharifying Agent in Fermenter Mashes	Saccharifying Agent in Yeast Culture Mashes	Average Alcohol Yield per Standard Bushel (gal, 190 proof)	
			(proof gal)	proof)
299	10% malt	22% malt	4.77	2.41
847	9–10% malt	8.6% malt plus 4.3% mold bran	5.17	2.72
6	4% mold bran	8.6% malt plus 4.3% mold bran	5.24	2.76
12	9–10% malt	8.6% malt plus 4.3% mold bran	5.5	2.71
7	3.9–6.2% malt plus 2.2–0.9% mold bran	8.6% malt plus 4.3% mold bran	5.26	2.77
12	9–10% malt	8.6% malt plus 4.3% mold bran	5.23	2.75

After Underkofler and others (1947).

Underkofler and others (1947) reported that for commercial and semicommercial production of mold bran, the simplest incubation system involves the use of trays with a bran depth of not over 2 in. They also used "incubation cells" in which the fungus was cultured in thicker layers of bran through which air was forced.

LeMense and his co-workers (1947) have found that fungus starch-digesting enzymes may also be produced in submerged cultures in deep vats. These investigators cultured strains of *Aspergillus niger* under submerged aerobic conditions and found in laboratory trials that the culture liquor could be used to replace barley malt completely in the alcoholic fermentation of grain mashes. Pilot plant operations were conducted in which fungi were propagated with continuous aeration and agitation in 250-gal quantities of medium composed of thin stillage, 1 per cent corn meal, and 0.5 per cent calcium carbonate. Enzyme potencies reached a maximum after about sixty hours. Saccharification was satisfactory and alcohol yields were comparable to those obtained with barley malt converted mashes when fungus culture liquor equivalent to 6–10 per cent of the final mash volume was used. LeMense and others estimated the cost of this amylase to be 6.06 cents per bushel of grain processed as compared with 12.1 cents for malt. More evidence is accumulating to support the view that starch conversion can be conducted more economically in the grain alcohol industry through the use of fungal amylases. As has already been pointed out, however, the use of enzymes of such origin in the production of beverage alcohol is still prevented by law.

Although mold bran as prepared by Takamine and the more recent workers mentioned above can be used directly as a substitute for malt, a more-or-less purified preparation can be readily made by extracting the enzymes from mold bran by percolating water through it and then precipitating out the enzyme from water solution by adding strong alcohol until the alcohol content of the mixture is 70 per cent by volume. The white, flocculent precipitate can then be dehydrated with strong alcohol. The precipitate so prepared is a white or yellowish-white powder which is usually marketed under the name of Taka Diastase. A precipitate prepared in this way has a very high amylolytic power, but it is not pure amylase, consisting actually of a mixture of many enzymes. Harada (1931) states that the following enzymes have been isolated from this type of preparation: maltase, dextrinase, invertase, lipase, peptase, ereptase, rennet, trypsin, amylase, catalase, lactase, inulase, sulfatase, amidase, glycerophosphatase, emulsin, and esterase.

Much of the emphasis on fungus starch-digesting enzymes has been placed on their use in the conversion of grain starches in the alcoholic fermentation industry, yet these enzymes have also been used in other processes. For example, Oshima and Church (1923) have reported the use of fungus amylase preparations as desizing agents in the textile industry. In certain fabrics woven from cotton, jute, or similar fibers, the textile manufacturer often finds it necessary to oversize the warp (longitudinal) threads in order to facilitate weaving. Such practice imparts added strength to the threads during the actual weaving process, but the heavily sized threads are undesirable in the finished cloth. After the fabric is woven, the extra sizing material (frequently starch) is removed by passing the cloth through a bath of starch-digesting enzyme solution.

Starch-digesting enzymes have also been used in the preparation of pectin and fruit juices. The presence of starch has always been a disturbing factor in the production of pectin from apple pomace. Daughters (1927) and Douglas (1932) have recommended the use of diastatic enzymes in the preparation of fruit juices and pectin, and Wallerstein (1939) states that fungus enzymes such as those produced by *A. oryzae* are especially suitable because of their marked activity at low *p*H values.

Other Uses of Fungus Enzymes

Pectin, like starch, is another material that creates difficulties in the preparation of clear fruit juices. Fungus enzymes have also been used to decompose pectins especially in the preparation of apple juice. Pectic compounds are colloidal in nature and hence cause considerable difficulty in the filtration of fruit juices. The enzyme pectinase catalyzes the conversion of pectins to simpler compounds which are not colloidal and hence do not interfere with filtration. According to Kertesz (1930), such enzyme preparations as "Taka Diastase," "Polyzyme," "Oryzyme," and "Protozyme" have been employed in the clarification of fruit juices. Kertesz reports that *Penicillium glaucum* is an excellent source of enzymes suitable for the clarification of cider. The effects of enzyme treatment on fresh apple juice are shown in Fig. 88.

It is not uncommon for tartrates to crystallize out of bottled grape juice—a phenomenon that apparently does not affect the palatability of the grape juice but may well arouse buyer resistance. Barton (1953) found that *Aspergillus versicolor* synthesizes an enzyme capable of destroying tartrates and recommended its use in the commercial preparation of grape juice.

Fungus proteases have been used to a certain extent in the tanning industry, and there are several manufacturers who market enzymes of this type. After fresh hides have undergone the processes of trimming, soaking, liming, fleshing, dehairing, and scudding they are subjected to the process of bating, the purpose of which is to prepare the hides for tanning. Early tanners conducted the bating process by putting hides in a suspension of bird or dog dung; however, in 1898 Wood demonstrated

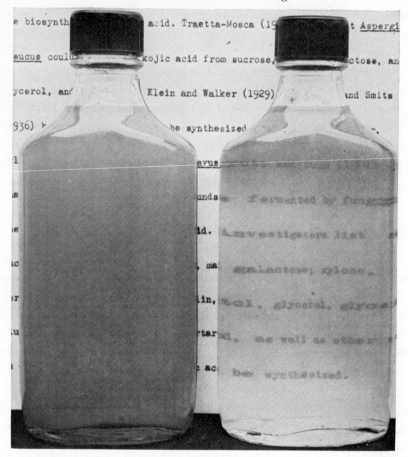

FIG. 88. *Samples of apple cider before and after clarification with mold enzyme preparations.*

that the bating action was due not to dung but to the action of enzymes which are synthesized by bacteria present in dung. Today the bating process is conducted with enzyme preparations, some of which are derived from fungi.

Coincidental with the widespread development of economical refrigeration in this country the growing demand that beer be served cold has created problems in the brewing industry that are not encountered in countries where beer is served at room temperature. One of the problems of the American brewer has been the production of a chill-proof beer, that is, one that does not become cloudy or turbid when cold. It has been common practice to add enzymes of green plant origin such as papain or bromelin (proteolytic enzymes) to produce greater stability in beer when cooled. Wallerstein (1937) recommends that fungus or bacterial enzyme preparations be added also, since he found that such preparations enhance the activity of the papain and bromelin.

A fungus enzyme recently placed on the market is glucose-oxidase (glucose aerodehydrogenase), which is obtained along with the enzyme catalase from *Aspergillus niger* by a submerged culture method (Lockwood, 1952). Marketed as a powder, this enzyme preparation is used to remove glucose from eggs before they are dried in order to prevent browning. Glucose aerodehydrogenase catalyzes the oxidation of glucose to gluconic acid with the simultaneous formation of hydrogen peroxide, which latter compound is destroyed by catalase (see Chapter 12).

Sizer and Prokesch (1945) recommend a rather unusual use for a fungus enzyme. These investigators found that purified mushroom tyrosinase (a phenol oxidase) catalyzes the oxidation of the toxic principles of a large number of different commercial poison ivy concentrates as well as extracts of related materials from poison oak, Japanese lac, and cashew nut shell. They found that tyrosinase would inactivate such toxicants not only *in vitro* but also when applied to the human skin simultaneously with or a few hours after the toxicants. On the basis of these findings, Sizer and Prokesch suggested the use of tyrosinase in the treatment of poison ivy dermatitis in its early stages.

Literature Cited

Atsuki, K. 1929. Sake brewing. *Jour. Soc. Chem. Ind. Japan* 32:57B–58B.

Barton, R. R. 1953. The production and action of a tartrate-decomposing enzyme. *Mycologia* 45:533–547.

Booker, J. P. 1919. Process for making cream centers for coated candy. U.S. Patent 1,309,979.

Boyer, J. W., and Underkofler, L. A. 1945. Mold bran aids production of grain alcohol. *Chem. & Met. Eng.* 52(12):110–111.

Daughters, M. L. 1927. The clarification and filtration of fruit juices. *Canning Age, May, 1927.* pp. 503–505.

Diehm, R. A. 1938. The potentialities of enzymes in the paper industry. *Paper Trade Jour.* 106(23):36–38.

Douglas, R. 1932. Process for preparing pectin. U.S. Patent 1,858,820.

Fox, A. S., and Gray, W. D. 1950. Immunogenetic and biochemical studies of

Neurospora crassa: differences in tyrosinase activity between mating types of Strain 15,300 (albino-2). *Proc. Nat. Acad. Sci. 36:*538–546.

Hao, L. C., Fulmer, E. I., and Underkofler, L. A. 1943. Fungal amylases as saccharifying agents in the alcoholic fermentation of corn. *Ind. Eng. Chem.* 35(7):814–818.

Harada, T. 1931. Preparation of *Aspergillus oryzae* enzymes. *Ind. Eng. Chem.* 23:1424.

Kertesz, Z. I. 1930. A new method for enzymic clarification of unfermented apple juice. *N. Y. State Agr. Expt. Sta. Bull.* 589.

LeMense, E. H., Sohns, V. E., Corman, J., Blom, R. H., VanLanen, J. M., and Langlykke, A. F. 1947. Submerged mold amylase as a saccharifying agent in grain alcohol fermentations. *Abstr. of Papers, Amer. Chem. Soc. 112th meeting, Sept. 15–19, 1947.*

Lockwood, L. B. 1952. Industrial enzymes. Production and use. *Trans. N. Y. Acad. Sci. 15:*2–5.

Oshima, K., and Church, M. B. 1923. Industrial mold enzymes. *Ind. Eng. Chem.* 15:67–70.

Owen, W. L. 1933. Production of industrial alcohol from grain by amylo process. *Ind. Eng. Chem. 25:*87–89.

Paine, H. S., and Hamilton, J. 1922. Process for preparing fondant or chocolate cream centers. U.S. Patent 1,437,816.

Prescott, S. C., and Dunn, C. G. 1940. *Industrial microbiology.* McGraw-Hill, New York.

Sizer, I. W., and Prokesch, C. E. 1945. The destruction by tyrosinase of the irritant principles of poison ivy and related toxicants. *Jour. Pharmacol. & Exper. Therap. 84:*363–374.

Takamine, J. 1913a. Process for producing diastatic product. U.S. Patent 1,054,324.

——. 1913b. Diastatic product. U.S. Patent 1,054,626.

——. 1914. Enzymes of *Aspergillus oryzae* and the application of its amyloclastic enzyme to the fermentation industry. *Jour. Ind. Eng. Chem. 6:*824–828.

——. 1915. Diastatic product and the process for producing the same. U.S. Patent 1,148,938.

——. 1918. Process for producing diastatic product. U.S. Patent 1,263,817.

——. 1923. Enzymic substance and process of making the same. U.S. Patent 1,460,736.

Underkofler, L. A., and Hickey, R. J. 1954. *Industrial fermentations.* Chemical Pub. Co., New York.

Underkofler, L. A., Fulmer, E. I., and Schoene, L. 1939. Saccharification of starchy grain mashes for the alcoholic fermentation industry. *Ind. Eng. Chem.* 31:734–738.

Underkofler, L. A., Severson, G. M. and Goering, K. J. 1946. Saccharification of grain mashes for alcoholic fermentation. *Ind. Eng. Chem. 38:*980–985.

————, and Christensen, L. M. 1947. Commercial production and use of mold bran. *Cereal Chem. 24:*1–22.

Wallerstein, L. 1933. Invertase preparations and method of making the same. U.S. Patent 1,919,675.

————. 1937. Process of chill-proofing and stabilizing beers and ales. U.S. Patent 2,077,447.

————. 1939. Enzyme preparations from microorganisms. *Ind. Eng. Chem. 31:*1218–1224.

Willaman, J. J. 1940. Industrial use of microbial enzymes. *Rept. of Proceedings, Third Int. Cong. for Microbiology, N. Y., Sept. 2–9,* 1939.

Wolf, F. A., and Wolf, F. T. 1947. *The fungi.* Vol. II. Wiley, New York

Wood, J. T. 1898. Notes on the constitution and mode of action of the dung bate in leather manufacture. *Jour. Soc. Chem. Ind. 17:*1010–1013.

16 · *Fermentation Process for Glycerol Production*

USES OF GLYCEROL

THE GLYCEROL FERMENTATION

RECENT DEVELOPMENTS IN THE GLYCEROL FERMENTATION

WE ORDINARILY THINK only of alcohol and carbon dioxide production in connection with a fermentation involving yeast. Pasteur (1858) demonstrated many years ago that in the course of the alcoholic fermentation small amounts of glycerol and succinic acid are also formed in addition to these two compounds. Glycerol, the simplest trihydric alcohol, is a common chemical compound and has many uses. It

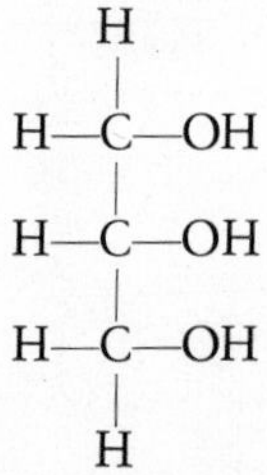

$$
\begin{array}{c}
\text{H} \\
| \\
\text{H}-\text{C}-\text{OH} \\
| \\
\text{H}-\text{C}-\text{OH} \\
| \\
\text{H}-\text{C}-\text{OH} \\
| \\
\text{H}
\end{array}
$$

is a clear, colorless, syrupy, almost odorless liquid having a sweet taste. It boils at 290 C, but if kept long at this temperature it undergoes partial decomposition. For this reason it is best purified by distillation under reduced pressure. Ordinarily glycerol is obtained by the hydrolysis of fats and oils and is a by-product of the soap industry, where the sodium salts of fatty acids (soaps) are prepared by heating animal or vegetable fats with sodium hydroxide. The reaction is given in the following equation, which illustrates the hydrolysis of tripalmitin, one of the constituent fats of beef tallow:

$$
\begin{array}{l}
\text{H} \\
\;\mid \quad\quad\; \text{O} \\
\text{H}-\text{C}-\text{O}-\overset{\displaystyle \parallel}{\text{C}}-\text{C}_{15}\text{H}_{31} \\[4pt]
\quad\quad\quad\quad \text{O} \\
\text{H}-\text{C}-\text{O}-\overset{\displaystyle \parallel}{\text{C}}-\text{C}_{15}\text{H}_{31} \;+\; 3\text{NaOH} \;\rightarrow\; \\[4pt]
\quad\quad\quad\quad \text{O} \\
\text{H}-\text{C}-\text{O}-\overset{\displaystyle \parallel}{\text{C}}-\text{C}_{15}\text{H}_{31} \\[4pt]
\;\mid \\
\text{H}
\end{array}
\qquad
\begin{array}{l}
\text{H} \\
\;\mid \\
\text{H}-\text{C}-\text{OH} \\[4pt]
\;\mid \\
\text{H}-\text{C}-\text{OH} \;+\; 3\text{C}_{15}\text{H}_{31}\text{COONa} \;+\; 3\text{H}_2\text{O} \\[4pt]
\;\mid \\
\text{H}-\text{C}-\text{OH} \\[4pt]
\;\mid \\
\text{H}
\end{array}
$$

tripalmitin   glycerol   sodium palmitate

Shortly before and during the early years of World War I, the German investigator Neuberg (1914, 1917, 1919), in studying the mechanism of the alcoholic fermentation, found that if sulphite is added to the alcoholic fermentation an increase in glycerol production results. According to Neuberg and his co-workers, sugar is fermented in the presence of sulphite to one molecule of glycerol per molecule of acetaldehyde according to the following equation:

$$C_6H_{12}O_6 \rightarrow CH_2OH \cdot CHOH \cdot CH_2OH + CH_3CHO + CO_2$$

Since the acetaldehyde combines with the sulphite,

$$CH_3CHO + Na_2SO_3 + H_2O \rightarrow CH_3CHOHSO_3Na + NaOH,$$

the reduction of acetaldehyde to ethyl alcohol which usually occurs in the alcoholic fermentation is prevented, and a triose formed from the hexose accepts the hydrogen (which ordinarily would be accepted by the acetaldehyde) and thus becomes reduced to glycerol (see diagram of the alcoholic fermentation, Chapter 9).

From Neuberg's equation it is evident that the theoretical maximum quantity of glycerol which could be derived from 100 grams of hexose sugar is 51 grams—provided enough sulphite is added to combine with 24.4 grams of acetaldehyde. Thus the weight ratio of acetaldehyde to glycerol should be 24.4 : 51, or 1 g acetaldehyde per 2.09 g glycerol. Table 27, taken from the work of Lawrie (1928) and based on Neuberg's studies, presents data which bear out these calculations and demonstrates that while the total quantity of glycerol synthesized during a fermentation is affected by the amount of sulphite added, the ratio of acetaldehyde to glycerol remains essentially the same—close to the theoretical 1 : 2.09.

Table 27.—Yields of glycerol and acetaldehyde with varying proportions of sodium sulphite

Parts Used		Parts Produced		Proportion of Aldehyde to Glycerol
Na_2SO_3	Sugar	Aldehyde	Glycerol	Glycerol
33	100	11.90	23.37	1:1.96
50	100	12.52	24.86	1:1.98
75	100	13.89	27.62	1:1.98
150	100	18.65	36.90	1:1.98

After Lawrie (1928).

Uses of Glycerol

Glycerol has many and varied uses. It is a component of nitro-glycerine and an important material in the manufacture of synthetic rubber, adhesives, antifreeze, as well as a solvent in numerous processes and industries. Glycerol is widely used in medicine (Lesser and Murphy, 1936a,b,c), one of its most important attributes being its hygroscopic nature. Many of the substances used in medicinal preparations (iodine, bromine, tannin, alkaloids, thymol, phenol, boric acid, etc.) are much more soluble in glycerol than in water.

Glycerol has been used as a sweetening agent in medicinal preparations. Because of its syrupy consistency it is a useful vehicle for many substances that would settle out of a less viscous substance such as water. It has definite antiseptic properties (probably because of its hygroscopic action and the slow rate at which it penetrates cell membranes) and is extensively employed as a vehicle for various vaccines and allergenic extracts. In the United States Pharmacopoeia XI, more than 12 per cent of the galenicals listed contain glycerol; in the National Formulary VI, it is an ingredient in more than 16 per cent of the 481 preparations listed.

The Glycerol Fermentation

Glycerol production by a fermentation process was apparently first accomplished in Germany during World War I as an outgrowth of the acute fat shortage in that country. The resulting shortage of glycerol, desperately needed for the production of explosives, led the Germans to attempt production of this compound by a yeast fermentation process— a process particularly feasible in the light of Neuberg's earlier work. The details of the German process were published after the war by Connstein and Lüdecke (1919) and Zerner (1920).

The German process for glycerol production was conducted as follows: A mixture consisting of sucrose, 1000 g; ammonium nitrate, 50 g; dibasic potassium phosphate, 7.5 g; and sodium sulphite, 400 g was dissolved in 10 liters of water and then inoculated with 100 g of fresh yeast (*S. cerevisiae*). The fermentation was allowed to proceed at 30 C for 48–60 hours at which time the easily volatilized constituents (alcohol and acetaldehyde) were removed by distillation. The residue after distillation was treated with lime and calcium chloride to remove the sulphite, and excess calcium was removed with sodium carbonate. The glycerol was then removed from the treated fermentation liquor by distillation under reduced pressure. The yield from 1000 g of sucrose was 200–250 g of glycerol, 300 g of ethyl alcohol, and 50 g of acetaldehyde. Using this process, technical grade glycerol was produced in Germany during the war at a rate of 1000 tons per month. According to Henneberg (1926), one fermentation plant used 60 tons of sugar and 6 tons of yeast daily, the fermentations being conducted in very large vats of about 135,000-gal capacity. It is believed that the ability of the Germans to produce glycerol in this manner enabled them to extend the war for an additional 12 months (Ramsbottom, 1945).

Shortly after the Germans initiated their work on the large-scale production of glycerol by a fermentation process, the problem was also assigned to government chemists in the United States. The process they developed, commonly called the Eoff process, was described by Eoff and his co-workers (1919). The essential feature is that the fermentation is conducted in an alkaline medium. Eoff and his associates screened a number of yeasts for their suitability for glycerol production and selected a strain of wine yeast, *Saccharomyces ellipsoideus*. Increasing the alkalinity of the fermentation medium results in an increase in glycerol production. The alkalinity may be produced by adding sodium carbonate, potassium carbonate, sodium hydroxide, or sodium perborate, but the most favorable materials are sodium carbonate and potassium carbonate. Best results were obtained when sodium carbonate was used in a total concentration of 5 per cent. The most favorable temperature was found to be 30–32 C, with optimum sugar concentration between 17.5 and 20 g per 100 ml. They "trained" their yeast strain by adding 0.5–1.0 per cent sodium carbonate to the medium in which the yeast was cultured in preparation for its use as inoculum. At completion of the fermentation, 20–25 per cent of the sugar initially present in the mash was converted to glycerol, practically all of the remaining sugar being converted to alcohol and carbon dioxide.

Cocking and Lilly (1922) developed and patented a modification of the German or sulphite fermentation process for glycerol production. Their process differs from that of Connstein and Lüdecke in that instead of adding sulphite to the fermentation, a mixture of sulphites and bisulphites is added. The addition of bisulphite causes acetaldehyde to be fixed at an earlier stage, but because of the antiseptic properties of bisulphites they cannot be added to a fermentation in any great quantity. Lilly (1935) states that the mixture of sulphite and bisulphite should be such that the medium has a nearly neutral reaction. When the fermentation is complete, soda ash or other mild alkali equal to or greater than the original bisulphite present is added; acetaldehyde and alcohol are then removed from the alkaline solution by distillation. The reaction of the residual liquor is restored with sulphur dioxide, sulphurous acid, or soluble bisulphite; fresh carbohydrate is added, and the liquor then used for a second fermentation. According to Lilly this procedure may be repeated several times.

From the time of the initial discovery up to 1928 (Lawrie, 1928), patents relative to the production of glycerol by fermentation processes similar to those discussed above have been issued as follows: United States, eight patents; Great Britain, eight; Germany, eleven; France, five; Japan, one. In addition to these patents granted, there were five applied for in Hungary, two applied for in Austria, and one applied for in Germany.

Recent Developments in The Glycerol Fermentation

During World War I and in the immediate postwar period there were numerous investigations of the glycerol fermentation, but after 1928 interest in this process diminished. The processes developed up to 1928 are known as "steered" fermentations, since the yeast metabolism is shunted from its usual pathway into one that results in glycerol formation. Such fermentations were steered by sulphites or alkali, either of which adds to the materials cost and increases the difficulty of recovering the glycerol.

Several organisms have since been found to be capable of synthesizing glycerol in unsteered fermentations. For example, McBee (1948) used two thermophilic, cellulose-decomposing bacteria in a fermentation of this type, and Neish and others (1947) were granted a patent for a process in which they used a strain of the common bacterium, *Bacillus subtilis.* Neish and his associates claimed yields of 29.4 lb of glycerol, 28.1 lb of 2,3-butanediol, 11.6 lb of lactic acid, and 2.2 lb of ethyl alcohol per 100 lb of sugar.

Nickerson (1943) isolated and named a new species of yeast (*Zygosaccharomyces acidifaciens*), which according to Nickerson and Carroll (1945) converted 22 per cent of the glucose fermented to glycerol in a ten-day fermentation period. Spencer, Roxburgh, and Sallans (1957) reported that preliminary work by Neish and his associates in their laboratory had shown that strong osmophilic yeasts, classified as *Saccharomyces rouxii* and *S. mellis,* also synthesized polyhydric alcohols without sulphite addition and with apparent yields of glycerol of nearly 50 per cent of the glucose fermented. Spencer and others used a yeast strain isolated from a sample of brood-comb pollen, which produced both glycerol and D-arabitol, another polyhydric alcohol. Their investigations of the effects of various factors on glycerol and D-arabitol production indicates that further studies of this type might lead to the development of an unsteered glycerol fermentation using a yeast as the organism for conducting the fermentation.

Notwithstanding its many uses, glycerol has never been prepared on a large scale in the United States by a fermentation process—probably because this country has never been "fat-poor," and because glycerol has always been obtained cheaply as a by-product of the soap industry. If fats become more expensive and less abundant, we may have to turn to one of the processes outlined above in order to supply our glycerol requirements.

Literature Cited

Cocking, A. T., and Lilly, C. H. 1922. Production of glycerine by fermentation. U.S. Patent 1,425,838. Aug. 15, 1922.

Connstein, W., and Lüdecke, K. 1919. Über Glycerin-Gewinnung durch Gärung. *Ber. deutsch. chem. Ges. 52:*1385–1391.

Eoff, J. R., Linder, W. V., and Beyer, G. F. 1919. Production of glycerin from sugar by fermentation. *Jour. Ind. Eng. Chem.* 11:842–845.

Henneberg, W. 1926. *Handbuch der Garungsbakteriologie.* Vol. II. Berlin.

Lawrie, J. W. 1928. *Glycerol and the glycols. Production, properties and analyses.* Chemical Catalog Co., New York.

Lesser, M. A., and Murphy, J. R. 1936a. Glycerin: its role in medicine. *Amer. Profess. Pharmacist, June, 1936:*18–20.

———. 1936b. Glycerin in pharmacy. *Amer. Profess. Pharmacist, July, 1936:* 20–23.

———. 1936c. The therapeutics of glycerin. *Amer. Profess. Pharmacist, Aug., 1936:*22–26.

Lilly, C. H. 1935. Manufacture of glycerine. U.S. Patent 1,987,260. Jan. 8, 1935.

McBee, R. H. 1948. The culture and physiology of a thermophilic cellulose-fermenting bacterium. *Jour. Bact.* 56:653–663.

Neish, A. C., Ledingham, G. A., and Blackwood, A. C. 1947. Production of glycerol by fermentation. U.S. Patent 2,432,032. Dec. 2, 1947.

Neuberg, C., and Kerb, J. 1914. Über zuckerfrei Hefegärungen. XIII. Zur Frage der Aldehydbildung bei der Gärung von Hexosen sowie bei der sog. Selbstgärung. *Biochem. Zeit.* 58:158–170.

——— and Farber, E. 1917. Über der Verlauf der alkoholischen Gärung bei alkalischer Reaktion. I. Zellfreie Gärung in alkalischen Lösungen. *Biochem. Zeit.* 78:238–263.

——— and Reinfurth, E. 1919. Weitere Untersuchungen über die korrelative Bildung von acetaldehyd und Glycerin bei der Zuckerspaltung und neue Beiträge zur Theorie der alkoholischen Gärung. *Ber. deutsch. chem. Ges.* 52B: 1677–1703.

Nickerson, W. J. 1943. *Zygosaccharomyces acidifaciens:* a new acetifying yeast. *Mycologia* 35:66–78.

——— and Carroll, W. R. 1945. On the metabolism of *Zygosaccharomyces. Arch. Biochem.* 7:257–271.

Pasteur, L. 1858. Production constante de glycérine dans la fermentation. *Compt. rend.* 46:857.

———. 1858. Nouvelles recherches sur la fermentation alcoolique. *Compt. rend.* 47:224.

Spencer, J. F. T., Roxburgh, J. M., and Sallans, H. R. 1957. Factors influencing the production of polyhydric alcohols by osmophilic yeasts. *Jour. Agr. & Food. Chem.* 5:64–67.

Ramsbottom, J. 1945. Fungi and modern affairs. *Smithsonian Institution Rept. for 1945:*313–326.

Zerner, E. 1920. Über den Chemismus der alkoholischen Gärung. *Ber. deutsch. chem. Ges.* 53:325–334.

17 · Fat Production

FUNGI THAT SYNTHESIZE FATS
FACTORS AFFECTING LIPID SYNTHESIS
COMPOSITION OF FUNGUS LIPIDS
YEASTS AND YEASTLIKE ORGANISMS AS A SOURCE OF FAT

THE POSSIBILITY OF UTILIZING microorganisms as a source of fat is one that has received sporadic attention, usually during or immediately following an actual or threatened food shortage. A very considerable amount of research has been done in the United States on the problem of fat synthesis by fungi, but thus far we have not had to utilize these organisms as a source of fat because of our more than adequate supplies from other sources. Germany, not so fortunately endowed in this respect, used microorganisms for fat production during both world wars.

Late in the nineteenth century Marschall (1897) reported that the lipid content of fungus mycelia varies between 1 and 40 per cent. A few years later, Browne (1906) reported that scums formed on molasses and syrups by *"Citromyces"* (*Penicillium*) had a fat content of 27.5 per cent.

There is some evidence that the nature of the fats formed by fungi may differ with the conditions under which the organisms are cultured. For example, Pearson and Raper (1927) were able to demonstrate that the fatty acids formed by *Aspergillus niger* and *Rhizopus nigricans* were qualitatively different when these organisms were cultured at different temperatures. Pearson and Raper cultured *A. niger* at 18, 25, and 35 C, and *R. nigricans* at 18 and 25 C. They then extracted the fats from the mycelia, hydrolyzed them, separated out the fatty acids, and determined the iodine numbers in order to ascertain the degree of saturation of these fatty acids. With both species tested, greater quantities of unsaturated fatty acids were formed at the lower temperature. The work of Barber (1929) indicates that the nature of the fat is not affected by carbon source. He cultured a species of *Penicillium* isolated from corn starch paste on media containing glucose, sucrose, xylose, or glycerol as the carbon source, and found that the same fat or mixture of fats was formed on each type of medium. Barber also reported that the fat synthesized by this organism consisted of palmitic, stearic, oleic, and α and β linoleic acids, both free and as glycerides.

Fungi That Synthesize Fats

As far as is known all fungi are capable of synthesizing lipids (fats and fatlike materials), but some have received especial attention with respect to this capacity. Pruess and others (1934) determined the total lipid contents of 24 species of fungi (*Paecilomyces*, 1; *Penicillium* 4; and *Aspergillus*, 19) and found that the fat content not only varied with the species of fungus but also with the type of medium on which the organisms were cultured. Fat content varied from 1.1 per cent in *Aspergillus carbonarius* to 19.9 per cent in *Aspergillus nidulans* (on glucose-inorganic salts medium) and varied from 1.5 per cent in *Aspergillus citrosporus* to 24.4 per cent in *Aspergillus insuetus* when cultured on glucose-malt sprouts medium.

Lockwood and others (1934) surveyed 120 cultures of Aspergilli for their capacity to produce fat, and Ward and his co-workers (1935) studied 22 Aspergilli and 39 Penicillia for this same purpose. These latter investigators extracted the crude fats and found that of the 61 fungi studied, ten contained more than 15 per cent crude fat; of these, six contained more than 20 per cent. None of the species of *Aspergillus* contained more than 20 per cent and only one contained more than 15 per cent. These findings seem to indicate that of these two genera of very common molds, members of the genus *Penicillium* are somewhat better sources of fat than are members of the genus *Aspergillus* (Table 28).

Many other species of fungi have been used in fat-synthesis research, but the fungi most commonly studied are species of *Penicillium* or *Aspergillus*. For example, Lockwood and others (*loc. cit.*) used *P. javanicum*; Kroeker and others (1935) used *P. aurantio-brunneum*;

Table 28.—*Crude fat content of fungi*

Species	Crude Fat Content of Dried Mycelium (%)
Penicillium flavocinerium	28.5
" piscarum	26–28
" oxalicum	24.4
" roqueforti	22.9
" javanicum	22.2
" soppi	20.2
" hirsutum	18.4
" citrinum	18.1
" bialowiezense	17.0
Aspergillus flavus	16.0

After Ward and others (1935).

Prill and others (1935) used *A. fischeri,* and Strong and Peterson (1934) used *A. sydowi.* In addition to the filamentous fungi, yeasts and yeastlike organisms have also been considered as potential sources of fat; however, these organisms will be treated separately later.

Factors Affecting Lipid Synthesis

One of the most extensive investigations of the factors influencing the yields of lipids synthesized by filamentous fungi was reported by Lockwood and others (1934), who used *P. javanicum* for their researches. They used 200 ml Erlenmeyer flasks containing 75 ml of nutrient medium for their studies and incubated the cultures for periods of from four to sixty days. The mycelial mats continued to gain weight throughout the sixty-day incubation period, but their analyses showed that maximum percentage of fat was attained after twenty-eight days (Table 29).

The studies by Lockwood and his co-workers on the relation of sugar concentration to fat formation were conducted in small flasks with a twelve-day incubation period. They found that while the greatest percentage of fat was formed when the fungus was cultured in medium of 40 per cent sugar concentration, the greatest total quantity of fat was formed in medium of 30 per cent sugar concentration (Table 30).

Table 29.—Relation of culture age and lipid
content of Penicillium javanicum

Age (days)	Mat Weight (g)	Fat (%)	Culture Acid Equivalent (cc N/10 acid)	Glucose Consumed (g)
4	0.405	21.3	14	1.9
8	1.584	24.3	47	6.7
12	2.396	22.1	123	10.0
16	2.660	28.1	174	12.6
20	3.001	32.7	220	14.5
24	3.271	29.5	188	14.7
28	2.823	32.6	166	14.0
32	3.212	32.1	129	15.3
36	3.465	25.5	100	15.3
44	3.645	28.3	133	15.3
52	3.870	27.5	123	16.0
60	3.977	27.3	131	16.5

From Lockwood and others (1934).

Table 30.—Effect of glucose concentration on fat
formation by Penicillium javanicum

Glucose (%)	Mat Weight (g)	Fat (%)	Culture Acid Equivalent (cc N/10 acid)	Glucose Consumed (g)
20	2.522	29.0	149	10.3
30	2.400	34.6	209	11.3
40	1.964	41.5	148	9.9
50	1.021	35.2	20	5.2

From Lockwood and others (1934).

Lockwood and his associates also considered such factors as $MgSO_4$ and KH_2PO_4 concentrations, effect of pressure, pH, type of carbon source, effect of various ions, and surface-volume ratio. Their highest lipid yields were obtained when the $MgSO_4 \cdot 7H_2O$ concentration was 4 g per liter and the KH_2PO_4 concentration 0.15. Cultures were incubated for eight days under air pressures ranging from one to eight atmospheres. It was found that increasing the air pressure resulted in a decrease in sugar utilization, mycelial weight, and titratable acidity, as well as lipid content.

Cultures were prepared using media in which the initial pH varied from 2.1 to 7.9, but the range of tolerance of this organism was so great that it was concluded that for ordinary purposes it is not necessary to regulate pH.

The ratio of surface area of medium to volume of medium in the culture flask was found to have a marked effect upon fat production. The highest yield was obtained when this ratio was 0.413 (Table 31).

Table 31.—*Relation of surface area-volume ratio to fat formation by* Penicillium javanicum

Surface-Volume Ratio	Volume (ml)	Mat Weight (g)	Culture Acid Equivalent (cc N/10 acid)	Glucose Consumed (g)	Total Fat (g)	Fat (%)
0.413	111	3.418	243	14.0	0.724	21.2
0.207	222	4.103	164	15.8	0.697	17.0
0.133	333	4.263	169	18.6	0.733	17.2
0.103	444	4.276	148	21.0	0.675	15.8

After Lockwood and others (1934).

Changing the surface-volume ratio had a very great effect upon the efficiency of the process whereby glucose was converted to fat, since 19.3 g of glucose were required at a ratio of 0.413 for the production of one gram of fat, as compared with 31.1 g required at a ratio of 0.103.

Inconclusive results were obtained when 52 compounds were added singly to cultures in order to test the effects of various ions on fat formation. Some were toxic and others apparently resulted in slight increases in fat synthesis. Of twenty-two compounds tested for their suitability as carbon sources for fat formation, it was found that xylose and glucose were most suitable for this purpose, these two sugars being utilized nearly equally well.

Ward, Lockwood, May, and Herrick (1935) later reported on the production of fat from glucose by *P. javanicum* in a large-scale laboratory apparatus.

Prill, Wenck, and Peterson (1935) also studied some of the factors influencing the synthesis of fat, but employed in their work a different organism from that used by Lockwood and his associates. These investigators screened nine different cultures of *Aspergillus fischeri* and then selected for further studies the one yielding the greatest amount of fat. They investigated the effect of nitrogen content of the medium, using NH_4NO_3 in concentrations ranging from 0.2 to 10 per cent. A greater percentage of glucose was utilized when the NH_4NO_3 content was 0.2 per cent—a predictable finding, since if an organism is supplied with adequate amounts of sugar and a high concentration of a suitable nitrogen source it would synthesize protein rather than fat.

Prill and his co-workers cultured *A. fischeri* at 20, 30, and 37 C and found that the greatest percentage of fat was formed at 30 C (25.7 per cent), although this value was only slightly higher than the percentage of fat in mycelia cultured at 20 C. They concluded from their studies that aeration has no significant effect upon fat production. Like Lockwood and his associates, however, they found that initial concentration of glucose has a marked effect upon the percentage of fat formed in the mycelium (Table 32).

Table 32.—Effect of initial glucose concentration upon synthesis of fat by Aspergillus fischeri

Glucose Added to 100 ml of Solution (g)	Glucose Utilized (g)	Period of Incubation (days)	Mycelium per gram of Glucose Utilized	Fat (%)
1	0.84	4	0.38	10.4
3	2.55	5	0.37	11.8
5	4.65	7	0.34	10.8
10	9.5	8	0.33	13.1
15	14.4	10	0.32	15.6
20	19.2	12	0.29	18.0
30	29.0	14	0.28	23.3
40	39.4	16	0.26	28.1
55	49.5	22	0.26	33.3
70	68.6	28	0.23	36.0

After Prill and others (1935).

Composition of Fungus Lipids

Several investigators have cultured various fungi, extracted the lipids from the mycelia with fat solvents of one type or another, and then analyzed the extracted lipids. Browne reported on the nature of the fat synthesized by *"Citromyces,"* Barber on an unnamed species of *Penicillium*, Ward and Jamieson (1934) on *Penicillium javanicum,* Strong and Peterson (1934) on *A. sydowi,* and Peterson and others (1933) on *Penicillium aurantio-brunneum.* The composition of the simple lipids of *A. sydowi* as reported by Strong and Peterson is shown in Table 33.

Table 33.—Composition of the simple lipids of Aspergillus sydowi

	%
Fatty acids	80.8
Volatile acids (calculated as butyric)	0.46
Saturated acids	22.6
Palmitic	8.8
Stearic	11.0
n-Tetracosanic	0.9
Unsaturated acids	52.9
Oleic	29.6
Linoleic	16.3
Higher acids	1.7
Unsaponifiable	8.18
Total sterols	5.36
Glycerol	4.2

From Strong and Peterson (1934).

Ward and Jamieson state that the fat obtained from *P. javanicum* is entirely different from the fat isolated by Browne from *"Citromyces"* but somewhat similar to the fat isolated by Barber from a species of *Penicillium.* It would be expected that fats from different species of fungi would have different characteristics; the report of Pearson and

Raper would also indicate that there is a possibility of varying the composition of the fat synthesized by a single species by the adjustment of certain environmental conditions.

Yeast and Yeastlike Organisms as a Source of Fat

The lipids of yeasts and yeastlike organisms have been extensively studied, the investigation of their production for food purposes receiving considerable impetus by the food shortages of both world wars. The study of yeast lipids goes back at least as far as 1879 to the work of Hoppe-Seyler. Since that date many papers have appeared on this subject. Most of the earlier work on yeast lipids was conducted with bakers' and brewers' yeasts (*Saccharomyces cerevisiae*); Welter (1915) reported that in that year Lindner produced a yeast containing 17 per cent fat, based on dry weight. When this yeast was cultured on cloth in a large pan at 20 C, as much as 50 per cent of the dry weight was lipid. The yeast could be removed from the cloth easily, then pressed and dried. The fat thus obtained seemed similar to olive oil and could be used to produce a good soap. During the years 1920 to 1928, Smedley-MacLean and her associates published a series of papers on the mechanism of fat formation in yeast and the influence of certain conditions on the amount and nature of the lipids produced. Several of the papers of this series are listed in the literature citations at the end of this chapter.

A number of other yeasts and yeastlike organisms besides *S. cerevisiae* seem far more promising, from the standpoint of their capacities to synthesize fats, than the common yeast of the baking and brewing industries. According to Reichel (1940), *Endomyces vernalis* was used for the large-scale production of fat for food use in Germany. The organism was cultured in shallow pans on a molasses medium and yielded a fat that was not very suitable for food purposes, since it soon became rancid. Its production ceased after the war. Nadson and Konokotina (1924) found that when cultured on beer wort medium, 25 per cent of the dry weight of *E. vernalis* was fat.

Dooren de Jong (1926) isolated a new yeast, *Torulopsis (Torula) lipofera,* which was used for studies of lipid synthesis by Kleinzeller (1944). This latter investigator reported that the lipid content of this nonsporulating yeast varied from 18 to 43 per cent of the dry weight. Nilsson and others (1943) cultivated several yeasts both on plates and in submerged cultures in their search for a suitable organism for the production of food fats. They used *Torulopsis pulcherrima* var. *variabilis, T. lipofera, E. vernalis, Rhodotorula glutinis,* and *S. cerevisiae* and on plate cultures all of these organisms contained over 15 per cent lipids, but only *R. glutinis* gave satisfactory yields in submerged culture. The lipid yield of this organism could be raised to 35 per cent of the dry weight by varying the substrate.

Enebo and others (1946) used *R. gracilis* in their studies on the production of food fats by yeasts and found that under optimum conditions of growth the composition of the cells of this organism was as follows: protein, 13 per cent; carbohydrate, 24 per cent; lipid, 60 per cent; minerals, 3 per cent.

Sufficient evidence has been presented in the above brief accounts to indicate that yeasts or yeastlike organisms seem to represent a potentially greater source of fat than the filamentous fungi that have been studied and reported on thus far. Not only are the percentages of fat higher in the yeasts than in the filamentous fungi, but the culturing of yeast on a large scale is usually conducted with considerably less difficulty than the large-scale culture of filamentous fungi. Yeast multiply rapidly when maintained under the proper conditions; moreover, the problems of obtaining sufficient inoculum for large-scale cultures are not encountered, since with these organisms vegetative cells rather than spores are used as inoculum.

Literature Cited

Barber, H. H. 1929. The production of fat from carbohydrate and similar media by a species of *Penicillium. Biochem. Jour. 23:*1158.

Browne, C. A. 1906. The fermentation of sugar cane products. *J. Am. Chem. Soc. 28:*453–469.

Dooren de Jong, Ir. L. E. 1926. A new fat-producing yeast. *Nederland. Tijdschr. Hyg. Microbiol. Serol. 1:*135–147. (*Chem. Abst. 21:*1135; 1927).

Enebo, L., Anderson, L. G., and Lundin, H. 1946. Microbiological fat synthesis by means of *Rhodotorula* yeast. *Arch. Biochem. 11:*383.

Hoppe-Seyler, F. 1879. Ueber Licithin in der Hefe. *Z. physiol. Chem. 3:*374.

Kleinzeller, A. 1944. Fat formation in *Torulopsis lipofera. Biochem. Jour. 38:*480–492.

Kroeker, E. H., Strong, F. M., and Peterson, W. H. 1935. The chemistry of mold tissue. VII. The lipids of *Penicillium aurantio-brunneum. J. Am. Chem. Soc. 57:*354–356.

Lockwood, L. B., Ward, G. E., May, O. E., Herrick, H. T., and O'Neill, H. T. 1934. The production of fat by *Penicillium javanicum* van Beijma. *Zentr. Bakt., Parasiten. u. Infectionskrank. Abt. II 90:*411–425

Marschall, Dr. 1897. Ueber die Zusammensetzung des Schimmelpilz-Mycels. *Arch. f. Hyg. 28:*16–29.

Nadson, G. H., and Konokotina, H. G. 1924. Fat yeast, *Endomyces vernalis* Ludw., as a source of fat for foods and technical purposes. *Wochs. Brau. 41:* 249–251. (*Chem. Abst. 19:*2219; 1925).

Nilsson, R., Enebo, L., Lundin, H., and Myrbäck, K. 1943. Microbial synthesis of fat with *Rhodotorula glutinis*. *Svensk. Kemi. Tid. 55:*41–51.

Pearson, L. K., and Raper, H. S. 1927. The influence of temperature on the nature of the fat formed by living organisms. *Biochem. Jour. 21:*875–879.

Peterson, W. H., Pruess, L. M., Gorcia, H. J., and Greene, H. C. 1933. Large-scale laboratory cultivation of molds. *Ind. Eng. Chem. 25:*213–215.

Pruess, L. M., Eichinger, E. C., and Peterson, W. H. 1934. The chemistry of mold tissue. III: Composition of certain molds with special reference to lipid content. *Zentr. Bakt., Parasiten. u. Infectionskrank. Abt. II 89:*37–377.

Prill, E. A., Wenck, P. R., and Peterson, W. H. 1935. The chemistry of mould tissue. VI: Factors influencing the amount and nature of the fat produced by *Aspergillus fischeri*. *Biochem. Jour. 29:*21–33.

Reichel, L. 1940. Biologische Fettsynthese. *Angew. Chem. 53:*577–579.

Smedley-MacLean, I., and Thomas, E. M. 1920. The nature of yeast fat. *Biochem. Jour. 14:*483–493.

Smedley-MacLean I. 1922. The conditions influencing the formation of fat by the yeast cell. *Biochem. Jour. 16:*370–379.

Smedley-MacLean, I., and Hoffert, D. 1923. Carbohydrate and fat metabolism in yeast. *Biochem. Jour. 17:*720.

———. 1924. Carbohydrate and fat metabolism of yeast. II: The influence of phosphates on the storage of fat and carbohydrate in the cell. *Biochem. Jour. 18:*1273–1278.

———. 1926. The carbohydrate and fat metabolism of yeast. *Biochem. Jour. 20:*343–357.

Smedley-MacLean I. 1928. The isolation of a second sterol from yeast fat. *Biochem. Jour. 22:*22–26.

Strong, F. M., and Peterson, W. H. 1934. The chemistry of mold tissue. IV: The lipids of *Aspergillus sydowi*. *J. Am. Chem. Soc. 56:*952–955.

Ward, G. E., and Jamieson, G. S. 1934. The chemical composition of the fat produced by *Penicillium javanicum* van Beijma. *J. Am. Chem. Soc. 56:*973–975.

Ward, G. E., Lockwood, L. B., May, O. E., and Herrick, H. T. 1935. Production of fat from glucose by molds. Cultivation of *Penicillium javanicum* van Beijma in large-scale laboratory apparatus. *Ind. Eng. Chem. 27:*318.

Welter, A. 1915. Yeast fat, a new source of fat. *Seifenfabrikant 35:*845–846.

18 · *Miscellaneous Fungus Activities*

PRODUCTION OF PLASTIC MATERIALS
USE OF FUNGI AS AGENTS OF BIOLIGICAL CONTROL
BOTRYTIZED GRAPES AND THE PRODUCTION OF SWEET TABLE WINES
SYNTHESIS OF GROWTH-PROMOTING SUBSTANCES
ROLE OF FUNGI IN SOIL STRUCTURE IMPROVEMENT
FUNGI AND THE WEATHERING OF ROCKS
FUNGI AND COAL FORMATION
MISCELLANEOUS METABOLIC PRODUCTS OF FUNGI
POTENTIALITIES OF FUNGI AS AGENTS OF BIOSYNTHESIS

SOME OF THE BENEFICIAL ACTIVITIES of fungi discussed in the preceding chapters are quite fortuitous, while others are controlled and directed by man. An example of the latter type is provided by the commercial production of antibiotics, which has become a large and growing industry in recent years. Other beneficial fungus activities that may be further exploited to man's advantage are described below.

Production of Plastic Materials

At the present time, the greatest potential contribution of mycology to the plastics industry lies in the production of itaconic acid by means of a fungus fermentation (Chapter 13). Esters of this acid may be polymerized to provide new resins that produce plastics of unique characteristics.

Prior to the development of a good fermentation process for the large-scale production of itaconic acid by *Aspergillus terreus,* it was suggested that some plastics could be made from slightly cruder fungus materials. Sanborn (1936) proposed the use of certain fungus agglom-

Fig. 89. (Top to bottom) *Crude gum, sheets of gum, objects made from hardened gum, and pressed cake of* Oidium *gum.* (*From Sanborn, 1936.*)

erates as gums in the manufacture of stoppers, buttons, and similar useful objects (Fig. 89). This investigator found that a species of fungus resembling *Oidium lactis* (often referred to as the "milk fungus"—see Chapter 24) produces high yields of gums from glucose, glycerol, and mannose, which could be variously moulded and hardened. Much earlier Herzog (*cf.* Sanborn) had been granted a patent for a process involving a similar use for fungus gums.

Although little consideration seems to be given to the use of such crude gums today, there may exist some fungus species that form gums suitable for use in making plastic objects having certain desirable properties.

Use of Fungi as Agents of Biological Control

Species of living organisms have long been known to prey upon or parasitize other living species. The biological balance thus established between these species is maintained until it is disturbed by outside agents. Man himself is probably one of the greatest disturbers of biological balances. Though in many instances such disturbances are necessary or intentional, the result is that man often creates additional environmental problems for himself.

For example, the clearing of wooded land may result in a gross reduction in the bird population of the area; thereupon the insect population, no longer kept within ecological bounds, may increase and inflict serious damage to food crops. Sometimes it becomes necessary to re-establish the original bird population by reforestation in order to maintain some measure of control over the insects.

The use of one species of living organism to eliminate or hold in check another species is known as biological control. Farmers sometimes introduce blacksnakes in grain fields to destroy small rodents that cause crop damage; if in time the blacksnakes threaten to grow too numerous, a knowing farmer merely turns his hogs into the field after harvest to reduce the snake population. Western man's eating habits, especially with reference to his preferred protein foods, is in a sense a form of large-scale biological control. In India, where it is sacred and hence not eaten, the cow has become a destructive pest.

Biological control was practiced during World War I when army surgeons, unaided by modern penicillin and similar antibiotics, had recourse to "maggot therapy" for the treatment and prevention of wound infections. Control of infectious microorganisms was frequently effected simply by placing fly larvae on open wounds. The larvae disinfected the wound by consuming dead tissue together with the microorganisms growing in the tissue.

The use of fungi in the control of insect pests offers intriguing possibilities, since many fungi are known to parasitize insects (Fig. 90, 91). Entomogenous fungi (fungi that parasitize insects) are widely distributed, but Shanor (1949) states that a larger number of species are

FIG. 90. *Some entomogenous fungi. Left,* Aschersonia aleyrodis *on scale insects. Right (above),* Isaria farinosa *on moth pupa. Right (below),* Empusa sepulchralis *on crane flies. (From Shanor, 1949.)*

Fig. 91. *Entomogenous fungi and their hosts. Above,* Cordyceps melolonthae *on may beetle larva. Below,* Cordyceps militaris *on buried moth pupa. (From Shanor, 1949.)*

found in tropical regions than in temperate regions. This difference in distribution may well be due to the fact that the generally higher temperatures and humidities prevailing in the tropics greatly influence the growth of fungi.

Like other parasites, entomogenous fungi may be either quite limited in their host range or may parasitize a great many different species of insects. Some quickly kill the insect host, others appear to inflict little if any injury.

In order to use fungi for the effective control of insects, man-made epidemics must be generated, the success of this operation depending to a large extent upon prevailing climatic conditions. There is considerable doubt that fungi may be successfully used to control large numbers of insects except in regions where climatic conditions greatly favor the establishment of the parasitic relationship and permit the rapid development of epidemics among insect populations. According to Shanor such conditions exist in certain parts of the Gulf States and in Florida, where fungi have been used successfully to reduce infestations of San Jose Scale and Citrus White Fly. He also states that among the most effective

FIG. 92.   *Fruiting bodies of* Podonectria coccicola *which have developed on scale insects.* (*From Shanor, 1949.*)

fungi used in Florida for the control of scale insects are *Sphaerostilbe auranticola* and *Podonectria coccicola* (Fig. 92), and that infestations by these two species have been initiated by tying twigs infected with scale insects to branches of trees. This same author states that *Beauveria globuliferum* was used unsuccessfully in the control of chinch bug in Illinois, but that *Metarrhizium anisopliae* has been used in controlling the beet weevil in Europe and the frog hopper of sugar beet in Trinidad. The use of *M. anisopliae* has been suggested for restricting the spread of Japanese beetles.

Botrytized Grapes and the Production of Sweet Table Wines

Although the imperfect fungus *Botrytis cinerea* is often found on grapes in many climates, the greatest amount of infection of mature or nearly mature grapes by this organism occurs in regions where the relative humidity is high. It is seldom encountered in hot dry regions. Infection of grapes by *Botrytis* under the proper set of conditions may, paradoxically, be a helpful fungus activity; fine sweet table wines like Sauternes are made from grapes infected with *B. cinerea,* or "botrytized" grapes. The effects on the fruit after infection by *B. cinerea* are not always the same. Laborde (1908) noted that cold, wet weather following infection caused an excessive growth of the fungus unaccompanied by drying of the fruit. On the other hand, if infection is followed by warm sunny weather, the berries lose moisture, shrivel (Fig. 93), and the percentage of sugar increases.

Müller-Thurgau (1888) reported that the must (unfermented juice) from 100 botrytized White Riesling grapes contained 30.26 per cent sugar, compared with 18.24 per cent sugar in must from uninfected grapes. The molded grapes yielded only 52 ml of must, while the uninfected grapes yielded 100 ml. Thus the effect of the fungus is to reduce only slightly the total sugar content while greatly increasing the percentage of sugar per unit volume of must. The total acidity of the must from infected berries was 0.79, compared with 0.89 per cent in the must from sound berries; hence the fungus reduced the total amount of acid to a quantity somewhat less than one half that of the original. In addition, *Botrytis* imparts a particularly desirable odor to the wine.

The use of botrytized grapes for the production of fine wines has been practiced in various European countries for many years. For example, Laborde (*loc. cit.*) reported that this practice occurred in the Sauternes

FIG. 93. *"Botrytized" grapes. Both of the above clusters were infected with* Botrytis cinerea; *however, the cluster at the left was incubated under conditions of 81–86 per cent relative humidity, while the cluster at the right was incubated under conditions of 40–52 per cent relative humidity. Note the greater amount of visible fungus growth on the left cluster and the greater amount of shriveling of grapes in the right cluster. The grapes on the right are properly botrytized and could be used in the production of fine table wines of the Sauternes type. (From Nelson and Amerine, 1957b.)*

region of Bordeaux, France as early as 1845. This method of wine production has been practiced also in Germany and Hungary (Muller,
1930), Russia (Khovrenko, 1910), Italy (Garino-Canina and others,
1951), and Portugal (Everett, 1954). Preobrazhanskii (1947) conducted some experimentation in inducing infection by inoculating clusters with spore suspensions or placing infected berries in uninfected
clusters.

Nelson and Amerine (1957a) state that the California viticulture industry has been unable to produce a Sauternes-type wine because climatic conditions prevailing in California prevent *B. cinerea* from developing as it does in certain European areas. These investigators conducted a series of experiments designed to determine if grapes could
be artificially infected and conditions then so controlled that desirable
musts might be obtained. Their studies involved the inoculation of
grapes (both on and off the vine) with conidia of *Botrytis*, but in most
of their experiments the grapes were inoculated after they had been
harvested. After inoculation, the grapes were first placed under humid
conditions to permit infection and then under dry conditions to facilitate
water loss. Various combinations of temperatures and relative humidities as well as length of the infection and drying periods were tried and
evaluated. Their attempts to produce musts of high sugar content from
grapes inoculated on the vine were unsuccessful. High daytime temperatures made it difficult to maintain the high moisture conditions
necessary for infection for periods of time sufficiently long. They did,
however, find that musts of the desired type could be obtained by harvesting only mature fruit, inoculating it, and then maintaining it under
controlled conditions during the incubation period. On the basis of
their experimental results Nelson and Amerine concluded that in California the production of wine from botrytized grapes required carefully
controlled conditions, but eventually might result in a new and desirable wine type.

Synthesis of Growth-Promoting Substances by Fungi

"Bakanae-byo," a common plant disease of the Orient, was
first reported in Japan by Hori in 1898 (Stodala and others, 1955).
This disease is incited by an imperfect fungus, *Fusarium moniliforme,*

the perfect stage of which is an Ascomycete, *Gibberella fujikuroi.* Since first reported occurring in rice nurseries in Japan, the disease has subsequently been observed in China, India, the Philippines, Ceylon, and British Guiana (Peiris, 1951). A characteristic feature of Bakanae-byo on rice is that infected seedlings grow to abnormal length. Kurosawa (*cf.* Stodala and others, 1955) demonstrated in 1926 that filtrates from cultures of the Bakanae fungus accelerated growth in length of rice seedlings in much the same manner as the fungus itself.

Yabuta and Hayashi (1939) who isolated a colorless, amorphous powder from sterilized culture filtrates of the Bakanae fungus found this powder to be effective on rice seedlings in very minute amounts (0.00002 per cent solution). Later, Yabuta and Sumiki resolved the amorphous powder into two crystalline substances named Gibberellin A and Gibberellin B—the former active in promoting growth, the latter less potent.

Stodala and others (*loc. cit.*) have produced growth-promoting substances on a pilot-plant scale by gradually building up the quantity of inoculum of a selected strain of *Fusarium moniliforme* and using it to inoculate 154 gal of medium in a 300-gal stainless steel fermenter equipped with both air sparger and agitator. After a sixty-five-hour incubation period during which the medium was aerated and agitated, recovery operations began, and about 12 g of crude crystalline gibberellin was obtained. This was a mixture of Gibberellin A and a compound which they called Gibberellin X ($C_{19}H_{22}O_6$).

Curtis and Cross (1954) attempted to isolate Gibberellin A from culture filtrates but instead isolated another compound with similar biological properties which they named Gibberellic Acid. Just as the discovery of penicillin led to an extensive search for other antibiotics among the fungi, so has the discovery of gibberellin led to the search for other fungi which synthesize growth-promoting substances. An example of this is provided by the work of Curtis (1957), who surveyed about 1000 fungi and 500 actinomycetes for their capacities to form growth-promoting substances, but was unable to demonstrate the existence of such substances using corn seedlings as the test organism.

Research on the mode of action of gibberellin as well as on its practical applications has currently become fashionable in certain plant-science areas; as a result it is now being produced by several different manufacturers: Imperial Chemical Industries, Eli Lilly, Merck, Pfizer, S. B. Penick, Abbott, and American Cyanamid (Beesch and Shull, 1957). During the early stages of its production gibberellin was quite expensive but it has recently been priced in large quantities at $10 per gram.

A substance with growth-promoting activities somewhat similar to those of gibberellin may have been involved in the studies conducted by Jump (1938). This investigator noted the prevalence of abnormal bifurcation of red pine trees in sections of the northeastern United States and found that this condition was caused by extraseasonal lateral shoot elongation (Fig. 94). This condition resulted in a greater susceptibility to the ravages of wood-decaying fungi, because in this type of forking the inner surfaces of the fork do not unite completely during subsequent diametric growth of the branches, and open fissures are formed through which wood-decaying fungi may gain entry (Fig. 95). Jump made isolations from buds of abnormally elongated lateral branches and recovered *Dematium pullulans* in the majority of cases. Subsequent experiments revealed that this fungus synthesizes a growth-promoting

Fig. 94.   (*left*) *Seven-year-old red pine tree with abnormal bifurcation caused by extraseasonal growth in a lateral branch. (From Jump, 1938.)*
Fig. 95.   (*right*) *Longitudinal section through abnormally forked red pine tree. Note the incomplete union of inner surfaces of branches and the fissure through which decay fungi have gained entry. (From Jump, 1938.)*

substance capable of causing elongation of etiolated lupine hypocotyl; Jump advanced the theory that extraseasonal growth of a pine bud may be initiated through the action of a phytohormone formed by the fungus living within the tissues.

Role of Fungi in Soil Structure Improvement

Soil scientists, agronomists and agriculturists have known for many years that the plowing under of green manures decidedly improves soil structure—a rather common practice when the structure of a soil is not especially good. It has been definitely established, however, that green manures *per se* do not improve soil structure. The importance of green manure is indirect in that it provides a source of raw materials from which soil-dwelling organisms may synthesize the complex materials that lead to an improved soil structure.

Soil contains inorganic particles of clay, silt, and sand, which by themselves form a soil with very poor structure. Improvement in structure is attained when the particles of inorganic material are "cemented" together into groups called soil aggregates. The "cementing" material consists of long-chain polysaccharide polymers containing uronic acid (sugar acids with an aldehyde group) units. Apparently such microorganisms as filamentous fungi, bacteria, actinomycetes, and yeast are capable of synthesizing these "cementing" materials; it is generally believed, however, that filamentous fungi are most important in this capacity. Gum-producing fungi are, of course, also important in the synthesis of soil-cementing materials. Among others, species of *Absidia, Mucor, Rhizopus, Chaetomium, Fusarium,* and *Aspergillus* are known to produce materials that assist in the formation of soil aggregates.

Since fungus-synthesized polysaccharides are not permanent soil components because of their susceptibility to digestion by a variety of soil microorganisms, the soil-cementing materials must be continuously replaced by soil fungi if good soil structure is to be maintained. In comparatively recent years attempts have been made to improve soil structure by the addition of synthetic polyelectrolytes (for example, Krillium) which are not destroyed by microorganisms. Such synthetic materials serve quite well in the formation of soil aggregates, but at present their high price prevents their economical use on a large scale.

Fungi and the Weathering of Rocks

The type of soil that develops on rock surfaces is the result of many physical, chemical and biological factors. Not the least important in the initial processes of soil formation is the action of lichens (Fig. 96), which are dual plants consisting of both a fungus and an alga.

FIG. 96. *Foliose lichen growing on a bare rock surface. (Courtesy of Robert Giesy.)*

These organisms, which have the capacity to grow under very dry conditions, are often the first occupants of a bare rock surface. Their growth leads to a weakening of the rocks, since lichens use some of the more soluble rock constituents and cause the rocks to retain a greater amount of moisture. Moisture retention makes for a more rapid breaking up of the rocks through the mechanism of freezing and thawing. Moreover, temperature changes cause expansion and contraction which results in the formation of still smaller rock fragments. When these fragments become mixed with the decaying remains of the licehen thalli, a thin layer of soil is formed, thus changing the environment sufficiently so that eventually other larger plants may become established.

This process of soil formation is obviously very slow, many years elapsing before vegetation other than lichens may grow on what was formerly bare rock. The succession of other plants contributes to further soil formation, since each in turn adds to the organic content of the soil and aids in further disintegration of the underlying rock. The later arrivals probably disintegrate more rock and add greater amounts of organic material to the developing soil, but in many instances the process is first initiated by lichens.

Fungi and Coal Formation

Any attempt to evaluate the possible role of fungi in coal formation must of necessity be highly speculative, yet there is little doubt that fungi, along with other microorganisms, were contributory to this important process. Waksman (1938) refers to coal as fossil humus and adds, *"Coal represents a number of humus types in an advanced state of decomposition, produced from various plant residues at different periods during prehistoric times, and later compressed by superimposed layers of mineral matter."*

Various theories have been advanced to explain coal formation. However, since chemical analyses of coal indicate its relationship with humus, it must be recognized that, regardless of what theory is judged most acceptable, the organisms of decay played a significant part in at least the early stages of coal formation because of their known roles in humus formation.

Miscellaneous Metabolic Products of Fungi

In addition to the commercial metabolic products of fungi already described in earlier chapters, a great many other chemical compounds have been isolated. Some of these are known to be synthesized only by fungi (in some instances by only one species of fungus), while others are synthesized by a variety of different living organisms. Without attempting to enumerate all of these compounds, certain categories with representative examples from each will be briefly mentioned here.

ALCOHOLS.   The commercial production of ethyl alcohol, using *Saccharomyces cerevisiae* as the agent of biosynthesis, is discussed in some detail in Chapter 9. Although the synthesis of ethyl alcohol is popularly believed to be a biochemical characteristic of yeast, many living organisms are capable of synthesizing this compound, and it may possibly play an important role in the functioning of many living cells. Many filamentous fungi (Perlman, 1950) also synthesize this alcohol, although none are as yet known that do so with the speed and efficiency of yeast. Other alcohols than ethyl are known to be synthesized by fungi. For example, Birkinshaw and others (1943) have reported finding gentisyl alcohol (2:5-dihydroxybenzyl alcohol) among the metabolic products of *Penicillium patulum;* and Birkinshaw *et al.* had previously described (1931) the synthesis of mannitol, the sugar alcohol, by several species of *Aspergillus.* In some instances yields of mannitol up to about 50 per cent were obtained.

ALDEHYDES.   The synthesis of acetaldehyde, a common intermediate metabolic product of many fungi, would naturally be expected to occur as a result of the activity of any fungus with a well-developed glycolysis mechanism. Another aldehyde—anisaldehyde—has also been reported as being synthesized by a fungus, since Birkinshaw and others (1944) detected this aldehyde among the products of metabolism of the Basidiomycete, *Trametes suaveolens.*

ESTERS.   The synthesis of esters by fungi has not been extensively investigated. Birkinshaw and others (1931) found that ethyl acetate was synthesized by *Penicillium digitatum,* the organism chiefly responsible for the decay of citrus fruits, Gray (1949) discovered it among the volatile neutral metabolic products of the yeast, *Hansenula anomala,* while Gordon (1950) reported that it was synthesized by *Endoconidiophora moniliformis.*

NITROGENOUS SUBSTANCES.   The capacities of many fungi to synthesize amino acids and proteins are obvious from their ability to thrive on a medium containing only mineral salts, a carbohydrate, and an inorganic nitrogen compound. Other nitrogenous compounds such as alkaloids, urea and choline are also known to be synthesized by fungi, although the synthesis of such substances by fungi has not been sufficiently investigated.

CHLORINE COMPOUNDS.   For the most part the biologist regards the metabolic products of living organisms as being composed of the essential chemical elements, yet organisms are known to be capable of incorporating certain nonessential elements into organic compounds which they synthesize. There is no evidence that chlorine is an essential element for fungi, but Raistrick and Smith (1936) reported the isolation of two chlorine-containing organic compounds which are synthesized by *Aspergillus terreus.* The molecular constitutions of these two compounds (geodin and erdin) were later established by Calam and others (1939), with empirical formulae as follows: $C_{15}H_6O_5Cl_2(OCH_3)_2$ (geodin), and $C_{15}H_7O_6Cl_2OCH_3$ (erdin). Another synthesis of organic compounds in which a nonessential element is incorporated into the molecule is that of arsenical organic compounds described in Chapter 19 on the use of fungi in biological assays.

SULPHUR COMPOUNDS.   There is at least one report of the synthesis by fungi of a sulphur-containing organic compound other than amino acids. Woolley and Peterson (1937), working on the chemistry of mold tissue, have reported that cyclic choline sulphate is formed by *Aspergillus sydowi.*

FUNGUS PIGMENTS.   In some species of fungi both the spores and mycelium are white, whereas in others one or both may be variously colored. It has frequently been suggested that perhaps certain fungi might be employed for the production of pigments for use as dyestuffs. According to Henrici (1947), *Monascus purpureus,* which forms a red pigment, has long been used by the Chinese for coloring rice and other materials. The use of *Chlorosplenium aeruginosum* for artificially coloring lumber is discussed in Chapter 21. A great variety of fungus pigments have been isolated, and studied, and have had their molecular structures established. Condensed ring structures with the anthracene or phenanthrene nucleus are common among fungus pigments. Aside from their possible commercial value, the study of such compounds may lead to information concerning their mode of synthesis

Table 34.—Some pigments synthesized by fungi

Pigment	Color	Synthesized by	Reference
Atromentin	Brown	*Paxillus atromentosus*	Kögl and Becker (1928)
Boletol	Blue	*Boletus luridus* *Boletus satanus*	Kögl and Deigs (1934)
Catenarin	Red	*Helminthosporium spp.*	Raistrick, Robinson and Todd (1934)
Citrinin	Yellow	*Penicillium citrinum*	Hetherington and Raistrick (1931)
Emodic acid	Orange	*Penicillium cyclopium*	Anslow, Breen and Raistrick (1940)
Fumigatin	Maroon	*Aspergillus fumigatus*	Anslow and Raistrick (1938)
Phoenicin	Yellow, red, or violet	*Penicillium phoeniceum*	Posternak (1938)
Spinulosin	Blue-purple	*Penicillium spinulosum*	Anslow and Raistrick (1938)
Telephoric acid	Indigo-blue	*Thelephora sp.*	Kögl, Erxleben and Janecke (1930)

by living cells. A few examples of fungus pigments are listed in Table 34; their chemical structures are illustrated in Fig. 97.

ACIDS. Among the various groups of living organisms the fungi seem to be acid formers *par excellence,* over forty different organic acids having been recovered from among the metabolic products of fungi. It is not surprising that acids are commonly syntheiszed by fungi, since these organisms are highly aerobic, and such oxidized compounds as organic acids would be expected to be synthesized in some quantity. Yet different strains of the same fungus species may exhibit unexpected variety with respect to acid synthesis. For example, one strain of *Aspergillus niger* may form citric acid in almost theoretical quantities, another may form gluconic acid exclusively, while still another may form gallic acid.

Another surprising feature of acid-forming fungi is the great variety of acids that may be synthesized. Acids known to be formed by fungi range from formic acid—the simplest of all organic acids—to compli-

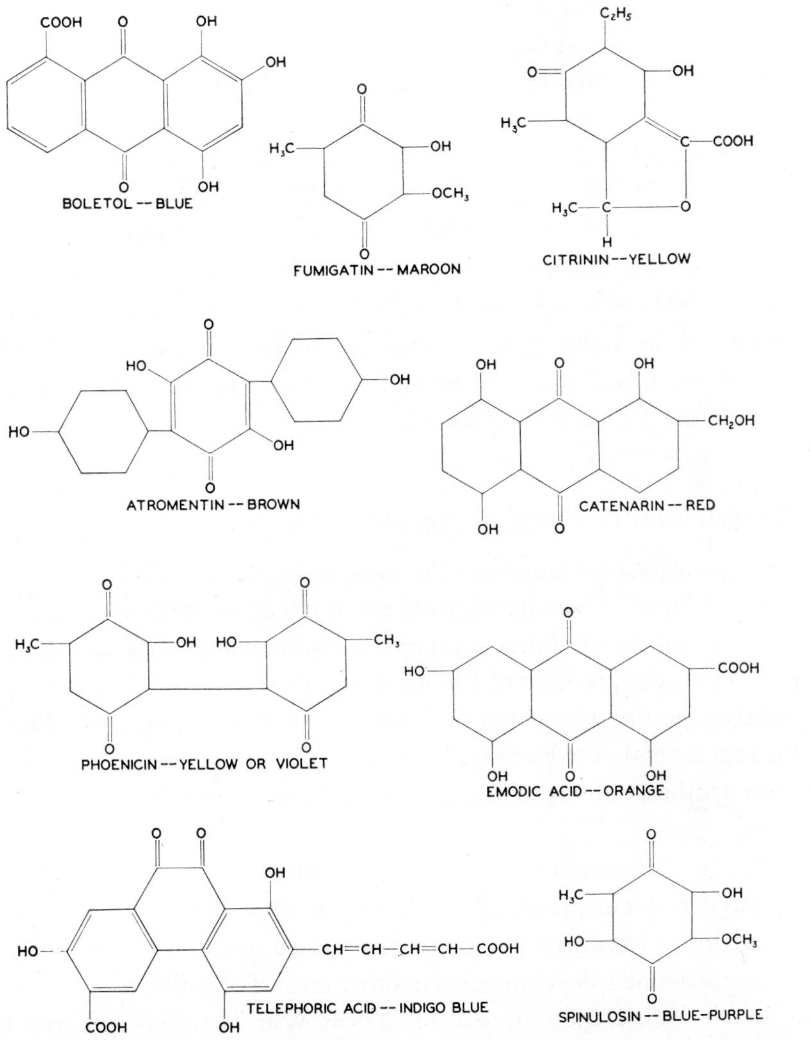

FIG. 97. *Molecular structures of some pigments synthesized by fungi.*

cated condensed-ring structures such as mycophenolic acid ($C_{17}H_{20}O_6$) (Clutterbuck and Raistrick, 1933). Thus far acids with 1, 2, 3, 4, 5, 6, 7, 8, 9, 10, 11, 14, 15, 16, 17, and 18 carbon atoms in the molecule have been reported as being synthesized by a variety of fungi. A single species of fungus may synthesize several different acids simultaneously (Bushnell 1955), but often it is possible to so adjust environmental conditions that a single principal acid is formed.

Most of the acids identified from fungus metabolic products, as well as many of the other compounds briefly mentioned here, are of academic interest only, but, as our chemical knowledge develops further and our chemical needs change a demand for some of these products may be created. Both Porter (1946) and Henrici (1947) have compiled extensive tables listing these compounds which should be consulted. Among the leaders in the field of fungus biochemistry are Raistrick and his colleagues at the London School of Hygiene and Tropical Medicine. For the serious student of fungus biochemistry, familiarity with the extensive works of this group is an absolute necessity. Their first eighteen papers are in Volume 220 (Series B) of the Philosophical Transactions of the Royal Society of London, and many of their later papers appear in the Biochemical Journal.

Potentialities of Fungi as Agents of Biosynthesis

When the number of commercial processes relying on the activity of fungi is compared with the number of species of fungi, or with the number of different organic chemical compounds known to occur among the products of fungus metabolism, it becomes quite apparent that the fungi have not been fully exploited commercially. During the past several decades fungi have been increasingly used for the large-scale synthesis of chemicals without exhausting the field of applications.

The development of the penicillin industry and other less spectacular fungus-dependent processes (citric acid, itaconic acid, glycerol) can be traced to an impetus created by emergencies or by heavy demands resulting from new developments in other areas. Penicillin was known for a decade before the outbreak of World War II, when suddenly this "miracle drug" became urgently needed for the treatment of war wounds. The fermentation process for citric acid production was developed only when heavy import duties were levied on citric acid and crude calcium citrate of citrus fruit origin. The rapid development of the plastics industry made itaconic acid of sufficient potential value to warrant the development of a process for synthesizing it biologically by means of *Aspergillus terreus*. The high price and scarcity of riboflavin led to the development of a less expensive method for its production— the fermentation process, involving the use of a fungus pathogenic to cotton. Similar cases can be made for the development of the other fermentation processes involving the use of fungi with the exception of the alcoholic fermentation, the initial development of which is lost in antiquity.

All too often the rapid developments of processes stimulated by emergency needs are possible only through tremendous expenditures of time, energy, and material resources. It would seem provident, therefore, to use some foresight in such matters and to provide for the meeting of emergencies before they actually arise. With ever-increasing industrialization the demands for organic chemicals are becoming heavier and more varied. For that reason it might be well to scrutinize the fungi much more closely as potential agents of large-scale biosynthesis.

The extended researches of Raistrick and his colleagues in England, as well as those of investigators in other countries, have clearly pointed the way to the great host of different chemical compounds which fungi are able to synthesize. Without implying any criticism of these excellent investigations, it is probable that the subject has just barely been touched upon, since systematic researches of this type have been conducted with a relatively small percentage of the total number of fungus species.

As the English group examined and identified the metabolic products of fungus after fungus, an increasingly greater number of complex chemical compounds came to light. On the basis of the work by Raistrick and his colleagues it seems safe to predict that as the fungi are still further systematically investigated, more and more different compounds will be discovered. Many of these may be of academic interest only, while others may be of immediate value to industry or medicine. One may cite an example from the field of bacteriology. The fact that certain bacteria could synthesize acetone was known many years before the outbreak of World War I, but the fermentation was not exploited simply because there was little demand for acetone. With the introduction of large-scale aerial warfare a heavy demand for this compound was created, because it was an important ingredient of the "dope" used in the construction of airplane wings. The allies went immediately to a large-scale fermentation process, marking the beginning of the commercial acetone-butyl alcohol process.

According to Foster (1949) there is no evidence that fungi form dissimilation products of any sort in a natural habitat such as the soil. His conclusion is that the fungi dwelling in soil oxidize their carbon-containing substrates completely to carbon dioxide and water, except for the portion converted to assimilation products (materials of cell constituents). Thus the question arises why fungi, when cultivated in the laboratory or industrial plant, synthesize large amounts of metabolic products other than those of cell material. Foster's explanation is that the metabolism of the fungus becomes deranged as a result of the influence of "abnormal" environmental—an explanation that is undoubtedly correct, since no phase of the physiological activities of fungi is more susceptible to alterations resulting from slight changes in environmental conditions than is carbon metabolism.

A change in environmental conditions commonly results in what is termed a metabolic shunt, several of which have already been described in preceding chapters. A striking example of shunt metabolism is provided by the glycerol fermentation involving yeast. Under natural conditions, or under the conditions usually maintained in the laboratory or plant for the cultivation of this organism, it is unlikely that sulphite or bisulphite is a constituent of its chemical environment, so that the acetaldehyde which it forms is reduced to ethyl alcohol. If the environment is altered by the addition of sulphite or bisulphite, however, acetaldehyde (which usually acts as a hydrogen acceptor from reduced DPN and hence is reduced to ethyl alcohol) is no longer available. As a result a three-carbon fragment formed earlier in the process of hexose breakdown functions as the hydrogen acceptor, and from this fragment glycerol is formed. Genetically the yeast was capable of forming glycerol, since the pathway leading to this compound was already in existence; all that the sulphite did was to alter the environmental conditions so that the major part of the hexose utilized was metabolized through one pathway rather than another.

Metabolic shunts are by no means characteristic only of the fungi. The farmer who adds too much high-nitrate fertilizer to his potato patch unwittingly changes the environment in such fashion that metabolism is shunted into a pathway other than the desired one. Under "luxury" conditions of available nitrogen, the potato plant uses much of its sugar in the synthesis of amino acids and proteins rather than starch, resulting in luxuriant top growth with little tuber production.

There are a number of common examples where fungus carbon metabolism is shunted into another pathway by changes in the chemical environment. In the course of the usual alcoholic fermentation, yeast does not synthesize acetylphenylcarbinol; however, if the chemical environment is altered by the addition of benzaldehyde, part of the acetaldehyde which would normally be reduced to ethyl alcohol reacts with the benzaldehyde with the resultant formation of acetylphenylcarbinol —a compound that may be used for the synthesis of *l*-ephedrine. The chemical precursors of the important hormone cortisone are formed in similar fashion: steroids are introduced into the chemical environment of a variety of different fungi with the result that the steroid may be altered in a number of ways and at a variety of positions in the molecule.

Changes in the physical environment may also result in a metabolic shunt. For example, slight changes in temperature may bring about marked changes in the ratio of one fungus metabolic product to another. On the basis of the various published reports it is obvious that a slight alteration of almost any one environmental factor may result in a considerably altered type of metabolism. When one contemplates all of the possible environmental changes, the large numbers of fungus species described, the number and variety of fungus metabolic products that have been isolated, and the variety of metabolic pathways described for living organisms, the potentialities of fungi as agents of biosynthesis appear overwhelmingly large.

Much of the systematic work on fungus metabolism has been concerned with fungi of the mold type (order Moniliales of the Fungi Imperfecti) and especially members of the genera *Aspergillus* and *Penicillium*. It is understandable that these two genera would have received intensive study, since they are easily cultivated and widely distributed; moreover, it was with them that the possibility of using fungi as agents of biosynthesis was first clearly demonstrated. It is now time to apply the thorough methods of Raistrick and others to still other groups of fungi. As far as antibiotics are concerned, Robbins and his colleagues have screened the various species of Basidiomycetes, and Gray and Bushnell (1955) have examined certain species of Ascomycetes and Basidiomycetes and pointed out that under the laboratory conditions they maintained, most of the species studied did not convert substrate carbon completely to assimilation products and carbon dioxide, but to soluble metabolic products which as yet have not been identified. Some species converted as much as 90 per cent of the carbon of the sugar utilized to products other than carbon dioxide and assimilation products. Further studies of this type may reveal the existence of species of fungi which convert most of the carbon of the substrate to valuable metabolic products.

Literature Cited

Anslow, W. K., Breen, J., and Raistrick, H. 1940. 26. Studies in the biochemistry of microorganisms. 64: Emodic acid (4:5:7-trihydroxyanthraquinone-2-carboxylic acid) and ω-hydroxyemodin (4:5:7-trihydroxy-2- (hydroxymethyl)-anthraquinone), metabolic products of a strain of *Penicillium cyclopium* Westling. *Biochem. Jour.* 34:159–168.

Anslow, W. K., and Raistrick, H. 1938. XCI. Studies in the biochemistry of microorganisms. LVII: Fumigatin (3-hydroxy-4-methoxy-2:5-toluquinone) and spinulosin (3:6-dihydroxy-4-methoxy-2:5-toluquinone), metabolic products respectively of *Aspergillus fumigatus* Fresenius and *Penicillium spinulosum* Thom. *Biochem. Jour.* 32:687–696, 803–806.

Beesch, S. C., and Shull, G. M. 1957. Fermentation. *Ind. Eng. Chem.* 49:1491–1505.

Birkinshaw, J. H., Bracken, A., and Findlay, W. P. K. 1944. Biochemistry of the wood-rotting fungi. 4: Metabolic products of *Trametes suaveolens* (Linn.) Fr. *Biochem. Jour.* 38:131–132.

Birkinshaw, J. H., Bracken, A., and Raistrick, H. 1943. Studies in the biochemistry of micro-organisms. 72: Gentisyl alcohol (2:5-dihydroxybenzyl alcohol), a metabolic product of *Penicillium patulum* Bainier. *Biochem. Jour.* 37:726–728.

Birkinshaw, J. H., Charles, J. H. V., Hetherington, A. C., and Raistrick, H. 1931. Studies in the biochemistry of micro-organisms. Part IX: On the production of mannitol from glucose by species of *Aspergillus*. *Phil. Trans. Roy. Soc. London, Ser. B,* 220:153–171.

Birkinshaw, J. H., Charles, J. H. V., and Raistrick, H. 1931. Studies in the biochemistry of micro-organisms. Part XVIII: Biochemical characteristics of species of *Penicillium* responsible for the rot of citrus fruits. *Phil. Trans. Roy. Soc. London, Ser. B,* 220:355–362.

Bushnell, W. R. 1955. Investigation of acid synthesis by *Polyporus sulphureus* (Bull.) Fr. *MSc Thesis, The Ohio State University* (unpublished).

Calam, C. T., Clutterbuck, P. W., Oxford, A. E., and Raistrick, H. 1939. LXXI: Studies in the biochemistry of micro-organisms. LXI: The molecular constitution of geodin and erdin, two chlorine-containing metabolic products of *Aspergillus terreus* Thom. Part II: Dihydrogeodin and dihydroerdin and the synthesis of their trimethyl esters. *Biochem. Jour.* 33:579–588.

Clutterbuck, P. W. and Raistrick, H. 1933. LXXXVI: Studies in the biochemistry of micro-organisms. XXXI: The molecular constitution of the metabolic products of *Penicillium brevi-compatum* Dierkx and related species. II: Mycophenolic acid. *Biochem. Jour.* 27:654–667.

Curtis, R. W. 1957. Survey of fungi and actinomycetes for compounds possessing gibberellinlike activity. *Science 125:*646.

Curtis, P. J., and Cross, B. E. 1954. Gibberellic acid. A new metabolite from the culture filtrates of *Gibberella fujikuroi*. *Chem. & Ind, 1954:*1068.

Everett, W. 1954. *The wines of Portugal. In:* House and Garden Wine Book, House and Garden, London.

Foster, J. W. 1949. *Chemical activities of fungi*. Academic Press, Inc., New York.

Garino-Canina, E., Capris, N., and Passera, U. 1951. Passito di Caluso. *Ann. Sperim. Agr. n.s. 5:*1349–1374.

Gordon, M. A. 1950. The physiology of a blue stain mold with special reference to production of ethyl acetate. *Mycologia 42:*167–185.

Gray, W. D. 1949. Initial studies on the metabolism of *Hansenula anomala* (Hansen) Sydow. *Amer. Jour. Bot. 36:*475–480.

―――― and Bushnell, W. R. 1955. Biosynthetic potentialities of higher fungi. *Mycologia 47:*646–663.

Henrici, A. T. 1947. *Molds, yeasts, and actinomycetes*. Wiley, New York. (2nd. ed. by Skinner, Emmons, and Tsuchiya).

Herzog, R. O. 1915. U.S. Patent 1,141,545.

Hetherington, A. C., and Raistrick, H. 1931. Studies in the biochemistry of micro-organisms. Part XIV: On the production and chemical constitution of a new yellow colouring material, citrinin, produced from glucose by *Penicillium citrinum* Thom. *Phil. Trans. Roy. Soc. London, Ser. B, 220:*269–295.

Jump, J. A. 1938. A study of forking in red pine. *Phytopath. 28:*3–16.

Khovrenko, M. A. 1910. Obshchee vinodelie. (*cf.* Preobrazhenskii, 1947).

Kögl, F. and Deijs, W. B. 1934. Untersuchungen über Pilzfarbstoffe. XI: Über Boletol, den Farbstoffe der blau anlaufenden Boleten. *Liebig's Ann. 515:* 10–33.

―――― and Becker, H. 1928. Untersuchungen über Pilzfarbstoffe. VI. Die Konstitution des Atromentins. *Liebig's Ann. 465:*211–242.

――――, Erxleben, H. und Jänecke, L. 1930. Untersuchungen über Pilzfarbstoffe. IX. Die Konstitution der Thelephorsäure. *Liebig's Ann. 482:*105–119.

Laborde, J. 1908. *Cours d'oenologie. VII.* Mulo, Paris.

Muller, K. 1930. *Weinbau Lexikon*. Parey, Berlin.

Müller-Thurgau, H. 1888. Die Edelfäule der Trauben. *Landw. Jahrb. 17:* 83–160.

Nelson, K. E., and Amerine, M. A. 1957a. The use of *Botrytis cinerea* Pers. in the production of sweet table wines. *Hilgardia 26:*521–563.

――――. 1957b. Further studies on the production of natural, sweet table wines from botrytized grapes. *Am. J. Enology 8:*127–134.

Peiris, J. W. L. 1951. Bakanae disease and foot rot of paddy. *Trop. Agric. (Ceylon) 107*(3):172–175.

Perlman, D. 1950. Observations on the production of ethanol by fungi and yeasts. *Amer. Jour. Bot. 37:*237–241.

Porter, J. R. 1946. *Bacterial chemistry and physiology.* Wiley, New York.

Posternak, T. 1938. Recherches su la biochimie des champignons inférieurs. II: Sur la constitution et la synthese de la phoenicine et sur quelques nouveaux dérivés de la 4,4'-ditoluquinone. *Helv. Chim. Acta. 21:*1326–1337.

Preobrazhenskii, A. A. 1947. Methods of artificial inoculation of grapes with *Botrytis cinerea* for the production of Shato-Ikem wine. (Russian). *Akademiya Nauk, Biokhemiya vinodeliya* 1:77–97.

Raistrick, H., Robinson, R., and Todd, A. R. 1934. LXXIX: Studies in the biochemistry of micro-organisms. XXXVII: (a) On the production of hydroxyanthraquinones by species of *Helminthosporium.* (b) Isolation of tritisporin, a new metabolic product of *Helminthosporium tritici-vulgaris* Nisikado. (c) The molecular constitution of catenarin. *Biochem. Jour. 28:*559–572.

——— and Smith, G. 1936. CLXXXVIII: Studies in the biochemistry of micro-organisms. LI: The metabolic products of *Aspergillus terreus* Thom. Part II. Two new chlorine-containing mould metabolic products, geodin and erdin. *Biochem. Jour. 30:*1315–1322.

Sanborn, J. R. 1936. Gums produced by fungi. *Ind. Eng. Chem. 28:*1189–1190.

Shanor, L. 1949. Not only fleas to bite 'em! *The Sci. Teacher 16:*115–117, 146, 170–172, 186.

Stodala, F. H., Raper, K. B., Fennell, D. I., Conway, H. F., Sohns, V. E., Langford, C. T., and Jackson, R. W. 1955. The microbiological production of gibberellins A and X. *Arch. Biochem. and Biophysics 54:*240–245.

Waksman, S. A. 1938. *Humus: origin, chemical composition and importance in nature.* Williams and Wilkins, Baltimore.

Woolley, D. W., and Peterson, W. H. 1937. The chemistry of mold tissue. XIV: Isolation of cyclic choline sulfate from *Aspergillus sydowi. J. Biol. Chem. 122:*213–218.

Yabuta, T., and Hayashi, T. 1939. Biochemical studies on "Bakanae" fungus of the rice. Part II: Isolation of "gibberellin," the active principal which makes the rice seedlings grow slenderly. *J. Agr. Chem. Soc. Japan 15:*257–266. (In Japanese with English abstract).

19 · *Use of Fungi in Biological Assays*

B-VITAMIN ASSAYS

ASSAYS FOR AMINO ACIDS

SOIL ANALYSIS

BIOASSAY FOR ARSENIC

GROWTH-SUBSTANCE ASSAY

ASSAY FOR MILDEW AND ROT RESISTANCE IN FABRICS

ONE OF THE FUNDAMENTAL OBJECTIVES in quantitative chemical analysis is to develop methods that yield results of the highest degree of accuracy combined with the greatest ease of manipulation. Unfortunately for the analyst, the quantitative determination of many compounds by purely chemical means is accomplished only through the use of extensive, time-consuming methods. Furthermore, with many complex compounds the values obtained through the use of the best chemical methods are not absolute, nor are existing methods for the determination of some compounds entirely reliable.

For quantitative analyses of certain complex compounds, a number of biological assays have been developed, especially in the quantitative estimation of physiologically active substances or in cases where easy, rapid manipulation is more desirable than an extremely high degree of accuracy. Such bio-assays involve the use of living test organisms for determining the presence or estimating the amounts of certain compounds. The quantity of any specific compound in the material under test is generally estimated by measuring the amount or rate of growth of the organism, or by measuring the rate of some specific physiological activity upon which the compound is known to have an accelerating or depressing effect. The feeding of certain food materials to rats in order to ascertain the Vitamin D content of such materials is an example of a bio-assay. By feeding different quantities of such materials (mixed with Vitamin-D-free rations) to different groups of rats and thus determining the minimum quantity required to prevent rickets, a very practical estimate of the Vitamin D content can be made. Sometimes biological assay methods need only be qualitative in character; examples of such methods are tests for pregnancy which involve the use of rabbits or frogs as test organisms.

A variety of different organisms, including the fungi, have been used in bio-assays; however, in actuality their possible uses as test organisms in a large number of assay methods have been relatively unexplored. Since the culturing and maintenance of fungi is a comparatively simple and inexpensive process, it would be profitable further to investigate their potentialities in this area.

A search of the literature reveals many reported methods for the quantitative determination of various sugars by strictly chemical means. Fermentable sugars were frequently determined quantitatively by earlier investigators by a method involving the use of brewer's yeast. The sugar-containing material was fermented with yeast and the alcohol thus produced was then determined quantitatively, the amount of sugar present in the original material being calculated on the basis of the following equation:

$$\underset{\text{(glucose)}}{C_6H_{12}O_6} \rightarrow \underset{\text{(alcohol)}}{2CH_3CH_2OH} + \underset{\text{(carbon dioxide)}}{2CO_2}$$

Obviously, such a method could yield only approximate results, since all of the sugar may not be converted to alcohol. Hence the method is hardly to be recommended in view of the faster, more accurate chemical methods extant.

In the quantitative estimation of sucrose and starch, fungus preparations are usually employed in certain steps of the analyses, although these analytical methods cannot be classed as bio-assays: Yeast invertase preparations are used to hydrolyze sucrose to reducing sugars prior to analysis, and filamentous fungus preparations (commonly from *Aspergillus oryzae*) are similarly employed to digest starch in an early step in the quantitative estimation of this polysaccharide.

The use of fungi in biological assays has probably had its widest application in assay methods for various B-complex vitamins. Many fungi are unable to synthesize some particular B vitamin, and hence must be supplied with the particular vitamin for which they are deficient if they are to be maintained in culture. With such organisms the amount or rate of growth is often directly proportional to the quantity of vitamin supplied in the culture medium, if a suitable range of concentrations is employed. By incorporating a known amount of the material being tested into a medium otherwise free of the vitamin being assayed—but complete in all other respects—the growth of the organism can be determined and compared with its growth on media containing known amounts of the vitamin. Since many environmental factors have a very marked effect on the growth of fungi, such assays must be conducted under a rigidly controlled set of standard conditions. Temperature, composition of culture medium, reaction of the medium and length of incubation period all are important and must be carefully controlled if reliable, replicable results are to be obtained. Of equal importance is the selection of the proper species and strain of test organism. The fact that one investigator reports the use of a species of fungus as a test organism for a particular bio-assay does not necessarily mean that other strains of the same species may be so used.

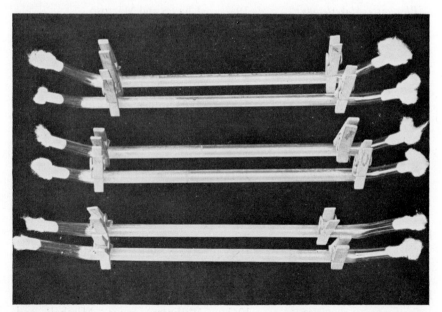

FIG. 98. *Long culture tubes used for the determination of growth rates of fungi. In the above tubes* Neurospora crassa *is growing on media with different amounts of organic nitrogen, ranging from low concentration in the top pair of tubes to high concentration in the lowermost pair.*

The growth of fungi can be determined by various means, although the most accurate method is probably that in which the mycelium is removed from the culture medium, dried, and weighed. Growth is estimated in some of the proposed assay methods by measuring the diameters of colonies on petri plates. In others, growth rate is determined by measuring the advance of the mycelium over a narrow strip of agar medium in a long tube (Fig. 98), a method described by Fawcett (1925). With nonfilamentous fungi such as yeasts, which can be suspended uniformly throughout liquid medium, growth can be estimated by measuring the turbidity of cultures by suitable means. In Table 35 are listed a number of fungi which have been used by

Table 35.—Fungi used in bioassays for B-complex vitamins

Fungus	Date	Investigator
THIAMIN		
Saccharomyces cerevisiae	1941	Schultz, Atkin and Frey
" "	1941	Williams, McMahan and Eakin
Phycomyces blakesleeanus	1942	Chaves and Mattoso
" "	1943	Schopfer
Pythium ascophallon	1945	Leonian and Lilly
PYRIDOXINE		
Saccharomyces cerevisiae	1941	Williams, Eakin and McMahan
" *oviformis*	1943	Burkholder
" *carlsbergensis*	1943	Atkin, Schultz, Williams and Frey
Neurospora sitophila	1943	Stokes, Larsen, Woodward and Foster
Ceratostomella pleuriannulata	1945	Leonian and Lilly
" *montium*	1945	Leonian and Lilly
Mycoderma valida	1945	Leonian and Lilly
PANTOTHENIC ACID		
Saccharomyces carlsbergensis	1945	Atkin, Williams, Schultz and Frey
" *cerevisiae*	1945	Leonian and Lilly
INOSITOL		
Saccharomyces cerevisiae	1941	Williams, Stout, Mitchell and McMahan
" "	1941	Woolley
Neurospora crassa	1944	Beadle

Table 35.—*Fungi used in bioassays for B-complex vitamins*
(*Continued*)

Fungus	Date	Investigator
NICOTINIC ACID		
Zygosaccharomyces marxianus	1945	Leonian and Lilly
P-AMINOBENZOIC ACID		
Neurospora crassa	1942	Tatum and Beadle
`` ``	1943	Thompson, Isbell and Mitchell
BIOTIN		
Saccharomyces cerevisiae	1940	Snell, Eakin and Williams
`` ``	1943	Hertz
Zygosaccharomyces marxianus	1945	Leonian and Lilly
Debaryomyces matruchoti		
v. *subglobosus*	1945	`` ``
Ceratostomella ips	1945	`` ``
`` *montium*	1945	`` ``
`` *pini*	1945	`` ``
Sordaria fimicola	1945	`` ``
Neurospora crassa	1945	`` ``
`` *sitophila*	1945	`` ``
CHOLINE		
Neurospora crassa	1943	Horowitz and Beadle

various investigators for assaying B-complex vitamins. No attempt is made at completeness in this listing; however, the list serves to illustrate the kinds of fungi that have been used in bio-assays of this type. The several examples that follow illustrate the various procedures commonly followed in biological assays of the B vitamins. For more detailed descriptions of the various methods the original publications should be consulted.

B-Vitamin Assays

p-AMINOBENZOIC ACID. Tatum and Beadle (1942) developed an assay method for this vitamin using mutant strains of the red mold *Neurospora crassa,* incapable of synthesizing *p*-aminobenzoic acid. Because of their inability to synthesize this vitamin, such strains can be cultured only if it is included in the medium. Tatum and Beadle cultured such a strain in media in which the *p*-aminobenzoic acid concentration varied over a wide range, and found that after a three-day incubation period the relation between mycelial weight and vitamin content was almost linear up to a concentration of 0.25 gamma/25 ml. Using the same organisms, these investigators also developed a "long tube" assay method for *p*-aminobenzoic acid, recommending this method as more satisfactory than the method involving the harvesting, drying, and weighing of mycelium. In this latter assay method, vitamin content is estimated on the basis of the rate of progression of the mycelial front along the surface of the agar in a narrow, horizontally placed culture tube. Measurements can be made in a relatively short period of time, and the assay is rather easily performed. Fig. 99 illustrates the relationship between growth rate as measured in this fashion and *p*-aminobenzoic acid concentration of the medium.

Thompson, Isbell, and Mitchell (1943) also proposed an assay method for *p*-aminobenzoic acid using a mutant strain of *N. crassa* ob-

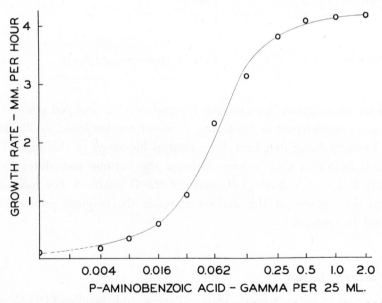

FIG. 99.   *Advance of mycelium of a "p-aminobenzoicless" strain of* Neurospora crassa *as a function of* p-*aminobenzoic acid content of the medium. (Redrawn from Tatum and Beadle, 1942.)*

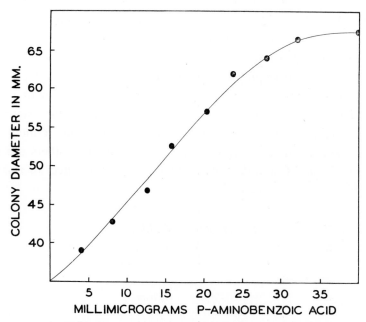

Fig. 100. *The relation between* p-aminobenzoic acid content of the medium and colony diameters of Neurospora crassa *after 24 hours incubation at 30 C°. (Redrawn from Thompson, Isbell, and Mitchell, 1943.)*

tained from Tatum and Beadle. Their method differs from those discussed above in that the tests are conducted on petri plates, and growth is estimated on the basis of fungus colony diameter after 24 hours incubation at 30 C. Figure 100 shows the type of standard curve obtained by these workers when colony diameter was plotted against millimicrograms of *p*-aminobenzoic acid. Thus an approximation of the amount of this vitamin in a material being assayed can be made by incorporating various quantities of the unknown in portions of the standard medium, then inoculating, incubating, and measuring the colony diameters. By interpolation on the standard curve an estimation of the vitamin content can be made.

THIAMIN. Several assays have been described for Vitamin B₁, but the one developed by Schultz, Atkin, and Frey (1941) is chosen for discussion here since it provides an example of a bio-assay in which the rate of a specific process is measured and in which the quantity of the vitamin in the substrate is estimated on the basis of this process rate. The test has its basis in the observation that, under a given set of conditions, added thiamin has a marked accelerating effect upon the rate of yeast fermentation. The test organism used by Schultz and his co-workers is baker's yeast (Fleischmann's), and the assays are conducted in a special respirometer which they call a fermentometer. Assays are made rapidly by this method, since the measurement of fermentation rate is accomplished simply by measuring the amount of carbon dioxide evolved during the course of a three-hour fermentation period. Data from the original paper by Schultz and others are presented in Table 36 and demonstrate the accelerating effect of thiamin upon fermentation rate of this yeast.

Table 36.—Effect of added thiamin on fermentation rate of Fleischmann's strain of baker's yeast

Bottle Number	Distilled Water (ml)	Thiamin Solution, 1 μg/ml (ml)	Gas Evolved in 3 hr
1	30	0	120
2	29	1.0	155
3	28	2.0	184
4	30	0	118
5	29	1.0	154
6	28	2.0	184

PYRIDOXINE.   A method for the determination of pyridoxine devised by Atkin, Schultz, Williams, and Frey (1943) also uses a yeast (*Saccharomyces carlsbergensis*) as the test organism. It differs, however, from any of the assay methods thus far described in that growth is measured turbidimetrically rather than by the longer and more laborious method of harvesting, drying, and weighing the fungus tissues. Assays are made by inoculating media containing various dilutions of the material under test, incubating at 30 C with continuous shaking for 16–18 hr, and then measuring the turbidity of the cultures. The amount of pyridoxine in the unknown is then estimated by interpolation on a reference curve which is based upon turbidity measurements

made on a set of tubes containing 0, 5, 10, 15, 20, 30, and 40 millimicrograms of pyridoxine. The authors of this method recommend that
such a standard series be included with each assay run. Figure 101

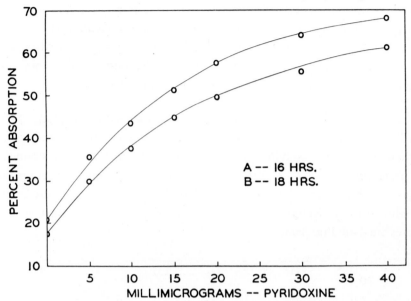

FIG. 101. *Reference curve used in pyridoxine assay by the method of
Atkin, Schultz, Williams, and Frey (1943).*

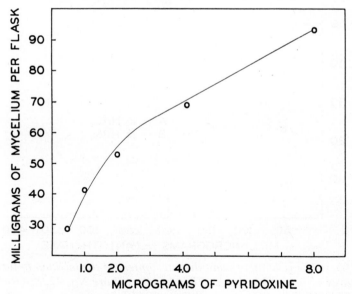

FIG. 102. *Reference curve obtained for pyridoxine in the* C. pleuriannulata *assay for this vitamin. (Redrawn from Leonian and Lilly, 1945.)*

shows the type of reference curve obtained when per cent light absorption is plotted against pyridoxine concentration.

Leonian and Lilly (1945) found that the various species of *Ceratostomella* with which they worked seem to require a number of accessory growth factors and subsequently used *C. pleuriannulata* and *C. montium* for the assay of pyridoxine. Growth was estimated on the basis of dry weight of mycelium. A reference curve which they obtained with *C. pleuriannulata* is shown in Fig. 102.

PANTOTHENIC ACID.   Atkin, Williams, Schultz, and Frey (1944) also developed a yeast bio-assay for this B vitamin, and, as in their method for assaying pyridoxine, the test organism is a strain of *Saccharomyces carlsbergensis*. The method is quite similar in its operation to their method for pyridoxine in that growth is measured turbidimetrically. Reference curves obtained by these investigators are presented in Fig. 103.

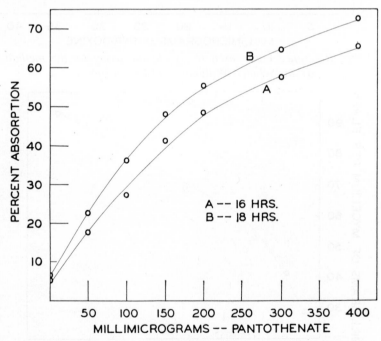

FIG. 103.   *The relation of pantothenate content of the medium to turbidity of cultures of* S. carlsbergensis: *Fleischmann culture No. 4228. (Redrawn from Atkin, Williams, Schultz, and Frey, 1944.)*

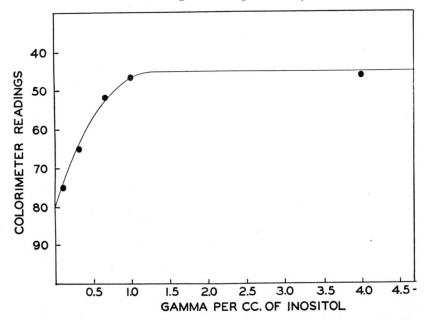

FIG. 104. *Standard curve for inositol assay by the method of Woolley using* S. cerevisiae *as the test organism. (Redrawn from Woolley, 1941.)*

INOSITOL.   For the estimation of this vitamin, Woolley (1941) recommended the use of a strain of *Saccharomyces cerevisiae*, the common yeast of industry. He found that within a certain range of inositol concentrations, growth (measured turbidimetrically) is proportional to concentration, and hence a standard curve can be derived simply by plotting turbidity readings (using an Evelyn photoelectric colorimeter) against inositol concentration as in Fig. 104. Williams and others (1941) also used *S. cerevisiae* in their assay for inositol, while Beadle (1944) employed a mutant strain of *Neurospora*.

NICOTINIC ACID.   Leonian and Lilly (1945) used a yeast, *Zygosaccharomyces marxianus* for the assay of nicotinic acid and measured growth both turbidimetrically and on the basis of dry weight of yeast cells formed. Their reference curves used in this assay method are shown in Fig. 105.

BIOTIN.   Snell, Eakin, and Williams (1940) reported on a biotin assay method based on the use of *S. cerevisiae* as the test organism; Hertz (1943) proposed a modification of this method involving

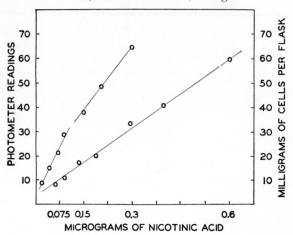

FIG. 105. *The relation of nicotinic acid content of the medium to culture turbidity and dry weight of cells formed by* Zygosaccharomyces marxianus. *(Redrawn from Leonian and Lilly, 1945.)*

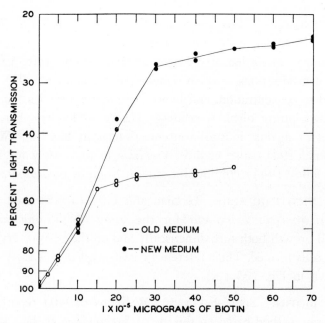

FIG. 106. *Yeast assay for biotin. References curves obtained with medium of Snell, Eakin, and Williams (1940) and medium of Hertz. (Redrawn from Hertz, 1943.)*

the inclusion of casein hydrolysate in the medium. Hertz claimed that the addition of biotin-free casein hydrolysate to the test medium increases both the specificity and the range of biotin determinations made by the method of Snell and his co-workers. Reference curves obtained by Hertz using both the medium devised by the earlier workers and the new medium which he proposed are included in Fig. 106.

CHOLINE. Whether or not choline should be classified as a vitamin is a debatable point; however, all agree that it is an important metabolite and for convenience it will be considered here with the B vitamins. Horowitz and Beadle (1943) developed an assay method for choline using a "cholineless" mutant of *Neurospora crassa* (No. 34486) derived from the "wild type" *N. crassa* through ultraviolet irradiation. They found that the growth rate of this mutant strain is a function of the choline concentration of the medium, and that growth increases with choline content up to a level of 30 gamma per 25 ml of medium. Growth was measured by harvesting, drying, and weighing the mycelium; the relationship between mycelial weight and choline content of the medium is shown in Fig. 107.

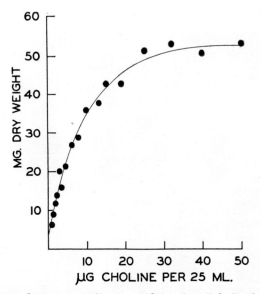

FIG. 107. *Growth (as mycelium weight) of a "cholineless" mutant of* Neurospora crassa *as a function of choline content of the culture medium.* (*Redrawn from Horowitz and Beadle, 1943.*)

Assays for Amino Acids

The production by irradiation of mutant strains of *Neurospora crassa* which are deficient for (unable to synthesize) certain of the essential amino acids has provided not only the tools for investigating the chemical steps involved in the synthesis of these important compounds, but also a number of test organisms for the assay of these acids. If a fungus is unable to synthesize one of the essential amino acids, this acid must be supplied in the culture medium in order to obtain growth (Fig. 108). Furthermore, within a certain concentration range, growth is proportional to the amount of the amino acid supplied. For example, Regnery (1944) reported obtaining a strain of *N. crassa* which was unable to synthesize leucine, and Ryan and Brand (1944) subsequently employed this strain for the quantitative determination of leucine in protein hydrolysates and foodstuffs. Their method is to culture the organism for 8.5 days at 30 C on leucine-free basal medium to which the material being assayed was added; at the end of the incubation period, the mycelium is harvested, dried, and weighed. They recommend that the samples of material under test be of such size that they contain 0.2 to 0.8 mg of leucine, and, as may be seen in Fig. 109,

FIG. 108. *Cultures of a "prolineless" mutant of* Neurospora crassa *in media with proline* (right) *and without proline* (left).

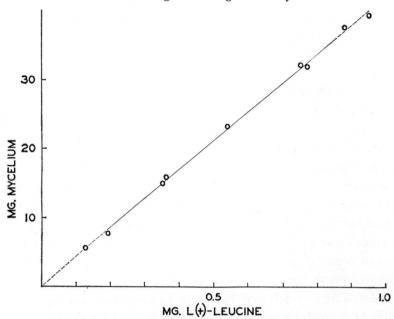

FIG. 109. *Relation of growth of mycelium of a "leucineless" mutant of* Neurospora crassa *to* l(+)*-leucine content of the culture medium.* (*Redrawn from Ryan and Brand, 1944.*)

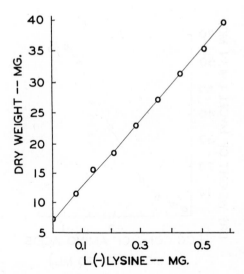

FIG. 110. *The relation between lysine content and mycelial growth of a "lysineless" mutant of* Neurospora crassa. (*Redrawn from Doermann, 1945.*)

a straight-line relationship exists between mycelium weight and $l(+)$-leucine content of the medium. Apparently the test is quite specific, since in their experiments there was no utilization of dl-isoleucine, an isomer of leucine which is separated from leucine chemically only with great difficulty.

A bio-assay for lysine has been developed by Doermann (1945) which also uses a mutant *Neurospora*. Doermann found that both lysine and biotin must be added to culture medium in order to obtain growth of Strain 4545, and that when both are present in the medium, growth is specifically a function of the available lysine (probably because of the very low biotin requirement of the fungus). Consequently he was able to employ this strain for bio-assay work, and obtained a reference curve such as that in Fig. 110, which shows that the relation between mycelial growth and $l(+)$-lysine is almost linear up to a concentration of 0.6 mg.

The research of Srb and Horowitz (1944) has provided mutant strains of *N. crassa* which could probably be used for the bio-assay of several compounds, although these investigators made no specific recommendations to this effect. They were primarily concerned with the genetic control of the ornithine cycle in *Neurospora* and studied a number of mutant strains which were unable to complete certain

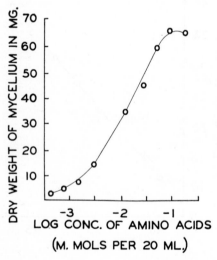

FIG. 111. *The relationship between mycelial weight of* Neurospora crassa *(Strain 36703) and arginine concentration of the medium. (Redrawn from Srb and Horowitz, 1944.)*

chemical steps in this cycle. According to these workers the steps in the synthesis of arginine from ornithine are as follows:

$$\rightarrow \rightarrow \rightarrow \rightarrow \text{ornithine} \rightarrow \rightarrow \text{citrulline} \rightarrow \text{arginine}$$

The seven mutant strains with which Srb and Horowitz worked were all arginineless (unable to grow in the absence of arginine or one of its precursors). Strains 21502, 27947, 29997, and 34105 would grow if ornithine was supplied, indicating that they were able to synthesize citrulline from ornithine and arginine from citrulline but unable to synthesize ornithine or one of its precursors. Strains 33442 and 30300 were unable to grow with ornithine but would grow if citrulline or arginine was added, thus indicating a "genetic block" at the step in which citrulline was synthesized from ornithine. Strain 36703 would grow only if arginine was supplied; thus the genetic block in this strain involved the citrulline $\rightarrow$ arginine step. From these observations it seems evident that Strain 26703 could be used in a bio-assay for arginine, and the curve (Fig. 111), which shows the relation between mycelial weight and arginine content of the medium, might be used as a reference curve in such an assay.

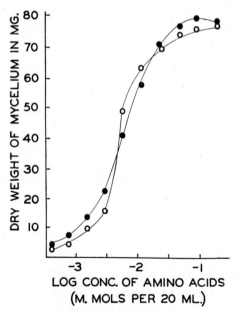

FIG. 112. *Growth of* Neurospora crassa (*Strain 33442*) *as a function of* dl-*citrulline or* l(+)-*arginine concentration of the medium.* (*Redrawn from Srb and Horowitz, 1944.*)

Strain 33442 might also be employed in arginine assay work provided no citrulline was present in the medium, and conversely this same strain might be used for the assay of citrulline if the medium contained no arginine. Figure 112 illustrates the relationship between mycelial weight and arginine concentration or citrulline concentration.

Soil Analyses

The use of fungi as test organisms for the biological assay of certain soil constituents in order to determine fertilizer requirements has been suggested by several investigators. Mehlich, Fred, and Truog (1934) proposed a method for measuring available soil phosphorus using either *Cunninghamella elegans* or *C. blakesleeana* as the test organism. The method is quite simple in operation: the soil under test is thoroughly mixed with phosphorus-free mineral salt solution, smoothed soil plaques are then prepared in petri dishes, and a drop of spore suspension of *Cunninghamella* is introduced in the center of each soil plaque. After a 48- to 50-hr incubation at 28–29 C, growth is estimated on the basis of the diameter of the fungus colony. Mehlich and others suggest that the approximate relationship between lateral growth of the fungus and phosphate fertilizer requirements is as follows:

Colony Diameter, mm	Phosphate Fertilizer Requirement
10	great need
11–15	moderate need
16–21	slight need
22	no need

The above values will vary somewhat, depending upon the kind of crops to be planted and the species of *Cunninghamella* used in the test. Nevertheless this test seems to be a rather reliable one, since the results obtained with soils from widely separated areas showed good agreement of field results. The authors particularly recommended the test for use with calcareous soils that give great difficulty with other methods used for the determination of available phosphorus. Figure 113 illustrates the growth of *Cunninghamella* on phosphate-poor soil to which varying amounts of phosphate have been added.

Several workers have used *Aspergillus niger* for the estimation of

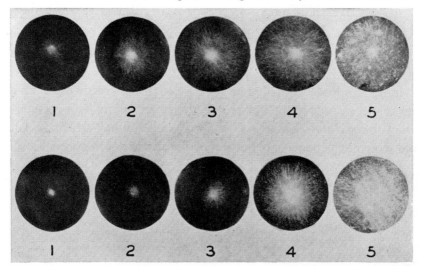

FIG. 113. *Growth of* Cunninghamella *on soils with different amounts of available phosphorus (Mehlich, Truog, and Fred, 1934).*

Upper *row: a soil containing 12 ppm available phosphorus and treated with the following increasing ppm of soluble phosphorus:* (1), 0; (2), 20; (3), 40; (4), 60; and (5) 80.

Lower *row: soils, untreated, containing the following amounts of available phosphorus, as revealed by chemical method:*

    (1),   4 ppm   *Responds markedly to phosphate in the field.*
    (2),   12 ppm   *Responds markedly to phosphate in the field.*
    (3),   17 ppm   *Responds moderately to phosphate in the field.*
    (4),   64 ppm   *No response to phosphate in the field.*
    (5), 152 ppm   *No response to phosphate in the field.*

certain mineral constituents of the soil. Butkewitsch (1909) apparently was the first to employ this well-known fungus for biological assays of this type, and various other workers have since used it in similar fashion. More recently the Wisconsin workers (Mehlich, Truog, and Fred, 1933) have recommended the use of *A. niger* as a test organism for measuring the amount of available potassium in soil. In brief, their method is conducted as follows: 2.5-g portions of sieved soil are placed in flasks containing 30 ml of potassium-free mineral salt solution. After inoculation with 0.5 ml of spore suspension of *A. niger,* the flasks are incubated at 35 C for 4½ days. The mycelium is then harvested and weighed, and the amount of available potassium in the soil is estimated by interpolation on a curve such as that in Fig. 114 or by determining the percentage of potassium in the mycelium.

For a comparison of the *Cunninghamella* and *A. niger* methods described above with the older Neubauer method (1925), which utilizes rye as the test organism, the reader should consult the work of Mooers (1938).

In 1938 Mulder (*cf.* Foster, 1939) described a method for assaying copper in soils using *A. niger* as the test organism. This method is based on the correlation between copper content of the nutrient medium and spore production and pigmentation in this species. In nutrient media

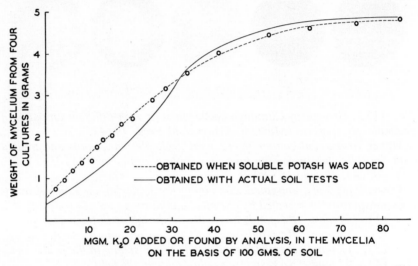

FIG. 114.   *The relation of potassium to mycelial weight of* Aspergillus niger. (*Redrawn from Mehlich, Truog, and Fred, 1933.*)

of very low copper content, the mycelium is white and completely without spores. With increase in copper content, however, spores are formed and the intensity of pigmentation increases with copper content through colors from yellow to yellow-brown to black. Mulder added soil samples to purified nutrient solution, inoculated with *A. niger,* incubated the cultures, and then compared spore pigmentation with that of cultures growing in a series of standards containing known amounts of copper. Maximum pigmentation occurred with 6.25 micrograms of copper per 100 ml.

Andrews (1937) proposed a novel method for estimating crop response to soil treatments utilizing the microorganisms occurring naturally in the soil as the test organisms. This investigator added 500 mg of mannitol to each 100 g soil sample to which water and fertilizer had been added; the soil was then incubated for 24 hours, the amount of carbon dioxide formed by the microorganisms during this period being determined by absorption on ascarite. Andrews found high correlation between the response of cotton to lime, phosphorus, and phosphorus and nitrogen and the formation of carbon dioxide in mannitol-treated soil. He noted that results obtained by this method tend to correlate with crop response to soil treatment in some cases but not in others. Obviously the method requires further study in order to determine if the inconsistencies may be eliminated by some modification of the test procedure. Copper, manganese, and zinc deficiencies could not be demonstrated by this method.

Bio-assay for Arsenic

The earlier practice of utilizing arsenic compounds in the pigments of wallpapers and plasters occasionally caused poisoning that sometimes resulted in death. According to Challenger (1935) a fatal case of this type occurred in England as recently as 1931. Apparently this type of poisoning was known in the early nineteenth century and received the attention of a number of workers who ascribed the poisoning to volatile arsenic compounds liberated from the wallpaper or plaster. Various suggestions were made as to the nature of the volatile material, but it was not until 1933 that it was definitely characterized chemically. The fact that the rooms where such poisonings occurred were damp and moldy led Gosio (*cf.* Challenger, 1935) to investigate the problem in 1891. He found that if potato mash containing arsenious oxide was exposed to air, an odor of garlic was produced when fungi developed on the mash. Several fungi were concerned: *Aspergillus glaucus, A. virens, Mucor mucedo,* and *Penicillium brevicaule;* of these organisms, *P. brevicaule* was found to be especially active in the production of the characteristic garlic odor which was due to a volatile arsenic compound. This volatile compound (often called Gosio gas) was found by Challenger, Higginbottom, and Ellis (1933) to be trimethylarsine, $(CH_3)_3As$. These same workers found that several other arsenic compounds could be synthesized by *P. brevicaule:* methyldiethylarsine from diethylarsonic acid, dimethyl-*n*-propylarsine from *n*-propylarsonic acid, and dimethylallylarsine from allylarsonic acid. Thom and Raper (1932) demonstrated that a variety of different fungi could produce arsenical gas.

Gosio developed a test for arsenic said to be more sensitive than the

Marsh test. Material suspected of containing arsenic is extracted with water, the extract concentrated, added to a sterilized potato slice which is then inoculated with *P. brevicaule* and incubated. A garlic odor will develop if arsenic is present, and the test reputedly can be used to detect this element in quantities as low as 0.000,001 gram of arsenious oxide per gram of material. Abba (1898), Abel and Buttenburg (1900), and Scholtz (1899) have attested to the extreme delicacy of this test for arsenic, although Lerrigo (1932) was unable to observe any volatile arsenic compounds formed as a result of mold growth.

Growth-Substance Assay

Worley and Duggar (1938) developed a bio-assay method in which one fungus species is used as a test organism to estimate the quantity of growth substance formed by another species. *Rhizopus suinus* synthesizes a heat-stable growth substance which exerts an influence on the dry weight yield of *Aspergillus niger* but does not cause curvature of oat coleoptile. By including various amounts of filtrate from liquid cultures of *R. suinus* in agar medium in petri plates they found that it was possible to estimate the strength of the filtrate by measuring diameter increments of colonies of *Colletotrichum circinans* growing in the plates.

Assay for Mildew and Rot Resistance in Fabrics

Since the length of service of many fabrics is very short unless they are treated with some type of fungicidal compound, it is common practice to incorporate some such material in fabrics that are to be used under conditions where they might rot or mildew. A variety of tests have been devised to determine rot and mildew resistances of materials so treated. These tests are discussed in Chapter 22 on Tropical Deterioration.

Literature Cited

Abba, F. 1898. Ueber die Feinheit der biologischen Methode beim Nachweis Arseniks. *Centralbl. Bakt. und Parasiten.* 4:806–808.

Abel, R., and Buttenburg, P. 1900. Über die Einwirkung von Schimmelpilzen auf Arsen und seine Verbindungen. Der Nachweis von Arsen auf biologischem Wege. *Chem. Centralbl. 1900.* (*1*):428–429.

Andrews, W. B. 1937. Carbon dioxide production in mannitol-treated soils as a measure of crop response to soil treatments. *J. Am. Soc. Agron. 29:*253–268.

Atkin, L., Schultz, A. S., Williams, W. L., and Frey, C. N. 1943. Yeast microbiological methods for determination of vitamins. Pyridoxine. *Ind. Eng. Chem. 15:*141–144.

———, Williams, W. L., Schultz, A. S., and Frey, C. N. 1944. Yeast microbiological methods for determination of vitamins. Pantothenic acid. *Ind. Eng. Chem. 16:*67–71.

Beadle, G. W. 1944. An inositolless mutant strain of *Neurospora* and its use in bioassays. *J. Biol. Chem. 156:*683–689.

Burkholder, P. R. 1943. Vitamin deficiencies in yeasts. *Am. J. Bot. 30:*206–211.

Butkewitsch, W. 1909. Die Kultur des Schimmelpilzes *Aspergillus niger,* als Mittel zur Bodeuntersuchung. *Zhur. Opytn. Agron.* (Russian *Jour. Exp. Landw.*) *10:*136–141.

Challenger, F. 1935. The biological methylation of compounds of arsenic and selenium. *Jour. Soc. Chem. Ind. 54:*657–662.

———, Higginbottom, C., and Ellis, L. 1933. The formation of organometalloidal compounds by microorganisms. Part I: Trimethylarsine and dimethylarsine. *Jour. Chem. Soc.,* 95–101.

Chaves, J. M. and Mattoso, I. V. 1942. Determination of thiamin. Modification of the Schopfer technique. *Annais. Assoc. Quim. Brazil 1:*250–263. (*Chem. Abst. 37:*2033–2034. 1943.)

Doermann, A. H. 1945. A bioassay for lysine by use of a mutant *Neurospora*. *J. Biol. Chem. 160:*95–103.

Fawcett, H. S. 1925. Maintained growth rates in fungus cultures of long duration. *Ann. Appl. Biol. 12:*191–198.

Foster, J. W. 1939. The heavy metal nutrition of fungi. *Bot. Rev. 5:*207–239.

Gosio, B. 1892. Azione di alcune nuffe sui composti fissi d'arsenico. *Revista d'Igiene e Sanita Publica III* (8/9):201–230; 261–273.

Hertz, R. 1943. Modification of the yeast-growth assay method for biotin. *Proc. Soc. Exp. Biol. and Med. 52:*15–17.

Horowitz, N. H., and Beadle, G. W. 1943. A microbiological method for the determination of choline by the use of a mutant *Neurospora*. *Jour. Biol. Chem. 150:*325–333.

Leonian, L. H., and Lilly, V. G. 1945. The comparative value of different test organisms in the microbiological assay of the B vitamins. *W. Va. Agr. Exp. Sta. Bull. 319.*

Lerrigo, A. F. 1932. The biological method for the detection of arsenic. *The Analyst 57:*155–158.

Mehlich, A., Fred, E. B., and Truog, E. 1934. The *Cunninghamella* plaque method of measuring available phosphorus in soil. *Soil Sci. 38:*445–460.

———, Truog, E., and Fred, E. B. 1933. The *Aspergillus niger* method of measuring the available potassium in soil. *Soil Sci. 35:*259–277.

Mooers, C. A. 1938. An evaluation of the Neubauer and the *Cunninghamella* and *Aspergillus niger* methods for the determination of the fertilizer needs of a soil. *Soil Sci. 46:*211–227.

Mulder, E. G. 1938. Over de beteekenis van koper voor de groewan planten en micro-organismen. *Diss., Wageningen.*

Neubauer, H. 1925. Die Bestimung des Dungebedurfniss des Bodens. *Ztschr. Pflanzenernähr., Düngung., u. Bodenk. 4B:*32–34.

Regnery, D. C. 1944. A leucineless strain of *Neurospora crassa. Jour. Biol. Chem. 154:*151–160.

Ryan, F. J., and Brand, E. 1944. A method for the determination of leucine in protein hydrolysates and in foodstuffs by the use of a *Neurospora* mutant. *Jour. Biol. Chem. 154:*161–175.

Scholtz, W. 1899. Uber den Nachweis von Arsen auf biologischen Wege in den Hautschuppen, Haaren, Schweiss, und Urin. *Chem. Centrbl. 1899. (II):*1032.

Schopfer, W. H. 1943. *Plants and vitamins.* Chronica Botanica, Waltham, Mass.

Schultz, A. S., Atkin, L., and Frey, C. N. 1941. Determination of Vitamin B_1 by yeast fermentation method. *Ind. Eng. Chem. 14:*35–39.

Snell, E. E., Eakin, R. E., and Williams, R. J. 1940. A quantitative test for biotin and observations regarding its occurrence and properties. *Jour. Am. Chem. Soc. 62:*175–178.

Srb, A. M., and Horowitz, N. H. 1944. The ornithine cycle in *Neurospora* and its genetic control. *J. Biol. Chem. 154:*129–139.

Stokes, J. L., Larsen, A., Woodward, C. R., and Foster, J. W. 1943. A *Neurospora* assay for pyridoxine. *J. Biol. Chem. 150:*17–24.

Tatum, E. L., and Beadle, G. W. 1942. Genetic control of biochemical reactions. *Proc. Nat. Acad. Sci. 28:*234–243.

Thom, C., and Raper, K. B. 1932. The arsenic fungi of Gosio. *Science 76:* 548–550.

Thompson, R. C., Isbell, E. R., and Mitchell, H. K. 1943. A microbiological assay method for *p*-aminobenzoic acid. *J. Biol. Chem. 148:*281–287.

Williams, R. J., Eakin, R. E., and McMahan, J. R. 1941. Studies on the vitamin content of tissues. I: Assay method for pyridoxin. *Univ. Tex. Pub. No. 4137:*24–26.

————, McMahan, J. R., and Eakin, R. E. 1941. Studies on the vitamin content of tissues. I: Assay method for thiamin. *Univ. Tex. Pub. No. 4137:*31–35.

————, Stout, A. K., Mitchell, H. K., and McMahan, J. R. 1941. Studies on the vitamin content of tissues. I: Assay method for inositol. *Univ. Tex. Pub. No. 4137:*27–30.

Woolley, D. W. 1941. A method for the estimation of inositol. *Jour. Biol. Chem. 140:*453–459.

Worley, C. L., and Duggar, B. M. 1938. *Colletotrichum circinans* as a semi-quantitative test unit for the growth substance produced by *Rhizopus suinus. Science 88:*132.

II

HARMFUL ACTIVITIES OF

FUNGI

20 · *Plant Disease*

IN PART I we have seen how the fungi, through their myriad activities, may react toward man's benefit in a variety of ways and hence have a very decided effect upon the many facets of his daily life. Unfortunately, however, all fungus activities cannot be recorded on the credit side of the ledger; a number are distinctly harmful to mankind.

Through the ages one of man's principal concerns has been food gathering. When he shifted from a nomadic to an agricultural existence the food problem (temporarily at least) seemed largely solved. However, man soon learned that his crops were subject to many vicissitudes—depredations of other animals, hail, drought, crowding by other plants (which he has since come to call weeds), fire, floods, insect damage, and disturbances referred to collectively in earlier times as "blights"—most of which were probably various types of plant diseases.

Periodically man suffers great losses because of the above factors, but to estimate the extent of agricultural losses due to any single agency is a rather difficult task, especially if they involve a large land area in which agriculture is quite diversified; reports concerning the magnitude of such losses are at best only estimates. In a more localized

FIG. 115. *Late Blight of potato caused by* Phytophthora infestans. *The plants at the right were sprayed with copper aerosol; those at the left were not sprayed, and the foliage is dead due to Late Blight.* (*Courtesy of C. W. Ellett.*)

situation such as that of the Irish famine of 1845–46, attributed to the failure of the potato crop as the result of a single plant disease (Fig. 115), it is possible to estimate the damage in a variety of ways—number of deaths due to starvation, number of people emigrating from a country, or reduction in total yield—although most agricultural losses are usually reported in terms of actual money losses. On the whole, it would appear that greatest losses of agricultural crops are the result of insect damage and plant diseases, with the latter probably the larger of the two factors.

Plant diseases are incited by several different agents: bacteria, viruses, nematodes (eel worms), and fungi. Of these various agents the fungi probably cause the most severe losses, although there are serious plant diseases caused by pathogens belonging to all of the four groups mentioned. The plant pathogenic fungi greatly outnumber the plant pathogenic bacteria and viruses. Ellett (1956) has estimated that in the state of Ohio there are 1000 diseases of plants incited by fungi and only 50 incited by bacteria (with about 100 caused by viruses). In estimates of crop damage, the losses due to plant diseases are usually not separated on the basis of the causal agents; from such reports, therefore, it is impossible to determine the extent of the losses due to fungus activity alone. We do know that such losses directly attributable to fungi are very considerable. Table 37 gives some concept of the losses sustained by agriculture as a result of plant diseases. This table, which includes figures taken from a U.S. Department of Agriculture report, is based on estimated annual losses in the United States, especially during

Table 37.—Estimated annual production and losses in the United States due to plant diseases

Type of Crop	Total Production (thousands of dollars)	Production Loss	
		(thousands of dollars)	(%)
Field crops	11,436,305	1,579,529	13.81
Forage crops	2,387,898	803,163	33.63
Fruit and nut crops	1,093,778	94,310	8.62
Vegetable crops	1,572,749	353,990	22.51
Drug plant crops	9,194	1,202	13.18
Ornamental crops	6,713,724	81,609	1.22
Totals	21,213,648	2,913,803	13.26 avg.

Based on *Losses in Agriculture: a preliminary appraisal for review*. Published by the Agricultural Research Service, U.S. Department of Agriculture, in cooperation with other departmental and federal agencies, June, 1954.

the years 1942–51, with the losses evaluated in terms of 1942–51 prices.

From Table 37, which is based upon the best estimates obtainable, it appears that agriculture sustains losses on the average of over 13 per cent annually as a result of plant diseases. It is true that the table shows only a money loss, but where crop production is equal to or only slightly in excess of crop consumption obviously a population increase or a season of unusually heavy disease incidence might involve a more serious loss.

It is sometimes impossible completely to assess the harm done to man's interests by a plant disease in terms other than dollar losses. For example, the disease of our native chestnut, Chestnut Blight (Fig. 116), which is caused by an introduced parasite (*Endothia parasitica*),

Fig. 116.   *Two views showing chestnut trees killed by* Endothia parasitica, *the causal agent of Chestnut Blight. Such views are typical throughout the entire range of the American Chestnut. (Courtesy of the Agricultural Research Service, U.S. Department of Agriculture, Beltsville, Maryland.)*

has for all practical purposes eliminated this valuable timber and nut-crop tree from the United States. The loss to succeeding generations cannot be estimated, nor can the value of this tree species be evaluated as a part of the soil- and moisture-holding vegetation on the steep mountain slopes in its natural range. Likewise it is impossible to estimate the loss sustained by the homeowner when large elm trees serving

FIG. 117. *Shade trees of American Elm which have died of Dutch Elm Disease. (Courtesy of Agricultural Research Service, U.S. Department of Agriculture.)*

landscaping and shade purposes are killed by *Ceratocystis ulmi,* the causal agent of Dutch Elm Disease (Fig. 117).

Fungi That Cause Plant Disease

Species of fungi which are the causal agents of plant diseases are not restricted to any one particular group of fungi but are found among the Phycomycetes, Ascomycetes, Basidiomycetes, and Fungi Imperfecti. No species of Myxomycetes are known to be parasites of vascular plants, but occasionally certain species of this class of animallike fungi do considerable damage to crops of cultivated mushrooms, and sometimes are the cause of unsightly areas on lawns when sporangia form on grass leaves. With the exception of the Myxomycetes, it cannot be said that one class is more important than another as causal

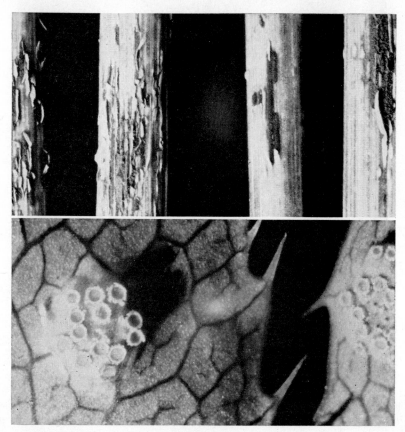

FIG. 118.   *Black Stem Rust of Wheat, incited by* Puccinia graminis. Top: *wheat stems with uredinial sori (red rust stage)*; bottom: *clusters of aecia on lower surface of barberry leaf. (Courtesy of C. W. Ellett.)*

agents of plant disease, since serious diseases are caused by members of all of the larger groups of fungi. For example, Downy Mildew of Grapes (Figs. 123, 124) and Late Blight of Potatoes (Figs. 115, 126) are diseases caused by Phycomycetes; Chestnut Blight (Fig. 116), Peach Leaf Curl (Figs. 127, 128), Dutch Elm Disease (Figs. 117, 130), and Net Blotch of Barley (Fig. 120) are caused by Ascomycetes; Rusts and Smuts (Figs. 118, 119) are caused by Basidiomycetes; Beet

FIG. 119. *Oat smuts. Plant at left with covered smut incited by* Ustilago kolleri; *plant at right with loose smut incited by* Ustilago avenae. (*Courtesy of C. W. Ellett.*)

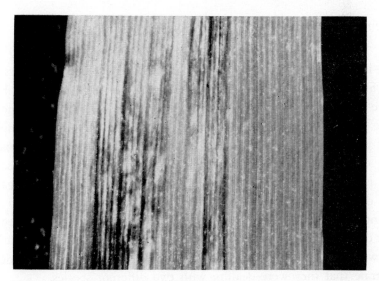

FIG. 120. *Barley leaf with Net Blotch. The causal agent of this disease is an Ascomycete, the imperfect stage of which is* Helminthosporium teres. (*Courtesy of C. W. Ellett.*)

Fig. 121. *Characteristic symptoms of Apple Blotch, a disease which is incited by* Phyllosticta solitaris. (*Courtesy of C. W. Ellett.*)

Leaf Spot (Figs. 131, 133), Apple Blotch (Fig. 121), and Maple Leaf Spot (Fig. 122) are caused by Fungi Imperfecti.

Number of Plant Pathogenic Fungi

The exact number of species of fungi capable of inciting disease in plants is not known—a situation that is due to several factors. In the first place, not all plant diseases are known or have been described, since the tendency of the plant pathologist has usually been to concentrate his efforts on studies of the diseases of only economically important plants. Another factor is our incomplete knowledge of the taxonomy of fungi. An investigator in one area may describe a plant disease and isolate and name the causal fungus, whereas another investigator in a different area may consider the disease to be due to an entirely different organism. Conversely, two different investigators may report that the same species of fungus is the responsible agent in the causation of two different diseases, and some subsequent investigator may demonstrate that they were dealing with two different species.

As early as 1913, Stevens, in his *Fungi which Cause Plant Disease,* listed over 2000 species of fungi which up to that time had been reported to be capable of causing a wide variety of plant diseases. Some

FIG. 122. *Maple Leaf Spot.* Top: *leaves showing characteristic spots;* bottom: *highly magnified spot in which pycnidia of* Phyllosticta minima, *the causal organism, may be seen.* (*Courtesy of C. W. Ellett.*)

of the species names that Stevens listed were undoubtedly synonyms, but others have since been shown to represent several entities, and there are undoubtedly omissions from the list. In the more than four decades since the first appearance of Stevens' book a great many new plant pathogenic fungi have been discovered and described, so that the list is now considerably larger. In spite of the fact that from the standpoint of numbers the plant pathogenic fungi seem to be very abundant, on a percentage basis they are still in the minority when all species of fungi are considered.

The Science of Plant Pathology

No field of plant science has had such a rapid and constantly expanding development as *plant pathology,* which is concerned with the study of plant diseases. Starting about the middle of the nineteenth century with the researches of the famous European botanist Anton de Bary, plant pathology as a recognized science has continuously expanded and is today one of the major fields of plant study. Although European in its origin, much of the development of plant pathology is directly attributable to American investigators.

The duties of the plant pathologist are myriad. He must consider many facets of the plant disease problems which he encounters— symptoms of disease, causal agents (including their correct identities and all of the details of their life histories), establishment and enforcement of quarantine measures to halt the geographic spread of a disease until some measure of control is attained, and the development of adequate control measures. Sometimes an extensive educational program must first be conducted as a prelude to the establishment of really effective control measures, as for example in the barberry eradication program set up in connection with the control of Black Stem Rust of Wheat, and the gooseberry and currant eradication program involved in the control of White Pine Blister Rust.

States in which agriculture is one of the major industries usually have one or more extension plant pathologists, who act in a consultant capacity for the agriculturists as well as initiate and implement education programs with lectures, distribution of literature, preparation of descriptive bulletins, and personal interviews. They may also conduct research programs on a number of plant diseases.

Both the state and federal governments make use of the services of a great many plant pathologists at experiment stations and similar government installations. The duty of most plant pathologists in these situations is primarily of a research nature, although in some instances they may also have extension and teaching duties. Private industry today also retains many plant pathologists, since research in the cure and prevention of plant diseases by means of specific chemical compounds receives considerable attention.

The major portion of the formal teaching of plant pathology is conducted by plant pathologists located at the various colleges and universities. In some institutions the field has grown so large that instruction is offered in separate Departments of Plant Pathology; in others it may be offered as a discipline in the large parent field of Botany, and in still others it may be variously combined with such fields of science as Bacteriology or Entomology.

The principal objective of the plant pathologist is the prevention of plant disease, but like his medical counterpart he must often be satisfied with partial control rather than prevention; however, partial control, is concerned with a community of plants rather than with single individuals. There are a variety of general categories of control measures, but with some diseases special control methods must be designed and employed. Control measures will be discussed in a later section and again in connection with the descriptions of specific diseases.

In addition to the applied aspects of plant pathology discussed above, problems of more fundamental nature are also studied by the plant pathologist. For example, many plant pathologists are engaged in the more basic realms of fungus genetics, fungus ecology, fungus physiology, host-parasite relationships, or host resistance,—a knowledge of which may be essential before the more practical applications may be made. While in the past there have been periods when plant pathology was referred to ironically as "botany with a dollar sign in front," such a categorization today has no basis in fact in the light of the fundamental problems which are currently under attack by plant pathologists.

Examples of Plant Diseases

In order to gain some general concepts of the nature of plant disease, the types of organisms which are the causal agents, and possible control measures that may be employed in combatting plant disease, several specific diseases will be discussed. One disease caused by a fungus from each of the four large groups will be described in detail to illustrate some of the major points; in no instance, however, should a single disease be considered as representative of the type of disease caused by all members of the large group to which it belongs.

DOWNY MILDEW OF GRAPES—A PHYCOMYCETOUS DIS-EASE. In a number of highly publicized instances the causal organisms of very devastating plant diseases have been introduced into the United States from other countries, and once introduced have become well established, causing great damage to certain valuable plant species. Notable among these introduced pathogens are the causal agents of Chestnut Blight, White Pine Blister Rust, and Dutch Elm Disease. However, the transportation of pathogenic fungi may be accomplished in two directions, the causal organism of Downy Mildew of Grape being an example of a plant pathogen which was introduced into France from America. According to Melhus and Kent (1939), this disease was known in America as early as 1834 but apparently was not introduced into France until 1875. The causal organism, *Plasmopara viticola*, was introduced into France on rootstocks of native American grape varieties, which were taken to France because of their resistance to a disturbance caused by an insect (*Phylloxera*), then a source of considerable trouble to the French grape growers. The pathogen has now spread to many other areas of the world. Losses due to Downy

FIG. 123.   *Downy Mildew of Grape, a disease incited by the Phycomycete,* Plasmopara viticola. (*Courtesy of C. C. Allison.*)

Mildew have been much greater in Europe than in the United States because of the greater susceptibility of the European grape varieties.

All parts of the grapevine except the root may be invaded by *P. viticola*. Plants may lose all of their leaves and tendrils, flowers may not set, and fruits may be destroyed. The early symptoms of the disease are round, light-green spots which have an oily appearance and occur on the upper surfaces of the leaves (Fig. 123). Tufts of white, downy hyphae soon appear on the lower surfaces of the leaves in the areas immediately below the light-green spots. The spots later become yellow or variegated (yellow and reddish-brown) and form patches between the larger veins of the leaf which are irregular in shape. At about this time, when the leaves are dying, the fungus enters the sexual stage of its life cycle and thick-walled, over-wintering spores form within the tissues of the leaf.

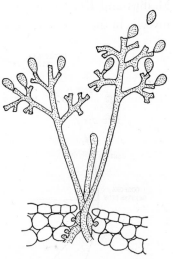

FIG. 124. *Diagram of conidia and conidiophores of* Plasmopara viticola *protruding through a stomate of an infected grape leaf.*

Being a Phycomycete, *P. viticola* has a nonseptate mycelium that grows intercellularly in the host tissues. The only parts of the mycelium that actually penetrate the walls of the host cells are small, specialized hyphal branches, *haustoria,* which are not unique to this organism but are developed by a number of other pathogenic fungi. Long, many-branched, white conidiophores develop from the intercellular mycelium and emerge in clusters from the stomates of the leaves (Fig. 124) and are responsible for the downy appearance of the lower leaf surface. Conidia, borne at the tips of the branches, are easily detached and may be blown by the wind to other plants, where they may germinate forming zoospores which may initiate other infections.

The sexual spores (oospores) develop in the tissues of the host, where the gametangia (antheridia and oogonia) were developing while the conidiophores and conidia were forming. The oospores are dark-colored, thick-walled spores which remain dormant during the winter but germinate when more favorable conditions prevail in the spring. Upon germination, the oospore forms a stout conidiophore bearing a single conidium which may be blown by the wind to a susceptible host. There the conidium germinates by forming zoospores which may then initiate primary infection. The host relations and sequence of events of the life history of *P. viticola* are represented in Fig. 125. According to Melhus and Kent (*loc. cit.*), the fungus can overwinter as perennial mycelia in the buds and crowns of plants as well as in the oospore stage.

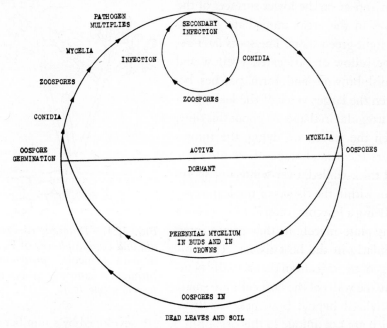

FIG. 125.   *Diagram of the host relation of* Plasmopara viticola, *a plant pathogenic fungus which survives the winter in the form of oöspores in plant refuse. (Based on Melhus and Kent, 1939.)*

Plasmopara viticola is closely related to *Phytophthora infestans,* the causal agent of Potato Late Blight (Fig. 126) and several other rather serious plant pathogens.

Control of Downy Mildew can be accomplished by the practice of sanitary measures in the vineyard and by spraying. Any dead grape leaves may contain oospores; therefore, primary invasion in the spring can be prevented to a certain extent if the fallen leaves are plowed under or raked and burned. According to Chester (1942), control of the disease depends not only upon destroying the dead leaves but also

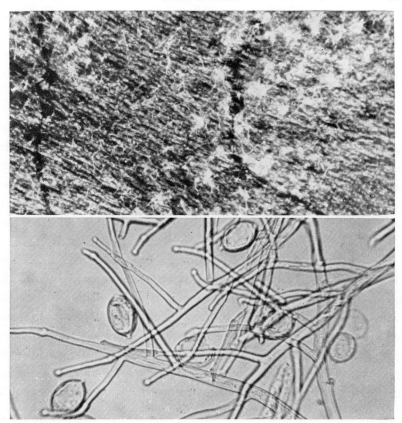

FIG. 126. *Potato Late Blight.* Top: *leaf surface magnified, showing downy clumps which are clusters of conidiophores emerging from the stomates;* bottom: *highly magnified conidiophores and conidia which were scraped from the leaf. (Courtesy of C. W. Ellett.)*

Table 38.—Plant diseases caused by species of Phycomycetes

Disease	Host or Hosts	Pathogen
Downy mildew of curcurbits	Cucumber	*Pseudoperonospora cubensis*
Downy mildew of spinach	Spinach	*Peronospora spinaciae*
White rust	Cruciferous plants	*Albugo candida*
Brown spot	Corn	*Physoderma zeae-maydis*
Club root	Cruciferous plants	*Plasmodiophora brassicae*
Damping-off	Many hosts	*Pythium debaryanum*
Soft rot	Sweet potato	*Rhizopus nigricans*
Powdery scab	Potato	*Spongospora subterranea*

upon the application, five or six times during the growing season, of a spray such as 8–8–100 Bordeaux mixture.

Many diseases of important economic plants are caused by other species of Phycomycetes; a few such diseases, with the host plants and pathogens, are listed in Table 38.

PEACH LEAF CURL—AN ASCOMYCETOUS DISEASE.—Leaf curl disease of peach and related trees is a common disease caused by the Ascomycete, *Taphrina deformans*. This organism is a member of the subclass Protoascomycetes (Hemiascomycetes), in which the asci are not grouped together in any type of characteristic fruiting body (ascocarp). According to Butler and Jones (1949), the disease occurs in America, Europe, Asia, Africa, Australia, and New Zealand.

The symptoms of Peach Leaf Curl are very striking and quite characteristic (Fig. 127). As the invaded young leaves emerge from the bud in the spring they are arched and reddened. Shortly after the leaves are well out of the bud, some of them appear to be distorted and fold over so that the tips are directed backwards. More heavily invaded leaves may curl so much that the lamina look like small, inflated paper bags. The blistered parts of the diseased leaves are softer and thicker than the uninvaded parts; they turn yellow and finally reddish-purple,

FIG. 127. *Twigs of peach tree which have several leaves infected by* Taphrina deformans, *the causal agent of Peach Leaf Curl.* (*Courtesy of C. W. Ellett.*)

soon becoming covered with a whitish bloom (usually on the upper part of the leaf). Leaves so diseased fall early, and premature defoliation in trees heavily diseased may occur in late spring. The tree may form a second crop of leaves, but if this disease occurs for several years the tree may be killed outright (Chester, 1942). The second crop of leaves does not become diseased, probably because the fungus cannot thrive at high temperatures. The minimum temperature for growth of *T. deformans* is below 10 C, the optimum at about 20 C, and the maximum between 26 and 30 C.

The whitish bloom that appears on the leaves consists of a large number of asci which develop in palisade fashion and break through

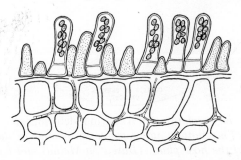

FIG. 128. *Diagram of leaf cross-section with mature and immature asci of* Taphrina deformans *arranged in palisade fashion on the leaf surface.*

the cuticle of the leaf (Fig. 128). Each ascus contains eight (sometimes fewer) globose ascospores. The ascospores may bud before or after they are expelled from the ascus, and the buds are small secondary spores which are usually referred to as conidia. The life history of *T. deformans* is outlined in Fig. 129.

The ascospores and/or conidia are forcibly ejected from the asci in early summer and may be blown about by the wind or splashed about in raindrops. Some of the conidia have thicker walls than the others and are referred to as resting conidia (Martin, 1925). Such thick-walled conidia apparently do not germinate by immediate budding but form a short germ-tube, from which thin-walled conidia are formed by budding.

It was believed by earlier workers that this pathogen survives the winter months as a perennial mycelium in the shoots, but according to Butler and Jones (*loc. cit.*), the general opinion now appears to be that primary inoculum in the spring consists of conidia that had lodged on

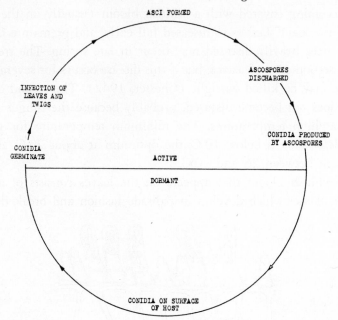

Fig. 129. *The host relation of* Taphrina deformans, *an ascomycetous plant pathogen. This fungus may survive the winter in the conidial stage on the surface of the host plant.* (*Based on Melhus and Kent, 1939.*)

some sheltered part of the host during the winter. Anderson (1956) concurs in this view and states that there is no evidence that the mycelium becomes perennial in infected twigs. Conidia present beneath the bud scales may constitute important inoculum.

Table 39.—*Some plant diseases caused by species of Ascomycetes*

Disease	Host or Hosts	Pathogen
Chestnut blight	American chestnut	*Endothia parasitica*
Brown rot	Stone fruits	*Sclerotinia fructicola*
Ergot	Rye	*Claviceps purpurea*
Leaf spot	Alfalfa	*Pseudopeziza medicaginis*
Scab	Apple	*Venturia inaequalis*
Powdery mildew	Grape	*Uncinula necator*
Scab	Cereals	*Gibberella zeae*
Blister canker	Apple	*Nummularia discreta*
Powdery mildew	Roses	*Sphaerotheca humuli*
Leaf spot	Cherry	*Coccomyces hiemalis*

FIG. 130. *Dutch Elm Disease, caused by* Ceratocystis ulmi. Top: *early symptoms of the disease; insert is a cross section of branch showing the brown discoloration of the annual rings of the wood.* Bottom: *Culture of* C. ulmi *on elm wood showing the appearance of the imperfect stage in which numerous coremia bearing thousands of conidia in droplets are formed. Conidia are carried by elm bark beetles and are the principal means of spread of the pathogen. (Courtesy of Agricultural Research Service, U.S. Department of Agriculture.)*

Considerable damage can be caused by Peach Leaf Curl. As noted above, repeated defoliation of the tree for several years will lead to its death; however, if defoliation is not this severe, the disease will lead to a reduced fruit set. Anderson (*loc. cit.*) states that this disease is one of the few serious diseases of peach which may be cheaply and effectively controlled, and notes that if sprays are applied at the correct time and if the correct materials are used, a 95 to 98 per cent control is usually attained. This writer notes that Leaf Curl cannot be controlled after the host tissue has been invaded in the spring and that applications of protectants must be made before the buds begin to swell.

A great many other diseases of economically important plants are caused by Ascomycetes; among these is Dutch Elm Disease (Fig. 130), which is caused by *Ceratocystis ulmi.* The causal organism of Dutch Elm Disease was first considered to be an imperfect fungus and was placed in the form genus *Graphium;* however, as the pathogen was further investigated, the perfect (sexual) stage was found. Other plant diseases which are caused by species of Ascomycetes are listed in Table 39.

CERCOSPORA LEAF SPOT OF BEET—INCITED BY AN IMPERFECT FUNGUS.   Leaf Spot of Beet, caused by *Cercospora beticola,*

FIG. 131.   *Beet leaf which has been extensively invaded by* Cercospora beticola, *an imperfect fungus which is the causal agent of Beet Leaf Spot.* (*Courtesy of C. C. Allison.*)

is a disease of the foliage of sugar beets, garden beets, mangel, and Swiss chard. It was formerly considered a very destructive disease of sugar beets, and in 1939 Melhus and Kent stated that in some sections of the United States losses of 50 per cent may result from defoliation, reduction in sugar percentage, and reduction in total tonnage yield of beets. The disease is no longer considered of significance on sugar beets,

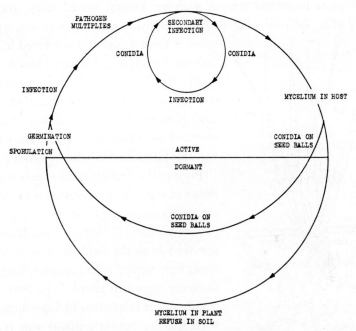

Fig. 132. *A diagram of the host relation of* Cercospora beticola, *an imperfect fungus. This plant pathogen survives the winter either as mycelium in plant refuse or as conidia on seed balls. (Based on Melhus and Kent, 1939.)*

since resistant varieties of sugar beet are now available (Walker, 1952).

The principal symptoms of the disease are the small spots (less than one centimeter in diameter) that develop on the leaf; these spots are brownish with reddish-purple borders but become ashen in color as a result of the production of conidia over the central portions. When infection is heavy (Fig. 131), the spots may be so numerous that they almost cover the entire leaf surface. When extensively invaded, the leaf turns yellow, shrivels, and dies. If environmental conditions favorable for the growth of the parasite prevail, it spreads to the next older leaves and thus continues to advance over the plant. New leaves continue to develop and in turn become invaded, which leads to the depletion of the supply of sugar accumulated in the root. As new leaves are formed and then destroyed, the crown of the plant becomes elongated and roughened.

Being an imperfect fungus with no known sexual stage, the life history of *C. beticola* (Fig. 132) is relatively simple. Only one type of spore is known, and this is formed in acervuli on the surface of invaded leaves (Fig. 133). Apparently the pathogen overwinters primarily as a mycelium on plant refuse; however, infected seed may also be a source of inoculum, although Walker states that this latter is of minor importance.

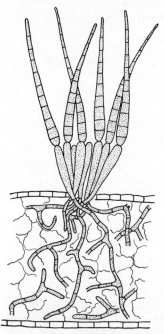

FIG. 133. *Diagram of acervulus of* Cercospora beticola *on beet leaf.*

Prior to the development of resistant varieties of sugar beet, sanitation was the best means of controlling *C. beticola;* it was usually recommended that diseased leaves be removed from the field or plowed under. Seeds were treated with a mercury dust, and since the organism invaded the host more readily under conditions of high humidity, wide spacing between plants was recommended. Melhus and Kent (*loc. cit.*) state that spraying has been recommended, but that in practice it was only partly successful and was too expensive. Since resistant sugar beets are now available, Leaf Spot is of no consequence in the production of this crop plant. Resistant varieties of garden beet have not, however, been developed, and the disease can cause damage to this plant. Walker states that while fungicides may be used to protect garden beets, this precaution is usually not necessary if proper rotation procedures are followed.

Many other plant diseases are caused by organisms now classified as imperfect fungi, a number of which are often called "wilts," "rots," and "anthracnoses." A few such diseases are listed in Table 40.

Table 40.—Some plant diseases caused by species of Fungi Imperfecti

Disease	Host or Hosts	Pathogen
Cotton wilt	Cotton	*Fusarium vasinfectum*
Tomato wilt	Tomato	*Fusarium lycopersici*
Stem rot	Sweet potato	*Fusarium batatatis*
Texas root rot	1700 species	*Phymatotrichum omnivorum*
Gray mold neck rot	Onions	*Botrytis allii*
Scab	Peach	*Cladosporium carpophilum*
Cereal anthracnose	Cereals	*Colletotrichum graminicolum*
Bean anthracnose	Beans	*Colletotrichum lindemuthianum*
Anthracnose	Clover & alfalfa	*Colletotrichum trifolii*
Blotch	Apple	*Phyllosticta solitaria*
Late blight	Celery	*Septoria apii*

WHITE PINE BLISTER RUST—A BASIDIOMYCETOUS DISEASE. Like the causal organisms of several other serious diseases of certain of our native trees, the causal organism of White Pine Blister Rust was introduced into this country from abroad. Melhus and Kent (*loc. cit.*) state that the pathogen is considered to be a native of the Baltic Provinces of the U.S.S.R., where it was first found on *Ribes* (currant and gooseberry) in 1854. The first collection of the organism in North America was made in New York in 1906.

The causal organism of White Pine Blister Rust, *Cronartium ribicola*, does not have a relatively simple life history as do the other plant pathogens discussed above, but instead forms a number of different spore types and is pathogenic on two unrelated groups of plants—the five-needle pines, of which the white pine is probably the most important, and gooseberries and currants, which are members of the genus *Ribes.* Not only does this pathogen invade and incite disease in both of these hosts, but it alternates between them in the course of its life cycle; if one or the other host is missing, the life cycle is not completed. Such a rust organism which alternates between two different hosts has the most complicated life cycle of all fungi and is known as an heteroecious rust.

Other heteroecious rust fungi are *Puccinia graminis,* the causal agent of Black Stem Rust of Wheat, which has the common barberry as its alternate host; *Gymnosporangium juniperi-virginianae,* the organism which causes Cedar-Apple Rust; and *Puccinia coronata,* the causal agent of Crown Rust of Oats, the alternate hosts of which are species of *Rhamnus* (buckthorn).

Apparently *C. ribicola* usually does not injure the *Ribes* host to any great extent, although defoliation by severe infection has been reported. Nevertheless the disease is extremely serious in white pine and could cause major losses throughout all of the white pine area of the United States and Canada. *Cronartium ribicola* may invade needles, twigs, branches, and main trunks of white pine trees, but it is on this latter that it causes greatest damage (Fig. 134). Trees may be killed or rendered commercially valueless in a period of five to ten years after initial invasion depending upon the size of the tree at the time it was first invaded. The infected tissues of the tree often swell into a more or less spindle-shaped enlargement on which one of the types of spores formed by this fungus develop. The first stage that develops on the pine is the spermagonial stage, which consists of small blisters that

FIG. 134.   *White Pine Blister Rust, incited by* Cronartium ribicola. *The blister rust canker has nearly girdled the main stem of this white pine tree. (Courtesy of C. C. Allison.)*

exude a sticky liquid containing small spermatia. The following year orange pustules are formed, and when the covering over the pustules breaks, a very fine yellow powder consisting of thousands of *aecio-spores* falls out and may be blown about by the wind. The mycelium in the wood continues to grow, and sporulation may occur again the next year, leading to the formation of large cankers which may completely girdle the stem. Resin exudes from such cankers and streams down the trunk, making white streaks with a characteristic appearance.

If aeciospores are carried by the wind to the surfaces of leaves of susceptible species of *Ribes,* they may germinate and initiate infection of that host. Early symptoms on the alternate host are small, yellow spots on the lower sides of the leaves. The *uredosori,* which are clusters of one-celled, thin-walled, stalked spores (*uredospores*) appear first in these spots and later there appear hornlike *telia,* on which are borne the *teliospores;* sometimes both the uredosori and the telia may be found simultaneously on the leaf (Fig. 135). The uredospores are the so-called repeating spores, which, if carried by some means to other currant or gooseberry leaves may initiate new sori. The teliospores are one-celled, thick-walled, dark-colored spores which germinate as soon as they are mature (forming basidia on which the basidiospores— often called sporidia—are borne). The basidiospores are thin-walled spores which are capable of initiating infection on pine. The complete

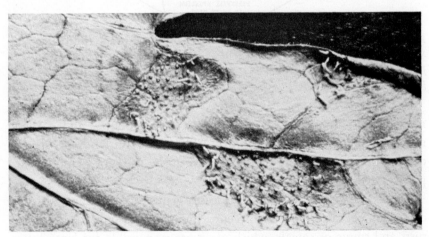

FIG. 135. *Lower surface of* Ribes *leaf magnified to show both the uredo-sori and telial horns in the spots infected with* Cronartium ribicola, *the causal organism of White Pine Blister Rust. (Courtesy of C. W. Ellett.)*

life history of *C. ribicola* in relation to both of its hosts is diagrammed in Fig. 136.

As a general rule, forest tree diseases are extremely difficult to eradicate, but control measures have been attempted in this country because of the great importance of white pine. These measures consist of both domestic and foreign quarantines and the eradication of susceptible *Ribes* species which are growing in the vicinity of five-

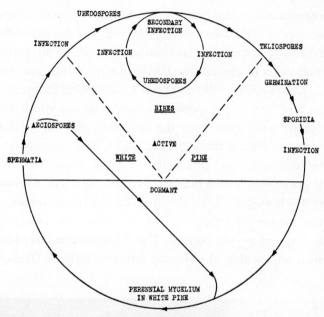

FIG. 136. *Diagram of the host relations of* Cronartium ribicola, *a Basidiomycete which is the causal agent of White Pine Blister Rust. This plant pathogen survives the winter as a perennial mycelium in the infected white pine.* (*Based on Melhus and Kent, 1939.*)

needle pines. The disease has spread over the country, and if these measures do not effectively control White Pine Blister Rust, species of pine other than white pine may have to be used for planting purposes.

Other tree diseases as well as diseases of herbaceous plants are also caused by species of Basidiomycetes. Important among these are the rusts and smuts of cereals, which often are responsible for large losses in agriculture. A few of the other diseases incited by species of Basidiomycetes are listed in Table 41.

Table 41.—Some plant diseases caused by species of Basidiomycetes

Disease	Host or Hosts	Pathogen
Stem rust	Grains and grasses	*Puccinia graminis*
Leaf rust	Wheat	*Puccinia recondita*
Orange rust	Cane fruits	*Gymnoconia interstitialis*
Carnation rust	Carnation	*Uromyces caryophillinus*
Flag smut	Wheat	*Urocystis tritici*
Corn smut	Corn	*Ustilago maydis*
Onion smut	Onion	*Urocystis cepulae*
White trunk rot	Broadleaf trees	*Fomes igniarius*
Shoestring root rot	Trees	*Armillaria mellea*
Black scurf	Potato	*Pellicularia filamentosa*

Principles of Plant Disease Control

For the effective control of plant diseases much information is required, since the chances are not very great of accidently discovering a good control measure as did Millardet (1885) when he discovered Bordeaux mixture. The complete life cycle of the organism should be known as well as the conditions under which the parasitic relationship is established, since when these facts are known control measures can frequently be developed, based upon knowledge of some vulnerable place in the life history of the organism. For example, the discovery that *Puccinia graminis,* the causal agent of Black Stem Rust of Wheat, alternates between two hosts in the course of its life cycle led to the control measure of eradicating barberry plants growing in the vicinity of wheat. Similarly, the work of Dickson (1923) lead to a recommendation which may prevent or minimize infection by the fungus which causes Seedling Blight of Wheat. This investigator found that wheat is not infected at temperatures of 12 C or lower and recommended that wheat be planted at the latest safe date in the fall or the earliest safe date in the spring in order to prevent or minimize infection by *Gibberella saubinetti.* There are other similar examples of disease control measures that have been developed after a thorough study of the parasite and the conditions affecting the establishment of the parasitic relationship have been made.

Methods of controlling plant diseases vary with the disease, but in general the approach to the problem of control can be divided into three main phases: (1) measures directed primarily against the pathogenic organism, (2) development of a host more resistant to disease, and (3) attempts to find out how the environment may be modified in order to prevent disease development or hold it to a minimum. As Butler and Jones (1949) have pointed out, quite frequently the control of a single plant disease may involve all three phases.

A variety of measures directed against the parasite have been employed. In some instances attempts have been made to keep the parasite from susceptible hosts by the establishment of quarantines to prevent the organism from being transported on infected material into an area where it is not established. Eradication of diseased plants is another measure in this category, since healthy susceptible plants may often be protected from disease by promptly removing and destroying diseased plants in the vicinity and thus eliminating the source of inoculum. General field sanitation is still another measure directed toward the reduction in amount of inoculum.

One of the most widely used measures directed against the pathogen is the application of protective substances to prevent invasion or colonization by the parasite. Such substances have been applied as either dusts or sprays and in the past have usually been copper or sulphur in one form or another. Today much work is being done in the development of new organic fungicidal compounds, with many of the major chemical companies directly involved in this development. While the earlier plant pathologists often merely tried a great number of different compounds in their search for effective materials to use in the control of plant disease, the plant pathologist today is interested in how a fungicide kills or inhibits the growth of a parasite, since information of this nature can lead to the scientific formulation of new and better fungicidal materials (see Horsfall, 1956). Another more recent development is the search for antibiotics which may be used effectively in the control of plant disease. Other measures that have been directed against the parasite are fumigation, soil sterilization, and seed disinfection. In instances where the spores of a parasitic fungus are known to be transported by insects from diseased to healthy plants, measures directed against the insect are employed; where a spray method is used, the spray material consists of a mixture of materials that kill both the insect and the parasite.

Most of the above measures are preventive in nature, but occasionally curative measures may be directed against an established parasite, such as in the removal of diseased branches or the excision of infected areas from the tree trunk. Especially intriguing from the standpoint of the development of curative measures is the possibility of introducing a chemical compound into a plant which will kill an invading pathogen or one already established.

Measures directed toward increasing the resistance of the host have consisted of (1) selection of naturally occurring disease-resistant plants for propagation or the breeding of other disease-resistant plants, and (2) the enhancement of disease resistance by means other than breeding. Examples of the latter are to be found in the work of Trelease and Trelease (1928), who reported that the susceptibility of wheat to mildew can be varied by changing the proportions of the mineral salts in the solution in which the wheat is cultured; and of Fischer (1935), who worked with both resistant and susceptible varieties of tomato and found that the concentration of several of the mineral elements affected the degree of resistance or susceptibility to tomato wilt.

Numerous measures have been directed toward the alteration of environmental conditions to make them less favorable for the development of the parasite. Crop rotation, which interposes several different crops between susceptible crops, undoubtedly results in the reduction in amount of inoculum and may also provide conditions less favorable for the growth of the parasite. Another example is the practice of providing good ventilation by wide spacing of plants that are more susceptible to invasion by a parasite under high humidity conditions. Better drainage also provides a better environment and is effective against parasites that thrive in very wet soil.

Summary

Adequately to cover a large, important, and rapidly expanding field such as plant pathology in a brief section of a general textbook is manifestly impossible. An attempt has been made, however, to point out the importance of this field to agriculture, industry, and human affairs in general. Also discussed were some of the problems confronting the plant pathologist, as well as various approaches to the solution of these problems. A tremendous responsibility rests with scientists in this field, since plant pathology must play an ever-increasing role in the provision of more food for a growing world population. The problems will be ever-changing, since as new conditions arise new plant diseases will also appear, and fungi may change their roles from non-pathogenic to pathogenic as new crops are brought into cultivation and new environmental conditions are created.

Literature Cited

Anderson, H. W. 1956. *Diseases of fruit crops.* McGraw-Hill, New York.

Butler, E. J., and Jones, S. G. 1949. *Plant pathology.* Macmillan, London.

Chester, K. S. 1942. *The nature and prevention of plant diseases.* Blakiston, Philadelphia.

Dickson, J. G. 1923. Influence of soil temperature and moisture on the development of the seedling blight of wheat and corn caused by *Gibberella saubinetti. Jour. Agr. Res. 23:*837–870.

Ellett, C. W. 1955. The parasitic fungi of Ohio plants. Ph.D. Dissertation, The Ohio State Univ.

Fischer, P. L. 1935. Physiological studies on the pathogenicity of *Fusarium lycopersici* for the tomato plant. *Bull. Md. Agr. Expt. Sta.* 374.

Horsfall, J. G. 1956. *Principles of fungicidal action.* Chronica Botanica, Waltham, Mass.

Martin, E. M. 1925. Cultural and morphological studies of some species of *Taphrina. Phytopath.* 15:67–76.

Melhus, I. E., and Kent, G. C. 1939. *Elements of plant pathology.* Macmillan, New York.

Stevens, F. L. 1913. *The fungi which cause plant disease.* Macmillan, New York.

Trelease, S. F., and Trelease, H. M. 1928. Susceptibility of wheat to mildew as influenced by salt nutrition. *Bull. Torrey Bot. Club.* 55:41–68.

Walker, J. C. 1952. *Diseases of vegetable crops.* McGraw-Hill, New York.

21 · *Destruction of Timber and Timber Products*

DECAY OF STANDING TREES

DECAY OF FELLED TIMBER

SAP STAINS

DECAY OF SAWN TIMBER

DECAY OF WOOD IN VARIOUS USES

NATURAL DURABILITY OF WOOD

AMONG THE MOST VALUABLE of all of our resources are our forests—not only because of their monetary value to the lumber business but because of the many thousands of useful products made from wood. For the most part we are inclined to take wood for granted because it is so commonplace, yet this attitude was hardly possible for many of the earlier settlers of the plains region, nor is wood an abundant commodity in the northernmost areas of the world where trees are scarce, stunted, or lacking altogether. To gain a better appreciation of the great value of wood one need but read accounts of the home-building problems encountered by the pioneers in the treeless prairie of the Midwest.

In spite of the seemingly boundless confidence of some individuals that the "age of plastics" we have entered will obviate our future need for wood, there is little evidence that many of the important objects now constructed from wood are likely to be replaced by plastics. Population increases always result in increased demands for basic raw materials, so we may safely anticipate increasing demands for timber and timber products. That our forest resources were unwisely exploited in earlier times is undeniable; however, a more sensible attitude toward the management of these important resources is becoming more and more apparent, and it would appear that with proper handling our timber supplies should be adequate for a considerable period.

It seems remarkable that many trees ever reach maturity when one considers the many harmful accidents that may occur from the time of seed germination until full growth is attained. The seed may be decayed by fungi, or eaten by birds or animals, and thus fail to germinate, or if the seed does germinate the young plant may be invaded by fungi and killed without even emerging above the soil line. If the seedling does emerge, it may be invaded by fungi at about the soil line, in which case it is destroyed by a disease commonly referred to as "damping off." Once the young tree is past the stage when it is susceptible to damping off, it is still subject to a great many vicissitudes. A variety of fungi may cause one or more tree diseases which result in weakening or death. The tree is also subject to damage from animals, wind, fire water, ice, and pathogenic organisms. All of these matters are more properly the concern of the forester and the forest pathologist, and need not be considered here.

In the present discussion the only diseases of living trees that will be considered are the heart rots. Actually there is some question as to whether or not a heart rot should be classed as a plant disease. Since these rots are confined principally to heartwood, which is composed of dead cells, it may be argued that the causal organisms are not parasitic. On the other hand, the life of a tree affected with heart rot is undoubtedly shortened even though no living tissue is invaded, so that the tree thus affected may be considered diseased. Whether or not heart rots are diseases in the strict sense, it should be noted that the major portion of the work conducted on such rots has been done by the forest pathologist.

A variety of factors may bring about the destruction and deterioration of timber and timber products. The main causes are mechanical wear, physical decomposition, chemical decomposition, insect damage, and decay by fungi. Some idea of the magnitude of the losses from these causes may be gained from the statement of Cartwright and Findlay (1946), who note that estimates made in the United States in 1924 indicate that an annual loss of wood products, when expressed in the equivalent of standing timber, may be nearly four billion cubic feet. The cause of wood deterioration depends on the use to which the wood is put; for example, the boards of a dry floor will probably deteriorate largely because of mechanical wear, whereas a fence post imbedded in moist soil is more likely to deteriorate as a result of fungal decay—the principal cause of wood deterioration in temperate regions.

Decay of Standing Trees

Many fungi are capable of growing in and causing decay of the heartwood of standing, living trees. The heart-rot fungi do not often grow in the living sapwood, and hence should probably not be considered true parasites. On the other hand they are somewhat different from saprophytes, which grow only on dead organic matter; the name

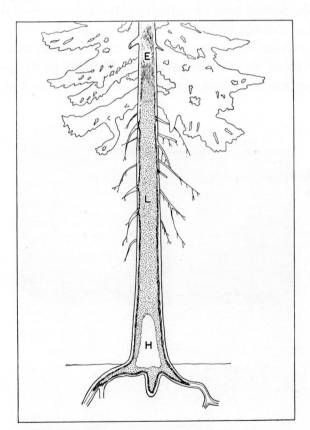

FIG. 137. *Heart rot in* Tsuga heterophylla *caused by the Indian paint fungus,* Echinodontium tinctorium. *Longitudinal section through living tree showing extent of decay with hollow cavity at* H, *late rot at* L, *and early rot at* E. (*Redrawn from Hubert, 1931.*)

pertophyte has been used for saprophytes that grow only in the nonliving parts of living trees. There are many fungi of this type, most of
which are of the class Basidiomycetes. Since these fungi do not grow in
living cells, their entry into the heartwood of trees is via wounds. Thus
infection takes place through roots which have died, through broken
branches, or other wounds (Fig. 137). Heart rot may occur in the butt
of the tree or in the upper part of the trunk (butt rot and top rot).

A heart rot fungus may live in a tree for many years before the tree
is killed, but the usable timber derived from the tree is decreased in
amount depending on the extent of the rot. In logging operations the
butt logs of trees frequently have to be discarded because of the presence of heart rot, or the rot may have progressed so far that no usable
logs may be derived from an entire tree. Boyce has pointed out that a
stand of trees should be felled when the amount of rotting occuring
each year exceeds the annual growth increment of the trees. This investigator found that in some stands of Douglas fir the growth increment exceeds the amount of rot until an age of 300 to 350 years has

FIG. 138. *Small pieces of oak wood cut to show early (top) and late
(bottom) stages of white pocket rot caused by* Stereum frustulosum.

Fig. 139. *Brown cubical rot. This piece of white pine sapwood was placed in a large test tube, sterilized, and inoculated with* Polyporus schweinitzii. *Note the dark color and cubical checking which is typical of the rot caused by this fungus.*

been reached. The amount of rot after that time equals the amount of growth and later exceeds it.

Both Cartwright and Findlay (1946) and Hubert (1931) list a variety of different rots, but for the present discussion it is not necessary to discuss these in detail. Prescott and Dunn (1940) have conveniently classified the rots into two major groups, the *white rots* and the *brown rots*. The white rots are further subdivided into *pocket* (Fig. 138), *stringy, flaky,* and *mottled* rots; the brown rots are divided into *pocket, stringy, mottled, ring,* and *cubical* rots (Fig. 139). The difference in color is due to the varying degree of destruction of wood constituents by different fungi. Thus, white-rot fungi destroy lignin principally, although in some instances they also destroy cellulose and effect a bleaching of the lignin; brown-rot fungi commonly destroy the cellulose. According to Boyce (1938) the most serious loss due to decay in this country is caused by Red Ring Rot (technically a white pocket rot). Brown rots are to be found in building timbers as well as in standing trees.

The problem of controlling heart rot and thus decreasing annual losses due to this decay of standing trees is a very large one indeed, and obviously, the control of rot in large stands of timber cannot be accomplished by giving attention to individual trees. However, the establishment of certain silvicultural practices will lead to some reduction of the losses. For example, the removal of crowding trees or trees damaged by lightning, ice storms, or previous cutting operations will reduce potential sources of infection and may result in the salvage of some usable timber. In old stands the trees should be cut down at an age when the annual growth increment is not exceeded by the progress of the rot. Since essentially all of the fungi that cause heart rot gain entry

Fig. 140. *This tree stump left after a logging operation has become invaded by a number of fungi, one of which is forming fruiting bodies. Shoots that develop from stumps often become infected very early with heart-rot fungi.*

into the heartwood by way of wounds, the avoidance of wounds is another way of diminishing the losses.

Wounding by natural causes cannot be controlled, but during logging operations in which clear cutting is not practiced the operations should be conducted in such fashion that there is a minimum of wounding of the trees that are not yet mature enough to be cut. Some heart rot can also be prevented by the use of proper reforestation practices, since Lorenz and Christensen (1937) stated that in 85 per cent of the cases of decay in unburned oak sprout stands studied in the Eastern states, the parent stump was the source of infection (Fig. 140). Thus it is advisable, at least with some species, to raise trees from seedlings rather than to let them develop from shoots.

Heart rot can be controlled to a certain extent in individual trees used for shade purposes or in park plantings, since damaged limbs can be sawed off close to the trunk and the wound treated with creosote, fungicidal paint, or similar material. With specimen trees, if the heart rot has not progressed too far the decayed portion may be cut out, the exposed sound wood treated, and the cavity filled with concrete or other type of masonry.

Decay of Felled Timber

It might be expected that the fungi capable of causing decay in the heartwood of standing trees would also cause decay of timber after it is felled, but apparently this does not usually occur. Some few fungi, such as *Polyporus schweinitzii,* continue growing but most others exhibit weak growth characteristics after the tree has been felled. Almost completely different fungus floras occur in trees affected with heart rot than occur in felled timber, a fact strikingly borne out by comparing the list of fungi recorded as causing heart rot with a similar list of those isolated from felled timber (Cartwright and Findlay, *loc. cit.*). The fungi involved in the decays of standing and felled timbers are of the same general type; why this difference in floras exists has never been clearly explained.

Although the wood of some species of trees is more resistant to decay than that of others, as soon as a tree is cut there are ample opportunities for it to become infected with a variety of different decay fungi. The bark is damaged in many places, branches are cut off, and the cut ends of logs present large unprotected areas of raw wood where the fungus may become established. One way of preventing losses at this stage of the lumbering operation is to get the cut logs to the sawmill with minimum delay. When this cannot be done quickly Cartwright and Findlay recommend brushing over the cut ends with creosote or other preservative material as soon after felling as possible. If logs cannot be hauled to the mill promptly, it is good practice to fell trees in winter, since environmental conditions in summer are more favorable for the development of fungi than during the winter months.

Sap Stains

In the above discussion we have dealt entirely with types of wood deterioration in which partial or entire destruction of the wood occurs. Since the decay fungi actually digest the walls of the cells of which wood is composed, wood infested with such fungi is weakened and thus rendered unfit for many purposes. In extreme cases it may be altogether destroyed. Besides the wood-rotting fungi there are other fungi that cause serious losses to the lumber industry, although they do

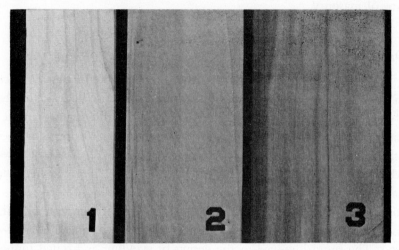

FIG. 141. *Effect of sap-stain fungi on wood. (1) unstained tulip poplar wood; (2) slightly stained tulip poplar wood; (3) heavily stained tulip poplar wood.*

not weaken lumber to an appreciable extent. The losses caused by the latter fungi consist mainly of forced downgrading, since the discoloration renders the wood unfit for many purposes. Lumber staining (Fig. 141) may be due to several causes, of which fungi is the most important economically. Most of these organisms do not develop and grow on living trees but are to be found on down timber, sawed timber, or wood products.

Most of the common wood-staining fungi are Ascomycetes, which grow principally in the sapwood. Occasionally the heartwood is also invaded. Some species of wood seem to be far more susceptible to fungus staining than others; for example, sycamore is quite susceptible to staining, and care must be taken in the stacking of freshly cut boards or considerable staining will result. The sap-stain fungi are often roughly classed into two groups on the basis of whether or not they penetrate the wood. If the mycelial growth is largely superficial, the stain does not penetrate the wood to a great extent and hence can be removed in the planing process; however, if the mycelium penetrates far into the wood, the blemishes are deep-seated and cannot be removed. If wood is to be left with a natural finish, stained lumber cannot be used, which is why the penetrating type of wood-staining fungi are responsible for the greater losses suffered by the lumber industry. In rare instances, as when an unusual wood pattern is desired, sap-stained lumber may be used for special cabinet work. In general the demand for such lumber is slight, so that sap-staining is a harmful rather than a helpful fungus activity. One species of Ascomycete, *Chlorosplenium aeruginosum,* imparts a very characteristic green color to oak and other hardwoods, and such stained wood has been used to a certain extent for inlay work (Tunbridge ware). Brooks (1913) proposed that wood be artificially infected with *C. aeruginosum* in order to stain it and was issued a British patent covering this process.

A number of sap stains have been described; they are usually named on the basis of the type of discoloration and type of wood affected. An example is the Grayish-Olive Stain of Hardwoods, first identified by Humphrey (1920) as being common on stored railroad ties of beech, red gum, and persimmon. The organism involved is *Lasiosphaeria pezizula,* which stains both the heartwood and sapwood. Other sap stains are the Yellow Stain of Hardwoods, which is caused by members of the *Penicillium divaricatum* group; the Red Stain of box elder caused by *Fusarium negundi;* and Blue Stain which may be caused by a number of wood-inhabiting fungi.

Sap-stain fungi develop most rapidly under conditions of abundant food supply, high moisture content of the wood, and warm weather. Some stains seem to occur very frequently; for example, Hubert (1931) has noted that Red Stain of box elder is of such frequent occurrence that it is popularly believed to be a reliable character for the identification of box elder wood.

Hubert (1924) has estimated that the annual loss in the United States due to sap-stain fungi (other than loss suffered by logs in storage) is over $10 million. This loss, of course, is a money loss rather than a physical loss of lumber, because a board so stained is still sound and usable for some purposes, yet must be downgraded and sold at a lower price.

Lumbermen and forest pathologists have been trying to solve the sap-stain problem in the United States since the latter part of the nineteenth century. According to Hubert (1931), no satisfactory method of preventing sap stain under all conditions has been developed. Methods

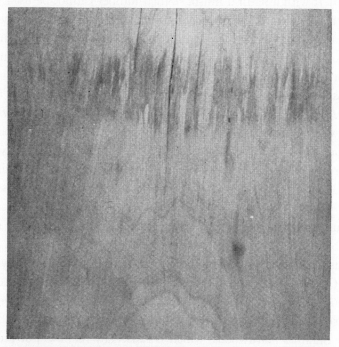

FIG. 142. *Sap-stain in sycamore. The darkened area extending across the upper part of the board is due to the growth of fungi in the area between the board and the stick which lay across it separating it from the board next above it in the stack.*

that have been tried include spraying with various chemicals, dipping into chemical solutions, coating the cut ends of logs with various materials, and storing logs under water.

The best preventive for stain in logs is to avoid long storage (especially during warm weather when conditions are favorable for growth of fungi), and to saw the logs as soon as possible after cutting. Even after logs are sawed into lumber, sap stain may still occur, but it can be reduced by dipping the lumber into a sodium carbonate-sodium bicarbonate solution and then stacking it in such manner that it will dry rapidly. One of the principal precautions to observe in the handling of freshly sawed boards is to stack them so that there is good air circulation around each board. Even this will not prevent some staining, especially in certain susceptible types of wood. In stacking sawed lumber for seasoning it is common practice to insert narrow wood "sticks" at intervals between the layers of freshly cut boards. Where a stick lays across the face of a board several square inches of the board are cut off from contact with the air; it is in this area that staining fungi may commonly develop (Fig. 142), since drying out of the board occurs more slowly there.

Decay of Sawn Timber

In order to prevent or at least diminish losses due to the growth of fungi, logs should be sawed into lumber as quickly as possible. When a living tree is felled the wood always contains considerable moisture; if the log is sawed into lumber shortly afterwards the lumber would contain a high percentage of water. The moisture content of freshly cut lumber is so high that it cannot be used for anything except rough or temporary building work.

The drying or seasoning of lumber is done in special drying kilns where the temperature and humidity can be controlled, or, more frequently, by piling in the open so that air can circulate freely around and through the lumber. Drying in the open requires a much longer period of time than kiln drying and its effectiveness is dependent upon the initial moisture content, the thickness of the timbers, environmental conditions, and the amount of care taken in stacking the boards. Sizable losses may be incurred if every precaution is not taken to insure rapid drying, since if boards are left moist for any prolonged period of time they will be invaded by a variety of harmful fungi (Fig. 143).

Many fungi are capable of growing on moist boards; some grow very rapidly and render a board unfit for use in a short period of time (Fig. 144). Usually if the moisture content of wood is reduced to a value below 20 per cent the chances of its becoming invaded by rotting fungi are slight. Sometimes "dry" boards are then stacked in solid piles; however, if their moisture content exceeds 22 per cent, solid stacking should never be practiced, since air cannot circulate and moisture may diffuse from the center of the board to the surface, where spores of wood-rotting

FIG. 143. *Rough-sawn sycamore board that was in the bottom layer of boards stacked for seasoning. Along the left side may be seen the fruiting body of a pore fungus, the mycelium of which has permeated much of the wood of that area; scattered over the remainder of the board are the dark stromata of an Ascomycete.*

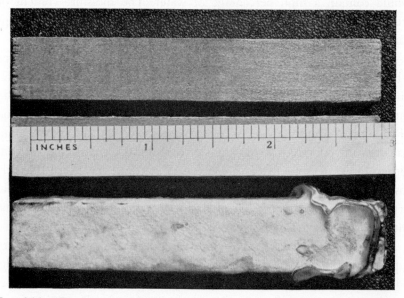

FIG. 144. *Birch wood blocks showing infected (bottom) and uninfected (top) blocks. The block on the bottom was placed in a large test tube with a small amount of nutrient medium, sterilized, and then inoculated with* Polyporus lucidus. *The picture was taken eight weeks after inoculation. When the block at the bottom was cleaned, dried and weighed, it had lost approximately 10 per cent of its initial weight.*

fungi may then germinate. Both staining fungi and rotting fungi may grow on the same boards; and with some types of wood staining can scarcely be avoided unless the boards are kiln-dried.

Boards that have been invaded by wood-rotting fungi are useless for most purposes; however, when the decay is not far advanced the lumber may be salvaged if the decayed area is superficial and if visibly affected surfaces can be removed by planing. If these boards are used for such purposes as furniture construction and thus kept permanently dry, no further difficulty will be encountered, but if the board is kept in a moist atmosphere, small infected areas that may have escaped notice will continue to develop. According to Cartwright and Findlay (*loc. cit.*), wood suspected of harboring decay can be sterilized by holding it at a temperature of 150F for 75 minutes in a humid atmosphere. This method has been used to preserve valuable carved and ornamental woodwork, but the method does not seem feasible for the sterilization of large-size lumber because of the excessive length of time necessary for

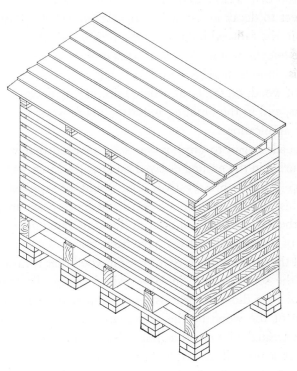

FIG. 145. *Proper method of stacking lumber for seasoning outside.*

heat penetration. Heat sterilization of entire buildings in which the timbers are heavily infected with dry rot has been attempted, but only with great difficulty. Although a variety of wood-preserving chemicals may be applied to finished lumber intended for building purposes, loss due to staining and decay can be best prevented, as previously indicated, by completing the logging and sawing operations as soon as possible and then stacking the sawn lumber properly (Fig. 145). For those interested in specific details of wood preservation the extensive work of Hunt and Garratt (1953) is recommended. This work covers the entire field of wood preservation, including descriptions of the more commonly used preservatives and their application.

Decay of Wood in Various Uses

Whether or not a piece of wood eventually decays in use depends upon the conditions of its application. Wood used in an application where moisture is continually present will obviously be subject to decay. Wood that is close to or in direct contact with the soil is particularly subject to decay unless it is properly protected. Moisture creates problems in the railroad industry in the prevention of decay of railroad ties; in the telephone and electric utilities industries, which utilize wood poles in distribution systems; in mines, where the shoring and roadways are made of wood; on the farm, where most of the fencing is fastened to wood posts, and in the building industry, where wood has hundreds of important applications.

As railroads began to grow it was soon realized that wooden crossties half buried in the ground decayed rapidly. Research was undertaken to develop suitable preservatives that could be applied to timbers used for this purpose. Telephone poles and fence posts are also partly buried in the soil and hence subject to the same rapid decay as crossties. A variety of wood preservatives have been tested, but apparently creosote is still the most satisfactory for use on wood that is in constant contact with the soil. Creosote in large cylinders may be applied under pressure, or by a dip-tank process, but in either method thorough impregnation of the wood by the preservative is essential. Crossties are completely treated with creosote, but poles and fence posts need only be treated over a prescribed length at the butt end.

The environmental conditions in many mines favor rapid growth of fungi. Mine timbers five to six inches in diameter may rot completely in less than a year (Cartwright and Findlay, *loc. cit.*). Pilat (1927) found many species of fungi in mines at depths of between 2000 and 4000 ft; in his studies of the silver mines at Pribram he found three elements in the fungus flora: (1) species common on wood on the surface of the earth in that locality, (2) species, such as *Paxillus panuoides,* which rarely occur above ground in central Europe, and (3) tropical or sub-tropical species which had been accidently introduced. Bryan and Richardson (1935) conducted trials in coal mines with mine props treated by the dip-tank process and found that a good measure of protection against decay was attained if the props were impregnated with a two per cent solution of Wolman salts, sodium fluoride, or zinc chloride. Wolman (1928) estimated that using treated wood for timbering mine roadways reduced to one-fifth the annual cost for such operations. This savings becomes quite significant when it is realized that the Rand gold mines in South Africa spent £3 million for mine timbers in one year.

Prior to the general use of steel for the construction of ships, the rotting of ships timbers remained a serious problem until the middle of the nineteenth century. Albion (1926) in his *Forests and Sea Power* has presented a history of the timber problems of the Royal Navy from 1652 to 1852. Ramsbottom (1937) has also discussed the early naval problems created by wood-rotting fungi. Apparently there was a period during the Napoleonic wars when ships timbers of British ships decayed even before the ships were launched. Excessive spending for defense is evidently not entirely a modern phenomenon; the *Queen Charlotte,* built in 1810, rotted so rapidly that she had to be completely rebuilt before she was commissioned. By 1816 the cost for repairs had amounted to £94,499 (in addition to the original cost of £88,254); by 1859 the total cost for repairs was £287,837.

Lumber, which forms an integral part of most buildings will decay like other wood products, but if proper construction methods are employed and the building is properly maintained, fungi usually present no serious problem. Building timbers will remain sound as long as they remain dry; the prevention of wood decay in buildings is therefore largely a matter of design and construction. Frame buildings (especially dwellings) in this country are generally so constructed that the rotting of timbers is a rare occurrence; however, in such countries as England, where higher humidities and lower temperatures prevail in dwellings, decay of the building timbers is of more serious concern.

The condition known as "dry rot" seems to be the greatest cause of decay of building timbers. Dry rot is characterized by a brown discoloration, a crumbly appearance, and cubelike cracking of the wood. According to Hubert (1931) there are two fungi of outstanding importance in the United States which cause dry rot in building timbers: *Merulius lacrymans* (the dry rot fungus), which has been studied by a number of European investigators, and *Poria incrassata* (the building poria), which has been studied in detail by Humphrey (1923). However, the consensus seems to be that in this country *P. incrassata* is the principal causal agent of dry rot, whereas in Europe *M. lacrymans* is the most important cause. The activities of these two fungi seem to be quite similar, and both are found primarily in connection with dry rot in buildings.

The term dry rot is somewhat misleading, since both of the fungi responsible for this condition need moisture in order for growth to be initiated. Both fungi develop best under warm, humid conditions, but they can spread from moist to dry wood by means of thick strands of mycelium through which enough water moves to enable them to grow in the new location. In this manner dry-rot fungi can grow from moist wood in a basement to dry wood in the upper stories. As wood is decomposed, the carbohydrates are respired to carbon dioxide and water, so that once wood is infected it becomes more moist, which in turn enables the fungus to spread still further. Miller (1932) measured the amount of water formed by *M. lacrymans* during the decomposition of wood cellulose and reported that it is nearly equal to the amount theoretically possible through the breakdown of cellulose to water and carbon dioxide. Bavendamm (1928) found that *M. lacrymans* as well as other wood-rotting fungi can thrive under conditions of reduced oxygen pressure, which partially explains the fact that the dry-rot fungus often starts its growth in wood that is poorly ventilated.

Hubert points out that the prevention of dry rot depends upon two factors—the control of moisture, and (where that is not possible) the application of preservatives to the wood. Basically the prevention of dry rot depends upon proper construction procedures which provide for adequate ventilation and prevent conditions of high moisture from developing. When dry rot is detected the rotted wood should be removed

Table 42.—*Relation of relative durability to specific gravity* [1]

CONIFERS		HARDWOODS	
Species	Specific Gravity *	Species	Specific Gravity *
VERY DURABLE WOODS †		VERY DURABLE WOODS †	
Pacific yew	.60	Osage orange	.77
Juniper	.48	Locust, black	.73
Redwood	.41	Mulberry, red	.59
Bald cypress	.41	Catalpa	.42
Western red cedar	.31	Walnut, black	.61
		DURABLE WOODS	
DURABLE WOODS		Chestnut	.45
S. yellow pine (dense)	.50	White oaks	.75
S. white cedar	.30	Locust, honey	.73
Douglas fir (dense)	.45	Oak, chestnut	.75
Douglas fir (Mont. & Wyo.)	.40	Elm	.72
Douglas fir (mill run)	.45	Gum, red	.59
Longleaf pine	.55		
Western larch	.48	LESS DURABLE WOODS	
Tamarack	.49	Elm, white	.65
		Butternut	.41
		Poplar, yellow	.42
LESS DURABLE WOODS		Oaks, red	.65
White pine	.36	Ash	.65
Western white pine	.39	Hickory, white	.74, .84
Shortleaf pine	.50	Beech	.69
Norway pine	.44	Magnolia, evergreen	.47
Western yellow pine	.38	Maple	.69
Pitch pine	.47	Birch	.58, .60
Sugar pine	.36	Sycamore	.57
Hemlock	.38	Gum, black, tupelo	.64
Spruce, Sitka, Englemann,		Basswood	.45
etc.	.34, .31	Cottonwood	.41, .46
Lodgepole pine	.38	Willow	.43, .45
Jack pine	.39	Aspen	.40
True firs	.31, .34	Alder, red	.37
	.35, .37		

[1] From Hubert (1931).
* From Record, "Economic Woods of the United States."
† Based on Table 40, in Weiss, H. F., *The Preservation of Structural Timber*, 1916.

and replaced with sound wood that has been treated with a preservative, and an effort made to control the development of high-humidity conditions in that particular location.

Natural Durability of Wood

The heartwood of most species of trees is more resistant to decay than the sapwood, and woods differ widely from species to species with respect to durability. Hubert (*loc. cit.*) indicates that such durable woods as oak, black locust, redwood, chestnut, and red mulberry contain tannins which may inhibit the growth of decay organisms. The reports of Schmitz (1922), Hawley and others (1924), and Sowder (1929) show that certain water-soluble materials present in some woods are toxic to fungi. Bateman (1925) has reported that resin and pine oils are toxic to wood-rotting fungi, and that resistance to decay of some woods may therefore be due to the presence of these materials. The specific gravity of wood seems to be an important factor in resistance to decay; Zeller (1917) has attempted to relate durability of woods such as oak and southern yellow pine to specific gravity alone. However, Hubert (1931) has pointed out that this relationship does not necessarily hold, and his contention is borne out by the data presented in Table 42.

From the data in Table 42, and from the reports of the various investigators who have attempted to relate natural durability of wood with some specific characteristic—such as the presence of some material or materials in the wood—it is apparent that no general statement can be made concerning the factors responsible for natural durability. Resistance of one type of wood to decay might well be due to the presence of some material toxic to fungi in that particular type of wood; in another type resistance might be attributable to the waterproofing effect of a resin, while in still other woods resistance to decay might be due to cell-wall thickness, size of cells, closeness of packing, or some combination of these various factors.

Literature Cited

Albion, R. G. 1926. *Forests and sea power.* Cambridge.
Bateman, E. 1925. What makes a pine stump last? *Southern Lumberman* 115:51.

Bavendamm, W. 1928. Neue Untersuchungen über die Lebensbedingungen holzzerstorender Pilze. *Zentralbl. Bakt. Abt. 2, 75:*426; 76:503.

Boyce, J. S. 1938. *Forest pathology.* McGraw-Hill, New York.

Brooks, F. T. 1913. Improvements in or relating to and/or preserving wood. British Patent 24595.

Bryan, J., and Richardson, N. A. 1935. Experiments on the preservation of mine timber. *For. Prod. Res. Record 3:*10 pp. H.M.S.O.

Cartwright, K. St. G., and Findlay, W. P. K. 1946. *Decay of timber and its prevention.* H.M.S.O., London.

Hawley, L. F., Fleck, L. C., and Richards, C. A. 1924. The relation between durability and chemical composition in wood. *Ind. Eng. Chem. 16:*699–700.

Hubert, E. E. 1924. The sap-stain problem and a ten-million dollar loss. *West Coast Lumberman 44:*28.

————. 1931. *An outline of forest pathology.* Wiley, New York.

Humphrey, C. J. 1920. The decay of ties in storage. *Proc. Amer. Wood Preservers Assoc. 16:*217–250.

————. 1923. Decay of lumber and building timbers due to *Poria incrassata. Mycologia 15:*258–276.

Hunt, G. M., and Garratt, G. A. 1953. *Wood preservation.* McGraw-Hill, New York.

Lorenz, R. C., and Christensen, C. M. 1937. A survey of forest tree diseases and their relation to stand improvement in the Lake and Central states. (Mimeo. report from *U.S.D.A. Bur. Pl. Ind.,* Oct. 7, 1937.)

Miller, V. V. 1932. Points in the biology and diagnosis of house fungi. I: The rotting process as a source of self-wetting for timber. *Pamph. State For. Tech. Pub. Leningrad. (Rev. Appl. Mycol. 12:*257).

Pilat, A. 1927. The mycoflora of the mines of Pribram. *Ann. Acad. Tchecosl. Agr.,* 1927, 455–553.

Prescott, S. C., and Dunn, C. G. 1940. *Industrial microbiology.* McGraw-Hill, New York.

Ramsbottom, J. 1937. Dry rot in ships. *Essex Naturalist 25:*231–267.

Schmitz, H. 1922. Preliminary note concerning the cause or causes of the durability of western red cedar, *Thuja plicata. Idaho Forester 4:*46–47.

Sowder, A. M. 1929. Toxicity of water-soluble extractives and the relative durability of water-treated flour of western red cedar. *Ind. Eng. Chem. 21:*981–984.

Wolman, K. 1928. Grubenbau. (In Mahlke-Troschel's "Handbuch der Holzkonservierung"; Berlin, 1928, pp. 358–379.)

22 · *Tropical Deterioration*

ELECTRICAL EQUIPMENT

LEATHER GOODS

PAPER GOODS

OPTICAL EQUIPMENT

TEXTILES

THE TERM "tropical deterioration" applied to the destruction of materials and objects by fungi can be misleading, since organic materials may deteriorate or be destroyed in temperate regions as well as in the tropics. Susceptible materials deteriorate much more rapidly, however, in a warm, humid climate where conditions are more favorable for fungus growth. Except in special instances, the deterioration of material often proceeds slowly, with only small amounts of material normally involved, so that, apart from the experience gained by military personnel in tropical countries, little concern has been evidenced over this form of fungal attack.

During World War II attention was focussed more sharply on the problems created by the deterioration of cellulosic and other materials when U.S. armed forces had to organize and supply a vast land, sea, and air campaign in the tropical and subtropical islands of the South Pacific. Under these conditions many types of materiel needed to wage a large-scale war were soon destroyed by fungi or rendered unfit for use. Materials such as clothing, tentage, optical equipment (binoculars, gunsights, cameras), leather goods, plastic objects, photographic film, paper goods, and electronic equipment were all subject to fungus growth, and hence the problem of tropical deterioration became a matter of immediate concern to the United States and her Allies. Accordingly, programs to study these problems were instituted in this country as well as in Australia,

India, England, Canada, and New Zealand. Close collaboration was maintained between the various groups, and information was freely exchanged.

Reports of investigations of tropical deterioration problems had appeared at intervals prior to World War II. Davis, Dreyfus, and Holland (1880) recognized that fungi are capable of causing mildew of cotton fabrics and isolated and identified several species of fungi from mildewed cotton materials. McBeth and Scales (1913) studied the destruction of cellulose by both bacteria and filamentous fungi. Thaysen and Bunker (1927) have summarized much of the literature prior to that time, so that no attempt will be made here to discuss in detail the earlier investigations, especially since much of the earlier work was concerned only with the deterioration of textile materials.

Electrical Equipment

According to Smith (1946), the first urgent problem in wartime tropical deterioration was that involving the growth of fungi of the mold type in radio and other electrical equipment. Such growth occurred primarily on insulation materials (Fig. 146), impregnating compounds such as waxes, laminated plastic materials, and cork packing. While there was little actual destruction of such materials, fungus

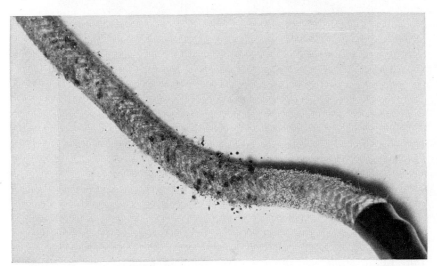

FIG. 146.   *Electrical cable with fungi growing on the insulation. (Courtesy C. K. Crocker, U.S. Testing Co., Inc., Hoboken, N. J.)*

growth led to leakage and short-circuiting via moist fungus hyphae (Fig. 147). Most such deterioration occurs only in unused equipment, because in operation a radio set or other electrical apparatus usually generates enough heat to maintain dryness and thus inhibit fungus growth. The solution to the problem of fungus-proofing electrical and electronic equipment lies in the use of suitable materials that do not provide a food source for the fungi. Thus, the substitution of polyvinyl chloride plastics for fabric in insulating applications prevents or greatly minimizes fungus growth on conductors (Fig. 148). Similarly, the selection of inert waxes or other impregnating compounds, or the incorporation of fungicidal materials into such compounds also prevents fungus growth, as does the use of paints containing fungicides, the elimination of cork, and the use of laminated plastics with inert fillers or suitable protective bonding agents. Smith states that with equipment not so pro-

FIG. 147. *Mold growth in a radio set with hyphae bridging some of the components.* (*From Smith, 1946; copied with permission from En-*deavour.)

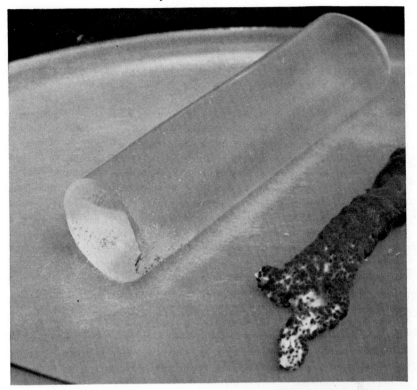

FIG. 148. *The growth of fungi on polyvinyl plastic as compared with growth on fabric.* Left: *polyvinyl plastic tubing inoculated with fungi;* right: *control specimen of twine. (Courtesy C. K. Crocker, U.S. Testing Company, Hoboken, N. J.)*

tected, fungus growth can be inhibited by spraying or painting the parts with a lacquer containing a fungicide.

Leather Goods

Whether or not fungi can digest collagen and thus actually cause destruction of leather is debatable. It is well known, however, that many molds will grow on the surface of leather, making it unpleasant to handle and requiring frequent cleaning. Furthermore, mold growth on leather instrument cases can spread to and possibly damage the enclosed instruments.

How well leather will support the growth of fungi depends upon the way it was tanned. Chrome-tanned leather is almost completely fungus-resistant because of the presence of chromic oxide; however, this type of leather is soft and unsuitable for many purposes. Shoe soles must be made of vegetable-tanned leather, which unfortunately supports the growth of fungi quite well. Failures in leather goods in service are often due to the rotting of the stitching threads as a result of fungus growth. It has been recommended that thread intended for this purpose be properly fungus-proofed by impregnation with chromic oxide or other fungicide. Smith (*loc. cit.*) states that fungus growth on leather can be prevented by using *p*-nitrophenol, which may be incorporated into the leather during manufacture or applied to the finished article. A somewhat less effective method is to apply a dubbin containing the fungicide to leather goods.

Paper Goods

The general problems encountered as a result of fungus growth on paper are discussed in Chapter 23. However, during the recent war problems not usually encountered were met and had to be solved. Paper is used in tremendous quantities in supplying a modern

FIG. 149. *Instruction booklet almost completely disintegrated by molds and moisture. (From Smith, 1946. Courtesy* Endeavour.)

army, and many of the paper products used in World War II were exposed to extreme tropical conditions (Fig. 149). During the war considerable research was devoted to the development of papers having high wet strength and resistance to the rotting effects of fungi. Materials such as sodium pentachlorophenate and copper naphthenate were used to mildew-proof papers. According to Smith (*loc. cit.*) the weak spots in built-up paper containers were the adhesives used, but that the substitution of modern plastic adhesives (such as urea-formaldehyde polymers) for older adhesives has resulted in great improvements.

Optical Equipment

One of the most persistent forms of wartime tropical deterioration was the growth of molds in or on optical equipment such as gun sights, binoculars, range finders, and telescopes. Although sterile glass does not support the growth of fungi, organic material on glass lenses or prisms, even in minute quantities, can serve as a substrate for fungus growth, which may spread over the glass surface. In many instances such mycelia may be simply wiped from the glass, but occasionally the glass is definitely etched and thus rendered unfit for further use.

The problems involved here are primarily problems of equipment construction. Instruments of the fixed-focus type will not support mold growth if they are assembled in a dry atmosphere and properly sealed. Instruments of the focusing type, however, cannot be air-sealed, and when used in a warm, moist climate, may be penetrated by moisture and small fragments of organic material. Organisms such as mites may also crawl into these instruments, where they may die and thus furnish sufficient substrate for the growth of fungi. Unfortunately, such mites generally carry fungus spores on their bodies, and thus furnish not only a substrate but also the inoculum. A first step in the construction of a fungus-proof instrument is to use greases, paints, or lacquers that do not support the growth of fungi. This helps in controlling fungus growth but does not protect the instrument when such organisms as mites gain entry. Protection against mold growth in such instruments has been partially solved by including in their construction a small capsule containing a desiccant or a volatile fungicide. Except in the emergency situation created in wartime, no severe problem exists because only a small number of such optical instruments are in use in the tropics. They can be easily cleaned at more or less regular intervals and any mold growth thus eliminated.

Textiles

That fungi will readily grow on many textiles is a fact known to many housewives, who are confronted at intervals with the "mildewing" of damp clothing. The advent of the power laundry and later the home clothes dryer has alleviated this problem to a great extent. During the war, however, by far the greatest problem of tropical deterioration was the damaging or destruction of textiles by fungi. The effects of fungi on textiles can be roughly classified as "mildews" and "rots." In mildew, fungi that grow on textiles do not actually attack the textile fiber, and hence do not cause a weakening or failure of the fiber. Nevertheless the growth of mildew fungi on textiles renders them unsightly and unfit for many purposes; or it may change the dye-fastness characteristics of the cloth. Rot fungi actually digest the textile fibers, causing a loss of fiber strength or complete destruction of the fabric.

Some textiles seem to be more susceptible to fungus growth than others. For example, Prindle (1935) has found that species of the genera *Alternaria, Stemphyllium, Oospora,* and *Penicillium* are especially destructive to wool, which is not readily susceptible to decay. Hardy (1943) has pointed out that silks and rayons may also support the growth of fungi, although deterioration of these fabrics is not frequently encountered. Hardy noted that acetate rayons are less affected by mildew organisms than the viscose and cuprammonium rayons. Marsh and Duske (1943) also studied the destruction of rayons by fungi and reported that the organisms responsible for the "tendering" of rayon yarns are molds of the common genera *Aspergillus* and *Penicillium.*

Most tropical deterioration of textiles occurs in cotton fabrics, which exhibit wide differences in susceptibility to fungus damage. Thaysen and Bunker (1924) have presented evidence that cotton fibers of different origin may vary considerably in their resistance to microbial deterioration. They found that American cotton was most resistant, Egyptian cotton less so, and that most rapid decay occurred in Indian cotton.

Davis and others (1880) observed that the spores of mildew-causing fungi are constantly present on cotton, so that cotton fabrics exposed to warmth and high humidity are likely to mildew. Intensified investigation in this country of tropical deterioration of textiles immediately prior to and during World War II had three phases: (1) isolation and identification of the fungi involved, (2) development of protective measures against deterioration, and (3) the development of reliable testing procedures for determining the efficacy of fungicidal treatments.

Many different species of fungi have been identified as causative agents in the deterioration of textiles. Davis and others (*loc. cit.*) early isolated several different fungi from mildewed cloth, as did Osborn (1912). Hardy (1943) stated that the chief textile mildewing fungi are species of *Penicillium, Mucor, Aspergillus, Fusarium,* and *Trichoderma,* but that the deterioration of cotton in storage is caused chiefly by a species of *Stachybotrys.* This same investigator stated that the species of fungus causing the greatest amount of damage to textile materials is *Chaetomium globosum* (Fig. 150) and that losses due to this organism are enormous. In his early studies of canvas deterioration in Malta and

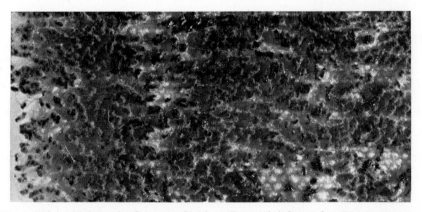

FIG. 150. *Enlarged photograph of surface of fabric showing numerous perithecia of* Chaetomium globosum; *the fabric was inoculated with spores of this fungus and incubated for 14 days. (Courtesy Institute of Home Economics, U.S. Department of Agriculture.)*

Italy, Broughton-Alcock (1919) attributed most of the deterioration to species of *Stemphyllium* (Fig. 151). The most extensive work in this area is that of White and others (1948), who assayed the cellulolytic activity of 453 cultures of fungi from 45 genera which had been isolated from fabrics and related items exposed in the tropics. These investigators estimated such activity by measuring the loss in tensile strength of strips of cotton fabric inoculated with pure cultures of the

various organisms under test. Many fungi were found to cause loss in
tensile strength, with considerable variation in destructiveness from one
species to another. Obviously a fungus capable of digesting cellulose
could under favorable environmental conditions cause serious deterioration of cotton fabric.

In the development of procedures designed to render fabrics more
resistant to mildew and rotting fungi, it was found necessary to devise

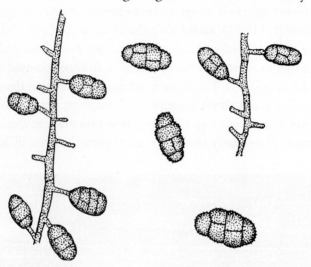

FIG. 151.   Stemphyllium sp., *an imperfect fungus often involved in the
deterioration of fabrics.* (*From Barnett, 1955.*)

methods of testing their resistance. Thom, Humfeld, and Holman
(1934), after experimenting with a number of fungi known to digest
cellulose, selected *Chaetomium globosum* as the most satisfactory species
for use in testing mildew resistance of treated fabrics designed for outdoor use. Their recommended laboratory test included the following
steps:

1. Sterilization of cloth strips which had been previously soaked in water.
2. Inoculation with a pure culture of *C. globosum.*
3. Incubation for fourteen days in petri dishes on agar jelly containing
mineral salts.
4. Washing and drying.
5. Ravelling the strips to reduce the width to a predetermined number of
threads equivalent to one inch of the original fabric.
6. Conditioning under controlled temperature and humidity.
7. Determining the tensile strength of the cloth.

According to these workers, tests in quintuplicate on treated and untreated cotton duck gave consistent results.

Rogers and others (1940), studying the deterioration of cotton duck by *Chaetomium globosum* as well as a bacterium (*Spirochaeta cytophaga*), developed a modified procedure in which 1½ × 6-in. strips of cloth were placed in 16-oz square bottles for incubation. The strips were

Fig. 152. *Incubation chambers for inoculated cloth strips.* Left, *strip treated with soap and cadmium chloride;* center, *strip treated with a double salt of chromium fluoride and sodium antimony fluoride;* right, *untreated strip.* (*From Furry, Robinson, and Humfeld, 1941; courtesy Institute of Home Economics, U.S. Department of Agriculture.*)

inoculated by pipetting 2 ml of inoculum (spore suspension) onto each strip. Furry and others (1941) used essentially the same procedure except that instead of pipetting inoculum onto the strips it was sprayed on with an atomizer (Fig. 152).

The method developed by Rogers and his co-workers was further modified by Greathouse and others (1942). These investigators also used 16-oz square bottles as individual incubation chambers for inoculated cloth strips but substituted a mat of glass fabric for the agar medium in each bottle. A cloth strip 6-in. long, which had been ravelled to a width of 1 in., was placed in each bottle. Uniform aeration of bottles was provided for by cutting a circle 4 cm in diameter from the center of each cap and inserting a filter of glass fabric. The following mineral-salts medium was found to be well suited for the growth of cellulose-decomposing fungi:

Mineral salt	Grams per liter
KH_2PO_4	1.3940
$MgSO_4$	0.7395
NH_4NO_3	1.0006
$CaCO_3$	0.0050
NaCl	0.0050
Fe, Zn, & Mn (as SO_4)	0.0010
H_2O to make 1 liter	

The details for making and assembling the individual incubation chambers used by Greathouse and his colleagues are illustrated in Fig. 153.

Modifications of the above testing procedures are basically similar in that the tests consist of inoculating sterilized pieces of fabric with pure cultures of some organism, and (after a suitable incubation period) determining if a loss in tensile strength has occurred. For example, cloth strips about 6 in. long and 1½ in. wide, ravelled to 1 in. in width, may be inserted in 1 × 8-in. test tubes containing a mineral salt solution into which the lower end of the strip extends. These may then be sterilized and inoculated with various fungi. This procedure was used by Gray and Martin (1947) in determining the cellulolytic activity of fungi isolated from asphalt-treated paper case liners, and also by White and others (*loc. cit.*) in their extensive investigations of the cellulolytic activities of fungi.

Disadvantages of the various pure culture testing methods are that when a single microorganism is used the possible reciprocal effects caused by the presence of other organisms is lacking, and the need for sterilizing the fabric. Bertolet (1944) developed a soil burial test which he claimed gave satisfactory results. Such a test has the obvious advantage that it brings the fabric under test into contact with a variety

FIG. 153. *Individual incubation chamber adapted to the use of liquid medium.* Upper right, *metal cap and wax paper filler with centers removed;* upper left, *glass cloth alone and in place in metal cap;* left center, *unsewed glass wick;* right center, *sewed glass wick;* bottom, *duck strip 6 in. long ravelled to 1-in. width;* center, *individual incubation chamber with glass wick and duck strip in place. (From Greathouse, Klemme, and Barker, 1942. Courtesy U.S. Department of Agriculture, Beltsville, Maryland.)*

of different microorganisms and eliminates the necessity for sterilization.

Marsh and others (1945) observed that great variation in results were reported by different laboratories even though the same type of material was tested in the different laboratories using the soil burial method. These differences can be attributed principally to two faults inherent in the method: seasonal effect when burial was out of doors or even in a greenhouse, and variation in soils used for burial of the fabric samples. Gray and Martin (1947) attempted to modify the soil burial method so as to eliminate or greatly minimize these faults. These investigators employed stainless steel pans equipped with plate glass covers; samples were buried in specially prepared compost in these pans, and were then maintained under controlled temperature and humidity conditions. Using the soil burial test, Gray and Martin demonstrated that variability in results between tests run with the same type of fabric could be greatly minimized.

Marsh and others (1945) stated that soil burial tests are much more drastic on a variety of treated fabrics than pure culture tests. These investigators concluded that the best test or combination of tests for determining the mildew resistance of a treated fabric depends on the service conditions for the fabric. A discussion of the problems involved in the standardization of testing methods is given in the work of Barker and others (1944).

Superficially the problem of making fabrics fungus resistant seems quite simple, since there are literally hundreds of chemical compounds that prevent or greatly inhibit the growth of fungi. Further examination shows the problem to be more complex, because many of these compounds have undesirable properties. For example, no water-soluble compound can be used on fabrics subjected to weathering or laundering. Some compounds may be colored, some may be toxic, some may actually deteriorate fabrics, and some may impart undesirable handling properties.

Various investigators who have studied the problem of finding suitable fungicides for use on fabrics have recommended an assortment of different chemical compounds. For example, Bright, Morris, and Summers stated in 1924 that the best known antiseptic at that time was zinc chloride, although this compound is little used as a fungus-proofing agent today. In the early work of Broughton-Alcock (*loc. cit.*) it was

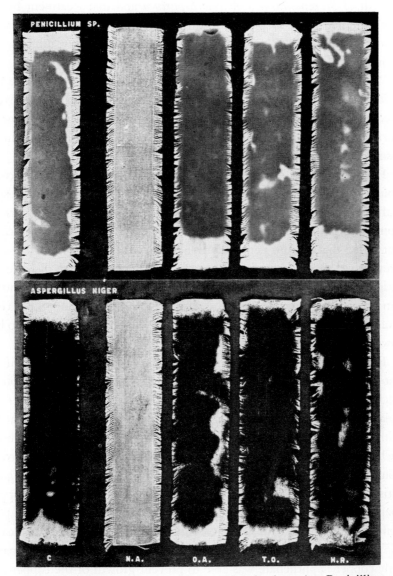

FIG. 154. *Fungicidal value of organic acid radicals against* Penicillium sp. *and* Aspergillus niger; *fabric treated at 1 per cent level. C, control; N.A., naphathenic acid; O.A., oleic acid; T.O., tall oil; H.R., hydrogenated resin. (From Marsh, Greathouse, Bollenbacher, and Butler, 1944. Courtesy U.S. Department of Agriculture, Beltsville, Maryland.)*

stated that cuprammonium or cutch treatment of canvas prevented the growth of *Stemphylium* and *Macrosporium* and that treatment by Piney's method (soft soap 1:5000 dilution, followed by a mixture of 1 per cent alum and 1 per cent copper sulphate) greatly inhibits the growth of these fungi.

"Shirlan" (salicylanilide), patented as an antiseptic in 1928 by the British Cotton Industries Research Association, has been extensively used as a fungicide in clothing and bedding and was in heavy demand during the war. However, Smith (*loc. cit.*) states that in preliminary tests mercaptobenzthiazole proved as effective as Shirlan.

Hardy (1943) reported that over 133 different chemical compounds were in use at that time for mildew-proofing fabrics. He especially recommended the use of Shirlan because it is colorless, odorless, nonvolatile in steam, and unaffected by sizing and finishing materials, but stated that sodium pentachlorophenate is also an effective, low-cost preventive. He recognized the importance of moisture in textile deterioration (as had Osborn as early as 1912) and stated that textile molds can be prevented by reducing the moisture content to below 8 per cent and the relative humidity of the atmosphere where they are stored to below 75 per cent.

Furry, Robinson, and Humfeld (1941) applied a great many different finishing treatments to degreased and desized unbleached cotton duck and estimated the mildew resistance of the treated samples by measuring loss in breaking strength after inoculation and incubation with *Chaetomium globosum*. They found that a great many compounds such as substituted phenols, dyes and mordants, organometallic compounds, metallic salts of organic acids, inorganic salts, and others gave satisfactory protection. Marsh and others (1944) used several copper soaps as protectants for fabrics and found that copper naphthenate prevents rotting of fabric at lower concentrations than does copper oleate, copper tallate, or copper hydrogenated resinate. Of these four soaps, only copper naphthenate was able to prevent growth of the copper-tolerant fungus, *Aspergillus niger*. These investigators also found that naphthenic acid alone is a potent fungicide (Fig. 154), which may explain the greater fungicidal action of the copper salt of this acid. In general copper naphthenate has been found to be a satisfactory preservative for application to fabrics (such as tentage materials) that do not come into prolonged contact with the skin, yet, Bayley and Weatherburn

(1945) have claimed that when cotton fabrics containing copper naphthenate are subjected to leaching in water, their ability to withstand microbial attack during the soil burial test is impaired. They stated that this effect is not due to the loss of copper during leaching, but to a change in the copper naphthenate whereby a portion of the copper is converted into a solvent-insoluble form.

In view of these and other favorable reports in the literature it seems apparent that a great many different compounds can be used successfully for treating fabrics as a measure directed against microbial deterioration. No general recommendation can be made here, since the selection of the proper fungicide for fabric treatment is in great part dependent upon the type of fabric and its service application.

Literature Cited

Barker, H. D., Greathouse, G. A., and Marsh, P. B. 1944. The problem of standardizing test methods for mildew and rot resistant treatments of textiles. *A.S.T.M. Bull. 126:*32–34.

Barnett, H. L. 1955. *Illustrated genera of imperfect fungi.* Burgess Publishing Co., Minneapolis.

Bayley, C. H., and Weatherburn, M. W. 1945. A study of the effect of leaching on the rot-proofing efficacy of copper naphthenate. *Amer. Dyestuff Reporter 34:*457–460, 471–473.

Bertolet, E. C. 1944. Observations on soil burial procedures. Symposium on mildew resistance. *AM. Soc. for Testing Mat. 23*–24, 1944.

Bright, T. B., Morris, L. E., and Summers, F. 1924. Mildew in cotton goods. *Jour. Text. Inst. 15:*T547–T558.

Broughton-Alcock, W. 1919. Canvas destroying fungi and their investigation in Malta and Italy. *Jour. Roy. Army Med. Corps 33:*482–485.

Davis, G. E., Dreyfus, C., and Holland, P. 1880. *Sizing and mildew in cotton goods.* 306 pp. Manchester, England.

Furry, M. S., Robinson, H. M., and Humfeld, H. 1941. Mildew-resistant treatments on fabrics. *Ind. Eng. Chem. 33:*538–545.

Gray, W. D., and Martin, G. W. 1947. Improvements on the soil burial testing method. *Mycologia 39:*358–367.

————. 1947. The growth of fungi on asphalt-treated paper. *Mycologia 39:*587–601.

Greathouse, G. A., Klemme, D. E., and Barker, H. D. 1942. Determining the deterioration of cellulose caused by fungi. *Ind. Eng. Chem. (Anal. Ed.) 14:*614–620.

Hardy, E. 1943. Fungi, molds and mildews in textiles. *Rayon Textile Monthly 24:*138–140.

Marsh, P. B., Greathouse, G. A., Bollenbacher, K., and Butler, M. 1944. Copper soaps as rot-proofing agents on fabrics. *Ind. Eng. Chem. (Ind. Ed.) 36:* 176–181.

——————, Butler, M., and Bollenbacher, K. 1945. Testing fabrics for resistance to mildew and rot. *U.S.D.A. Tech. Bull. 892.*

Marsh, W. S., and Duske, A. E. 1943. Destruction of rayon by "mildew" organisms. *Rayon Textile Monthly 24:*185–187, 242–244.

McBeth, I. G., and Scales, F. M. 1913. The destruction of cellulose by bacteria and filamentous fungi. *U.S.D.A. Bur. Plant Ind. Bull. 266.*

Osborn, T. G. B. 1912. Moulds and mildews: their relation to the damaging of grey cloth and prints. *Soc. Dyers and Colourists 28:*204–208.

Prindle, B. 1935. The microbiology of textile fibers. *Textile Res. 5:*542–568.

Rogers, R. E., Wheeler, H. C., and Humfeld, H. 1940. Physical and chemical changes produced in bleached cotton duck by *Chaetomium globosum* and *Spirochaeta cytophaga. U.S.D.A. Tech. Bull. 726:*1–35.

Smith, G. 1946. Moulds and tropical warfare. *Endeavour 5:*110–115.

Thaysen, A. C., and Bunker, H. J. 1924. Studies on the bacterial decay of textile fibers. I: Variations in the resistance of cottons of different origins to destruction by microorganisms. *Biochem. Jour. 18:*140–146.

——————. 1927. *The microbiology of cellulose, hemicelluloses, pectins and gums.* Oxford, London.

Thom, C., Humfeld, H., and Holman, H. P. 1934. Laboratory tests for mildew resistance in outdoor cotton fabrics. *Amer. Dyestuff Reporter 23:*581–586.

White, W. L., Darby, R. T., Stechert, G. M., and Sanderson, K. 1948. Assay of cellulolytic activity of molds isolated from fabrics and related items exposed in the tropics. *Mycologia 40:*34–84.

23 · *Fungi in the Paper Industry*

NO NATION is quite so profligate with paper as the United States. The amount of paper discarded annually in this country reaches staggering proportions and reflects the great abundance and relatively cheap price of this highly versatile material. The extensive forests which earlier covered the northern and eastern United States as well as the Great Lakes region, together with the proximity of the huge forested areas of Canada favored the large-scale development of the domestic paper industry. However, like many of other natural resources, the forests of America have been exploited without thought for the future, and as a result we may expect considerable reductions in the quantity of many types of wood available for pulping purposes, as well as a gradual increase in the cost of paper.

The increasing amount of paper used annually in the United States is taking a toll of our forest resources. Over 25 years ago Kress and his co-workers (1925) pointed out that pulpwood supplied to mills east of the Mississippi was being hauled for increasingly greater distances each year—an indication that the Eastern supplies had been largely depleted.

As pointed out in Chapter 2, the destruction of discarded paper and other cellulosic material through the digestive and respiratory activities of fungi is of direct benefit to man. On the other hand, the fungal destruction of supplies of unused paper or the deterioration of valuable books or manuscripts is obviously a harmful activity of fungi. Fungi do not destroy only finished paper. The paper industry faces the problem of combatting fungus activities at every step in the process of paper manufacture, starting with the living tree itself. The tree species used for paper pulp manufacture may be different from those used for lumber—and hence the pathogenic fungus species involved may also be different—but the basic problems are much the same and are largely in the province of the forest pathologist.

When a tree is cut for pulping purposes it may be shipped to the pulping mill immediately, but more commonly it is stored at some

FIG. 155.   *Pulpwood bolts stacked at woods point near scene of cutting. The above method is a good one to be used in stacking bolts, except that the two lowermost bolts in each stack are placed directly on the ground where they will undoubtedly decay if left too long. (Courtesy of American Forest Products Industries, Washington, D. C.)*

FIG. 156.   *Pulpwood bolts at the paper mill, showing method of storing in a large conical pile. (Courtesy of American Forest Products Industries, Washington, D. C.)*

woods point for varying periods of time (Fig. 155). In some instances storage at the woods point may be quite prolonged; for example, in southern Ohio it is not uncommon for a single pulpwood cutter to store his wood in the same spot until he has cut enough to fill a large box car. Winter is the best time for cutting pulp, since at this time the harmful fungi are more or less dormant. Furthermore, during the winter months there are few if any insects to carry the spores of wood-destroying fungi into the pile of pulpwood pieces. The bark should be removed as soon after cutting as possible in order to eliminate those insects living in or on the bark. If cut wood is stored for any length of time at a woods point, it should not be placed directly on the ground. Furthermore, the piles of wood should be separated and stacked lengthwise to the direction of the prevailing winds in order to facilitate drying.

Kress and others (*loc. cit.*) list the following species as causing extensive decay of pulpwood: *Polystictus hirsutus, P. versicolor, P. abietinus, Polyporus adustus, Stereum purpureum, S. sanguinolentum, Fomes roseus, Lenzites sepiaria,* and *Trametes pini.* Other fungi found to be responsible only occasionally for decay are *Fomes pinicola, Lenzites trabea, Trametes heteromorpha, T. peckii, Pleurotus ostreatus, Schizophyllum commune, Corticium galactinum, Stereum rugosiusculum,* and the Ascomycete *Hypoxylon cohaerens.* Many other species of

Fig. 157. *Pulpwood bolts at the paper mill, showing method of storing in long ricks. (Courtesy of R. C. Pratt, The Charmin Paper Products Company, Green Bay, Wis.)*

Basidiomycetes are also capable of causing wood decay if suitable environmental conditions prevail.

Once pulpwood is shipped from the point of cutting to the paper mill
it may be pulped immediately, but more commonly it is stored at the
mill for periods of time of up to one year or longer. During this period
any fungi present in the wood at the time it was removed from the
woods point will continue to grow unless proper precautions are taken.
At the mill, pulpwood may be stored in one of three ways: (1) completely immersed in water, (2) in conical piles (Fig. 156), or (3) in
ricks (Fig. 157). Complete immersion in water is best, since fungus
growth in the wood is prevented by the limited supply of oxygen; however, this method is not practicable at most mills. Ricking the pulpwood on weed-free, well-drained land in mill storage yards, where small
pieces of decayed wood are not allowed to accumulate, is preferable to
conical piling, although wood is sometimes stored in conical piles and
periodically sprayed with water to prevent decay.

Most paper mills try to carry a year's supply of wood in the storage
yard, but the cutting of pulpwood in winter leads to a seasonal peak in
pulpwood production which in turn results in periodic heavy influxes
of wood into the storage yards. Operators of mills may also overstock
wood when it is available in quantity in order to guard against a sudden
scarcity. Much of the storage loss is preventable if the wood is stacked
properly and if sanitation measures are rigidly enforced in the storage
yard. Wood should not be stored in utter disregard of species. Perishable
species such as poplar, balsam, and white fir, should be separated from
the more durable species. Badly infected shipments should always be
separated from noninfected woods in order to prevent the spread of
decay organisms.

Decay of wood either at the woods point or in the mill storage yard
is obviously a source of loss to the paper manufacturer because of the
reduction in actual weight of wood. In addition to these losses, still further losses may be sustained if decayed wood or partially decayed wood
is pulped, depending upon the type of pulping process employed. According to Kress and his co-workers, when mechanical pulp is prepared from decayed wood as the raw material, yields are characteristically low; moreover, the finished product has a darker color, and to
some extent a lower strength. On the other hand sulphite pulp (unless it

is prepared from badly deteriorated wood) does not differ greatly from pulp made from sound wood.

When decayed wood is used as raw material for paper manufacture, further losses may be sustained during the operation in which the wood bolts are chipped or ground. In wood that has been invaded by decay organisms, some of the fibers are partially destroyed; such wood is *brash,* and considerable losses may encountered because of the forma-

Table 43.—Data on grinding of sound and decayed spruce wood

Results of Grinding	Sound Wood	Decayed Wood
Quantity of wood (pieces)	140*	250†
Weight of rough wood (lb)	17,920	18,839
Weight of rough wood, oven dry (lb)	10,720	12,600
Loss in barking, based on oven dry wood (%)	32.4	31.3
Loss of barked wood, oven dry (lb)	7,250	8,650
Yield of pulp, oven dry weight (lb)	6,826	6,783
Yield of oven dry pulp, based on oven dry barked wood (%)	94.2	78.4
Yield of oven dry pulp, based on oven dry rough wood (%)	63.7	53.8

* 12-ft lengths
† 8-ft lengths
From Kress and others (1925).

Table 44.—Comparison of chipping losses sustained with sound and decayed spruce wood

Condition of Wood	Loss (%)
Sound	4.4
Relatively sound	5.6
Somewhat decayed	13.2
Considerably decayed	15.6
Badly decayed	17.0

From Kress and others (1925).

tion of an excessive amount of small particles during grinding or chipping. Tables 43 and 44 present data which indicate the magnitude of the losses that may be sustained during these operations.

The magnitude of losses sustained when paper pulp is stored depend on the type of pulp and the length of the storage period. Chemical pulps deteriorate less rapidly than ground wood pulps because they are usually stored for shorter periods of time and also because they are completely sterilized during the chemical process of pulping. Kress and others reported a $100,000 loss in one paper mill on ground wood stored inside for a comparatively short period of time; a loss of $10,000 was sustained at another mill on a 7500-ton lot of hydraulic-pressed ground spruce wood stored for two or three years. These workers point out that both wood-destroying fungi and fungi of the "mold" type may cause pulp deterioration, the former by decreasing the strength of the wood fibers and the latter by discoloring the pulp and binding the particles together—with the result that they do not beat up well and produce a lumpy, speckled paper. Although Kress and his colleagues state that the

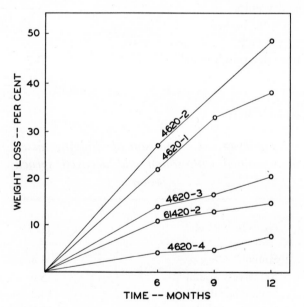

FIG. 158. *Graphs illustrating the rate of loss in weight of ground-wood pulp after infection in pure culture by various wood-destroying fungi. Figures on curves are isolate numbers. (Redrawn from Kress and others, 1925.)*

mold type of fungi are more likely to grow in pulp, they present evidence (Fig. 158) that weight losses may occur in pulp as a result of the growth of wood-destroying fungi.

Cartwright and Findlay (1946) state that ground wood pulp is usually imported into England in the form of sheets tightly baled together; that the pulp so handled contains approximately its own weight of water and is therefore excellent base material for the growth of both decay and "mold" types of fungi. These authors further state that considerable losses have been sustained due to the deterioration of pulp in all of the principal pulp-producing countries.

There is little evidence that the fungi in decayed or decaying pulp-wood are carried through the grinding and pulping processes. According to Sanborn (1933) the treatment of wood in sulphite digesters has a definite sterilizing effect, since the temperature at which digestion occurs is about 140–145C. The numbers of organisms in wood are also reduced in the preparation of ground wood pulp, because of the high temperature of grinding (85C). Fungal contamination occurring after the grinding and pulping processes must then enter the pulp from some source within or outside the mill. Sanborn states that microorganisms invade paper mills in water and to some extent in the raw materials, but Robak (1932) is of the opinion that air is a more important source of fungus contamination than either timber or water. Robak is probably correct in his view, since a greater fungus spore load would generally be expected in air than in water. He collected timber, logs, and wood pulp from all stages of paper manufacture and isolated fungi from these materials as well as from the woodwork in storage buildings and from backwater and slime deposits found in chutes and machine parts. He reported that the preponderating number of fungi isolated consisted of Hyphomycetes (order Moniliales) and other Fungi Imperfecti. Especially frequently isolated were *Cladosporium herbarum, Trichoderma lignorum, Hormonema pullulans,* and *Cadophora fastigiata.*

Robak cultured the organisms he had isolated in pulp and on sterilized filter paper and came to the conclusion that fungi ordinarily appearing on wood pulp are of no importance as fiber destroyers. He stressed the staining of pulp as being one of the most damaging results of the growth of fungi in wood pulp. Sanborn (*loc. cit.*) has also emphasized the discoloration of pulp and paper as being one of the principal damages that result from fungus growth in a paper mill, although he points out that economic loss and impaired quality can result from the formation of mill slimes and the actual deterioration of pulp and paper by fungi.

Slimes are frequently built up on the surfaces over which paper-pulp suspensions flow in paper mills. If particles of these slimes become a part of the finished paper, the result is the formation of shiny, sometimes translucent spots in the finished paper. Such slimes are never the

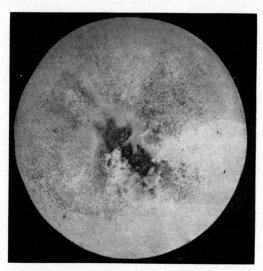

FIG. 159. *Growth of* Chaetomium globosum *on a piece of filter paper which was moistened, sterilized and then inoculated with spores and incubated under conditions of high relative humidity.*

result of the growth of a single species of organism, but consist of a variety of both bacteria and filamentous fungi. Sanborn isolated species of the following genera from such slimes: *Aspergillus, Mucor, Penicillium, Cladosporium, Chaetomium, Acrostalagmus, Trichoderma,* and *Alternaria.*

That paper itself is subject to decay as a result of fungal growth is obvious to anyone who has seen what can happen to discarded paper left on moist ground or in a damp basement for a period of time (Fig. 159). Paper used in book manufacture may sometimes be badly damaged by fungi. See (1919) isolated fungi from paper and books and found them to be species of *Chaetomium, Myxotridium, Eidamella, Aspergillus, Acrostalagmus, Spicaria, Torula, Cephalothecium, Stachy-*

botrys, Dematium, Cladosporium, Stemphyllium, Alternaria, Stysanus, and *Fusarium.* Sartory and others (1935) reported that species of *Cladosporium, Fusarium, Aspergillus,* and *Monilia* and an actinomycete may cause destruction of paper and that such organisms produce yellow, brown, black, or colorless spots on manufactured paper, known as "foxing." These investigators state that the action of such fungi may be very slow, as much as two years elapsing before any damage can be detected. Verona (1938) also studied the deterioration of paper and books by fungi and named new species of *Phoma, Coniosporium,* and *Cephalosporium* which he had isolated from such materials.

Asphalt-coated paper has been widely used to protect the contents of boxes and shipping cases, especially where the contents might be damaged by moisture and the growth of fungi, on the assumption that asphalt is fungicidal or at least fungistatic. Gray and Martin (1947) made isolations from asphalt-coated case liners which showed signs of fungus damage and obtained 19 fungi of the genera *Penicillium, Aspergillus, Chaetomium, Sepedonium,* and *Trichoderma.* Of these fungi, five were capable of causing marked loss in tensile strength of tentage cloth and hence were judged capable of digesting cellulose. Such fungi could, of course, weaken or perhaps completely destroy paper.

From the above brief accounts it is obvious that the paper manufacturer is faced with the problem of fungus damage from the time the tree is felled in the forest through all the stages of the manufacturing process up to and including the storage of the finished product. The paper fabricator and the ultimate user of the paper are also faced with the same problem, although to a lesser degree. Like most library books, valuable papers are usually kept under conditions that protect them from damage by fungi.

From the felling the tree up to the formation of wood pulp the principal fungi involved in the destruction of paper are probably wood-destroying species of Basidiomycetes, of which there are a great many. Damage to paper pulp appears to be caused primarily by the so-called mold type of fungi; of these, members of the Fungi Imperfecti seem to be principally involved. Various imperfect fungi are evidently responsible for most damage to finished paper and paper products, although there are some notable exceptions, such as species of *Chaetomium,* a genus of Ascomycetes.

Different procedures must be employed for the control of fungi in the manufacture of paper, depending upon the stage of the process. Control of wood-destroying fungi at the point of felling, in transit to the mill, and in the paper-mill storage yards depends largely upon proper stacking and sanitation measures. Pulpwood logs should be stacked well off the ground so that they are adequately aerated, thus permitting more rapid drying. Weeds should not be permitted to grow around the stacks, since this will prevent proper ventilation near the base of the stack and thus delay the drying-out process. If conditions permit, the pulpwood logs should be immersed in water at the mill until they are to be used. Neither dry wood nor wood saturated with water will decay, since in dry wood the moisture content is too low for the fungi to grow, while in saturated wood the oxygen content is likewise too low. Fungi will not grow in wood if the moisture content is lower than 20 per cent (Prescott and Dunn, 1940).

Many examples of the inhibitory effect of excess moisture upon wood decay can be cited. For example, the timber piles of the original London Bridge (built in 1176) have been recovered from time to time and are still sound. Another example of the inhibitory effect of water is provided by the fact that waterlogged timber recovered from river bottoms near sawmills is usually undecayed after many years of submersion.

Paper-mill storage yards should also be well drained and free of small pieces of rotting wood. Sound pulp wood logs should never be stacked in contact with decayed wood, otherwise the mycelia of wood-decaying fungi may grow from one piece of wood to another.

Pulped wood should not be stored for any longer period of time than is absolutely necessary. Rigid sanitation measures should be practiced in the mill to prevent the accumulation of microorganic slime on surfaces over which pulp suspensions pass. Sanborn (*loc. cit.*) recommends heavy chlorination of water for the control of mill slimes. If such widespread use of chlorine is undesirable because of the bleaching effect, copper compounds may be employed, and the direct application of calcium hypochlorite to surfaces where slimes commonly form will sometimes prevent their development. The most important aids in the prevention of slimes are vigilance in the detection and removal of slimes and the practice of general mill sanitation.

For the preservation of certain types of paper it is possible to incorporate a fungicide in the paper. Thus Gray and Martin reported that the incorporation of Dowicide G at a level of 0.7 per cent in kraft paper

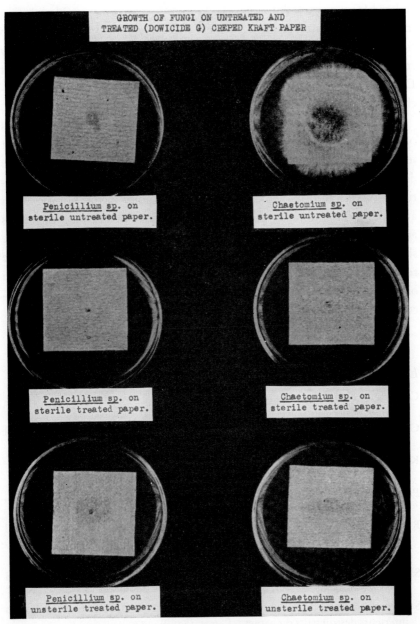

FIG. 160. *Growth of* Penicillium sp. *and* Chaetomium sp. *on creped kraft paper, with and without Dowicide G.* (*From Gray and Martin, 1947.*)

imparted complete protection against decay by fungi which had been isolated from paper (Fig. 160). Leaching of paper so treated by placing it in running water resulted in the excessive removal of fungicide so that it was no longer inhibitory; however, leaching can be prevented by coating the treated paper with asphalt. Paper containing 1.6 per cent Dowicide G and infused with asphalt containing 3.0 per cent pentachlorophenol was found to be completely resistant.

For the preservation of books and stored paper, the recommendations of See (*loc. cit.*) are probably adequate. On the basis of a number of tests, this worker recommended the use of formaldehyde vapors for the disinfection of books in the library. He also proposed the regular aeration of books and the avoidance of high humidity in the library. With air conditioning, libraries should encounter no serious amount of fungus activity; however, in older and congested libraries with inadequate shelf space, the problem may be more severe, especially in view of the report of Sartory and his colleagues regarding the slow action of fungi on paper products such as books, where considerable damage may occur before it becomes detectable.

Literature Cited

Cartwright, K. S. G., and Findlay, W. P. K. 1946. *Decay of timber and its prevention.* Forest Products Research Lab. London.

Gray, W. D., and Martin, G. W. 1947. The growth of fungi on asphalt-treated paper. *Mycologia 39:*587–601.

Kress, O., Humphrey, C. J., Richards, C. A., Bray, M. W., and Staidl, J. A. 1925. Control of decay in pulp and pulp wood. *U. S. Dept. Agr. Bull. 1298.*

Prescott, S. C., and Dunn, C. G. 1940. *Industrial microbiology.* McGraw-Hill, New York.

Robak, H. 1932. Investigations regarding fungi on Norwegian ground wood pulp and fungal infection at wood pulp mills. *Nyt Mag. for Naturvidenskaberne 32:*185–330.

Sanborn, J. R. 1933. Development and control of microorganisms in a pulp and paper mill system. *Jour. Bact. 26:*373–378.

Sartory, A., Sartory, R., Meyer, J., and Baumli, H. 1935. Quelques champignons inférieurs destructeurs du papier. *Papier 38:*529–542.

See, P. 1919. *Les maladies du papier piqué. Les champignons que les provoquent. Les modes de préservation.* O. Doin et Fils, Paris. 168 pp., 17 plates.

Verona, O. 1938. À propos des causes microbiennes de domage au papier et aux livres. *Boll. Soc. Int. Microbiol. Sez. Ital. 10:*91–92.

24 · Food Spoilage

ALTHOUGH A NUMBER of other factors may be responsible, the activities of microorganisms are the chief cause of food spoilage. To combat these activities a new science, food microbiology, has been developed.

Food microbiology is concerned with three major problems: (1) the prevention of food losses due to microbial action, (2) the prevention of food poisoning due to the growth of certain toxin-synthesizing organisms in the food, and (3) the prevention of the spread of certain human disease-producing organisms by way of foodstuffs. As far as the fungi are concerned the prevention of food losses is of most significance. One fungus, however (*Byssochlamys fulva,* an Ascomycete which creates problems in the fruit canning industry), synthesizes an acid known to be toxic to mice, and one investigator has reported that the fungus disease sporotrichosis may be contracted by eating certain green vegetables. Since food poisoning and the spread of disease involve bacteria and are of primary importance from the medical and health standpoint, a vast majority of the work done in the field of food microbiology has been concerned with food bacteriology. As a result, much remains to be learned about the mycology of foods.

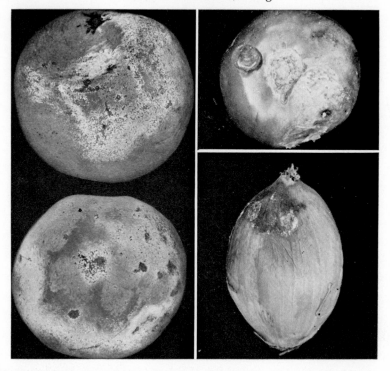

Fig. 161.   *Raw foodstuffs (grapefruits, tomato, onion) spoiled by fungus growth.*

Unless special precautions are taken, any type of food (Fig. 161) may become infected with and support the growth of a wide variety of fungi, rendering it unfit for consumption. Which fungus is principally involved in a case of food spoilage depends to a certain extent upon the type of food and the particular set of environmental conditions under which it is placed. Involved in this process are fungi of the mold type (order Moniliales of the Fungi Imperfecti), certain members of the Phycomycetous order Mucorales, and yeasts. Many fungus spores are commonly present upon foods. If conditions favorable for germination and growth exist, the food will become spoiled either in appearance or edibility. An example of spoiled appearance is provided by moldy bread: the fungi commonly found on bread are neither toxic nor pathogenic, and can be ingested without ill effect; but, because of its appearance, few people relish eating moldy bread unless goaded by hunger.

The storing of food under conditions unfavorable for the germination of spores and subsequent mycelial growth does not affect their viability. If the food is removed to a place where conditions are more favorable, fungi may grow. The work of Becquerel (1910) and others indicates that many fungus spores may remain viable for long periods of time, and McCrae (1923) has reported that spores of *Aspergillus oryzae* and *Rhizopus nigricans* have germinated after twenty-two years.

Losses Due to Spoilage of Food by Fungi

It is impossible to estimate the total losses sustained annually through the fungal deterioration of man's various foodstuffs, because no records are kept by food producers, food wholesalers, food retailers, or housewives of the quantities of food they destroy because of mold growth. In many food industries, however, it is possible to obtain fairly accurate estimates of the losses sustained through the activities of fungi. Two such estimates will be cited here to indicate the magnitude of such losses. Tanner (quoting a private communication from Pirrie, 1944) states that 100 million loaves of bread are annually discarded in the United States because they are moldy; at current prices this represents an annual loss to the baking industry of about $20 million. In his study of the microbiology of fruit, Tomkins (1936) estimated that the losses caused by *Penicillium digitatum* through the rotting of citrus fruits averages from two to three per cent of the total citrus fruit imports into England annually. Since about 20 million cases of oranges are imported into England each year, the loss of this one fruit alone would amount to between 400,000 and 600,000 cases.

Recent improvements in food preservation procedures have alleviated in part the staggering losses suffered annually due to food spoilage by fungi and other microorganisms. Man first preserved food by fermenting, salting, or drying it. These simple procedures are still adequate for some types of food products but obviously have limited applications. A great advance in food preservation was made when adequate canning procedures, employing heat sterilization, were developed. A second major advance was the use of low temperatures to preserve food by inhibiting the growth of microorganisms; the widespread use of electric refrigeration in the home is a primary factor in reducing the amount of food spoilage.

In spite of these and other advances, however, food spoilage continues to represent a serious economic loss to mankind. In some food industries spoilage is a chronic problem, while in others it is merely sporadic. The fungal spoilage of a number of major food types is discussed in this chapter.

Milk, Cream, and Dairy Products

General use of refrigeration has extended the potable life of fresh milk, and the development of pasteurizing, condensing, canning, and drying processes has made it possible to keep milk in a usable condition for much longer periods of time than formerly possible. However, a tremendous quantity of fresh milk is consumed directly, and fresh milk

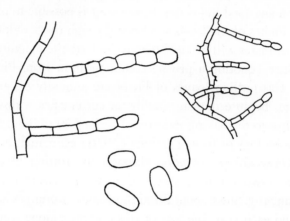

FIG. 162.   Oidium lactis, *an imperfect fungus, one of the fungi most commonly found in milk and cream.* (*From Barnett, 1955.*)

is unfortunately an excellent medium for the growth of filamentous fungi, yeasts, and bacteria.

Of the many different species of fungi found in milk supplies, *Oidium lactis* (Fig. 162) is, according to Tanner (1944), among the more common. Lactose-fermenting yeasts, which cause fermentation and gas production in milk and other dairy products, are also a source of trouble. From the standpoint of public health, the growth of fungi is not as serious as the presence of pathogenic bacteria in milk, since fungi only cause spoilage; however, fungus growths may be indicative of careless or insanitary handling. Elliker (1941) states that *O. lactis* enters milk and cream from dust, dirt, manure, and from carelessly washed utensils. Such materials are probably also the source of other species of fungi found in milk, since there is no evidence that fungi may come from the cow's udder as is true of certain bacteria.

Like milk, cream may contain a wide variety of fungus species, but *O. lactis* again seems to be the best known. Pasteurization is a reasonably effective means of controlling fungi in milk. The Thom and Ayers (1916), using fungus species from the genera *Aspergillus, Mucor, Penicillium, Oidium,* and *Fusarium,* found that normal pasteurization (heating milk to 145F and maintaining it at that temperature for 30 min) killed spores of every fungus species tested except conidia of *Aspergillus repens, A. flavus,* and *A. fumigatus.* The flash process (milk heated to 165F and held for 30 sec) destroyed the spores of all species tested with the exception of many spores of one form and occasional spores of three more forms. At 175F only occasional spores of two forms developed.

Both yeasts and filamentous fungi may grow in or on butter, and the "fishy" flavor of butter was early attributed to *O. lactis* by O'Callaghan (1901). However, Rogers (1909) studied this problem and was unable to produce fishy flavor in butter by inoculation with this fungus. Further inoculation experiments failed to connect this trouble with any one kind of bacterium, and Rogers concluded that fishy flavor is not produced by the action of a specific agent.

Butter may sometimes develop a yeasty flavor due to the growth of such yeasts as *Torula cremoris* and *T. spherica.* Rancid butter results when butter fats are hydrolyzed with the subsequent liberation of ill-smelling fatty acids. Many bacteria as well as the filamentous fungi, *Cladosporium butyri* and *O. lactis,* may be involved in the formation of rancid butter.

The problem of moldiness in butter was studied in some detail by Thom and Shaw (1915), who found that this condition usually appears in one of three forms: (1) orange-yellow areas with a submerged growth of mycelium which are caused by *O. lactis,* (2) smudged or dirty-green areas either entirely submerged or with some surface growth which are produced by species of *Alternaria* (Fig. 163) and *Cladosporium* (Fig. 164), and (3) green surface colonies caused by species of *Penicillium* (more rarely *Aspergillus*) which cause decomposition if growing directly on the butter or injure the market appearance if growing on the wrappings. Molds will not grow on butter exposed to relative humidities of 70 per cent or lower, since wet surfaces, wet wrappings, or high humidity are essential for the growth of fungi. Thom and Shaw found that species of *Oidium, Alternaria,* and *Cladosporium* cannot grow in butter containing 2.5 per cent salt, and stated that if salt is used in percentages of 2.5 to 3.0, mold growth may be eliminated or reduced to a negligible amount.

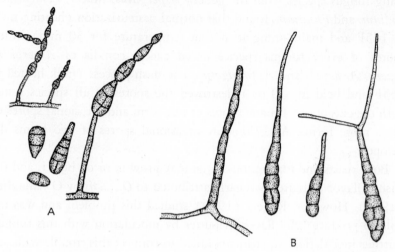

FIG. 163.   *A,* Alternaria sp.; *B,* Alternaria solani. *Species of the genus* Alternaria *sometimes cause moldiness in butter.* (*From Barnett, 1955.*)

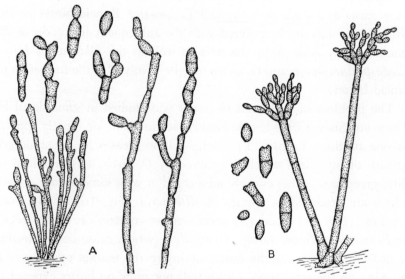

FIG. 164.   *A,* Cladosporium fulvum; *B,* Cladosporium herbarum. *Various members of the genus* Cladosporium *cause moldiness in butter similar to that caused by* Alternaria spp. (*From Barnett, 1955.*)

More recently Macy and others (1932) studied the changes that occur in the microflora during the manufacture and storage of butter and pointed out that, although pasteurization of the cream prior to churning destroyed 100 per cent of the molds, 88.98 to 100 per cent of the yeasts, and from 94.2 to 99.99 per cent of the bacteria, the cream could still be further contaminated during the butter-making process. They found that the churn was the most prolific source of contamination, especially for molds and yeasts. During storage at 35F, bacteria, yeasts, and molds increased in numbers in unsalted butter, but decreased in numbers in salted butter. The higher the salt content of butter the greater the effect on yeast and bacterial counts during storage, although this did not always hold true for mold counts. According to Tanner (*loc. cit.*), yeasts and molds are inhibited by 20 to 30 per cent salt solutions; this information, however, obviously cannot be applied in the preservation of butter for edible purposes.

Even canned condensed milk is not always completely free from fungus spoilage, since Rogers and others (1920) have reported a condition known as "button" formation in condensed milk which is fungal in origin. This condition, found to occur only in sweetened condensed milk, consists of a proliferation of reddish-brown masses of curd, usually regular in outline, and resembling a button in general form. Sometimes a slight fuzzy appearance may be observed on the surface, and microscopic examination usually reveals fungal hyphae in or on the button. According to Rogers and his co-workers, such buttons are caused by the growth of *Aspergillus repens* and possibly other species of fungi. Since the growth of the fungus is restricted when the oxygen in the can is exhausted, they stated that button formation is probably due to enzyme action which continues even after the death of the fungus. Fungi are destroyed during the condensing process, and hence contamination by molds leading to button formation must occur later in the handling of the milk. It was found that sealing the can under a vacuum of 20 in. or more is an effective means of controlling button formation.

In an earlier chapter dealing with the use of fungi in food processing it was pointed out that fungi are quite necessary for the ripening of certain types of cheeses, and thus may have a decidedly beneficial action in cheese manufacture. On the other hand, contamination of cheeses by certain other fungi may be harmful. Henrici (1947) states that *Geotrichum candidum* and *Scopulariopsis brevicaulis* frequently cause undesirable flavors in cheese.

Fruit and Fruit Products

Fresh fruits are relatively short-lived if stored under ordinary conditions of temperature and humidity, since the presence of large amounts of sugars and acids in fruits makes them excellent substrates for the growth of filamentous fungi, yeasts, and bacteria. Although there is no evidence that their tissues harbor any microorganisms, fresh fruits typically possess a quite varied flora of such organisms on their surfaces; once the covering tissues are broken these organisms enter and grow readily on the softer underlying tissues. The nature of the "protective" covering, and the ease by which this covering may be bruised or broken, varies with the kind of fruit. A very soft fruit like the strawberry with its thin covering tissue is much more readily invaded and destroyed by fungi than is a firmer fruit like the apple, with its thicker, cutinized outer tissue.

The fungus "spore load" on the surface of most fruits is probably acquired before harvesting from the plant, for in fruit-producing areas such as vineyards and orchards there is always some fallen and damaged fruit that provides adequate food for the growth of microorganisms and the building up of tremendous yeast, bacteria, and filamentous fungus populations. Washing does not remove all of the microorganisms from the surfaces of fresh fruit, and a variety of surface sterilizing treatments

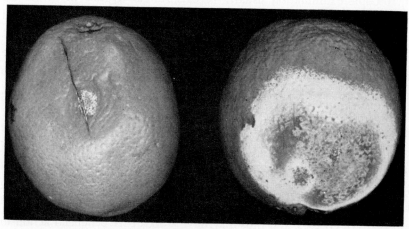

FIG. 165.　Penicillium digitatum *on oranges. The fruit on the left has a small fungus colony growing in it—the fungus apparently having entered the soft tissues of the fruit through a cut in the fruit wall. The fruit on the right shows a somewhat more advanced stage of the rot.*

designed to reduce the spore load have been tried, including dipping in hot water, formalin, or chloride of lime solution.

Fungus spores are prevalent on citrus fruits and much spoilage of such fruits occurs (Fig. 165). Tomkins (1936) has studied this problem in some detail and like others has found that one of the fungi chiefly responsible for the destruction of citrus fruits is *Penicillium digitatum*, a common green mold. This investigator found that the rate of rotting of stored citrus fruits by this organism is determined by the spore load, by the susceptibility of the fruit to invasion (such as mechanical injury), and by storage conditions. He recommends that mechanical injury and spore loads be kept at a minimum, and that fruits be stored at low temperature (40F). For reducing spore load, Tomkins also suggested that in instances of heavy orchard infection the fruits should be washed in mild disinfecting solutions and special wrappings should be used.

Drying, one of the earliest methods devised for the preserving of certain fruit, is not as widely practiced as it was before the development of better methods of preservation. The drying of fruits in no sense destroys the microorganisms on the surfaces; it merely reduces the water content and increases the concentration of sugar and other soluble materials to levels at which fungi cannot grow. As early as 1920 Prescott found that few dry foods are sterile and that the high concentrations of materials such as sugar in dried fruit were much more inhibitory to yeasts and bacteria than they were to filamentous fungi. However, he did note that several yeasts were capable of growing in and fermenting a 60 per cent sucrose solution.

Dried prunes and figs often become covered with a white, sugary substance during storage, before processing, and sometimes in the cartons after processing. It was formerly believed that this substance was mainly composed of sugar, but Baker and Mrak (1938) found that it consists of a mixture of sugar and yeast cells. These investigators made isolations from the sugary substance and recovered true yeasts, imperfect (nonsporulating) yeasts, and bacteria. In order of decreasing frequency of occurrence the yeast genera were listed as follows: *Zygosaccharomyces, Hansenula, Saccharomyces, Debaryomyces,* and *Zygopichia.* The souring of dried prunes both in storage and in the final package, and the souring of fresh dates after packaging, is a type of spoilage that occurs frequently. Esau and Cruess (1933) found that a number of yeasts were associated with this form of souring and recommended as a control measure that prunes be dried to a moisture content of less than 22 per cent. For control of souring of fresh dates they recommended pasteurization in sealed containers at a temperature of 60C or slightly higher. They pointed out that flavor is not appreciably affected by temperatures below 65C, but that at higher temperatures it may be seriously impaired.

The preservation of fruit by canning gives the consumer a product more closely resembling the fresh fruit than that attainable through drying; it also provides a better opportunity for the elimination of microorganisms, since elevated temperatures are typically employed in the canning process. However, too high a temperature may lead to undesirable changes in the product, such as undue softening or color and flavor changes. For the optimum preservation of fruit, the canner must rely upon a combination of three factors: (1) a concentrated sugar solution which will prevent the growth of most microorganisms; (2) a processing temperature high enough to eliminate many of the microorganisms, but not high enough to produce undesirable changes in the product; and (3) the exclusion of as much oxygen as possible from the final sealed container.

FIG. 166. *An example of fungus spoilage of commercially canned cherries.* Left, *side view of can showing thickness of fungus mass;* center, *view looking down on fungus colony;* right, *view of can with fungus mass and label removed showing irregular opening approximately ¼ × ½ in. Spoilage in this instance was probably due to can failure near the point indicated by the arrow; small amounts of solution probably leaked out through a minute hole in the can, thus providing moisture and food for the fungus. The can was then eroded by the high concentration of acid formed by the fungus in that area.*

In spite of all precautions, contamination and spoilage problems often arise in the canned fruit industry (Fig. 166). For example, Olliver and Rendle (1934) observed instances in which canned fruit disintegrated with no gas production, no abnormal flavor, and no evident color change and found that such spoilage was due to the activity of an Ascomycete which had previously been named *Byssochlamys fulva* by Olliver and Smith (1933). This fungus creates an important problem in fruit preservation in England, since it was found to be capable of disintegrating processed fruit even under conditions of reduced oxygen tension; the ascospores were found to be viable after being heated to 86–88C and held at this temperature for 30 min in fruit syrups. The organism probably comes into the cannery on fresh fruit, since it is known to be present on fruit in fields and orchards. Raistrick and Smith (1933) examined the metabolic products of *B. fulva* and found that while the product formed in greatest amount is mannitol, this fungus also synthesizes an acid which they named byssochlamic acid ($C_{18}H_{20}O_6$) in yields of about 0.5 per cent. Although byssochlamic acid was shown to be toxic to mice, no cases of human poisoning by this acid have been reported thus far.

Williams and others (1941) have reported a somewhat unusual type of mold contamination of canned fruit. These investigators found small colonies of a fungus (an unnamed species of *Penicillium*) growing in sealed cans of blueberries. Such growth occurred on the surface and only in enamel-lined cans. The blueberries had been placed in the cans at a temperature of 200F; the cans were then sealed, inverted, and air-cooled. This procedure results in a good vacuum in the can after cooling, the temperature of processing usually being adequate to destroy microorganisms of low heat resistance. They isolated a *Penicillium* from blueberries and from the soil of blueberry fields and found it capable of growing under high vacuum; one strain formed sclerotia which had unusually high resistance to heat.

The popularization and more widespread use of fruit juices in recent years has created additional problems for the canning industry. High temperatures cannot be used in processing, since they may alter the taste; fortunately, however, most filamentous fungi do not grow in canned fruit juice because of insufficient amounts of oxygen. According to Fabian (1933), grape juice normally contains filamentous fungi, bacteria, and yeasts, the latter predominating. The principal problem in the preservation of fruit juices is to devise a pasteurization process that will destroy yeasts without altering the quality of the product.

Except in an occasional instance encountered by the home canner, fungi present no great problems in the preservation of such fruit products as jams and jellies. According to Macara (1937), mold spores will not germinate in fruit jams containing 70 to 72 per cent solids if kept under conditions where the relative humidity is below 82 per cent.

Bread

The filamentous fungi are principally responsible for bread spoilage, although yeast and bacteria may, under unusual circumstances, occasionally be involved. This fact has been recognized in such early work as that of Smith (1885), who studied what he termed "musty" bread and mentioned *Aspergillus glaucus* and *Mucor mucedo* as fungi which are associated with this problem.

For some indeterminate reason the common Phycomycete, *Rhizopus nigricans,* has come to be popularly known as "bread mold" by many botanists. The implications of this common name as applied only to *R. nigricans* are quite misleading, and to continue to call this species bread mold is to simply promulgate a sort of botanical folklore. It is true that *R. nigricans* will usually grow on bread quite readily (if it is sliced, inoculated, placed in a moist chamber, and held at the correct temperature), but so will many other species of fungi, and a perusal of the literature on moldy bread does not give the impression that *R. nigricans* is the species principally involved in this problem. For example, Herter and Fournet (1919), in their study of the fungi found on bread, reported not only *R. nigricans* but eleven other species of fungi from the genera *Aspergillus, Penicillium, Mucor, Rhizopus,* and *Oospora.* Similarly, Thom and LeFevre (1921), who were concerned with the microbial flora of corn meal, isolated *Fusarium sp., Aspergillus repens, A. flavus, A. tamari, A. niger,* three species of *Penicillium, R. nigricans, Mucor sp., Syncephalastrum sp.,* as well as yeasts, yeastlike fungi, and bacteria. In the present writer's own experience, species of *Aspergillus* and *Penicillium* have been observed most commonly on accidently inoculated moldy bread. Reed (1924) cites a case in a small bakery in which *Neurospora (Monilia) sitophila* was the sole cause of bread spoilage. Bread baked in this bakery developed a shell pink color in four to five days, and the color increased in intensity until the loaf was eight to ten days old. Destruction of all infected material in the bakery, followed by cleaning and application of sodium hypochlorite solution, cleared up the trouble.

As sold in the United States, wrapped bread is a clean and attractive processed food. However, Tanner (loc. cit.) states that in 1913 the National Association of Master Bakers held that wrapping bread in waxed paper was not to be recommended, since it holds moisture upon the surface of the loaf and leads to injurious effects upon quality. Despite these early objections, most of the bread marketed in this country today is not only wrapped but also sliced. Wrapped and sliced bread is definitely a cleaner, more convenient product and represents a marked advance in the baking industry, but the introduction of slicing and wrapping machinery contributes greatly to the mold problem. The baker must prevent mold development for 96 hours, which is "freshness" life of the bread. As bread comes from the oven it is sterile so far as molds are concerned, for Owen (1932) has shown that bread collected in sterile paper bags as it comes from the oven and inserted after cooling into a sterile wrapper rarely develops mold, even if incubated at 90F. The spore load on bread, therefore, must accumulate during the time the bread leaves the oven until it is wrapped.

Under practical baking conditions it is almost impossible to prevent fungus spores from getting on bread, although modern air conditioning removes many of the air-borne spores. Not only is sliced bread more susceptible to molding than the whole loaf with unbroken crust, but according to Owen, the greatest source of contamination is at the bread slicer. At this point in the process slicing saws continually carry fungus

Table 45.—Effect of exposure to ultraviolet radiation on mold development on sliced bread

| | Average Number of Molds per Slice | Per cent of slices | | Average Number of Molds per Slice Infected |
		Free from Mold	Showing Mold	
Control	2.00	25	75	2.6
Exposed	0.55	45	55	0.99

Based on a table from Owen (1932).

spores from the surface to the moister and more susceptible inner portions of the loaf. Owen found that by irradiating bread with ultraviolet light during the slicing operation, the contamination was partly reduced; data obtained by this investigator are presented in Table 45.

Several attempts have been made to control bread mold by incorporating some type of fungus-inhibiting agent in the bread. For example, Jalade (*cf.* Owen, 1932) discovered that the addition of acetic acid in amounts sufficient to lower the pH to 3.1 usually corrects mold trouble in bread; Kirby and others (1935, 1937) recommended the use of fatty acids for controlling mold. They studied the effects of acids upon the growth of *Neurospora sitophila, R. nigricans,* four species of *Aspergillus,* two species of *Penicillium,* and an unidentified green mold, and stated that fatty acids were more toxic to fungi than mineral acids or such organic acids as lactic, citric, tartaric and maleic. These investigators also found that a film of very dilute acetic acid (such as

FIG 167.   *The effect of acetic acid on mold growth. The right half of the loaf was wiped with 90-grain vinegar; the left half was not treated. Both halves were then inoculated with* Rhizopus nigricans. (*From Kirby, Atkin, and Frey, 1937; Courtesy Fleischmann Laboratories, Standard Brands Incorporated.*)

vinegar) covering the surface of bread is very effective in preventing or retarding the development of mold (Fig. 167). Today sodium and calcium propionates (used under the name "Mycoban") are widely used as mold inhibitors in bread.

Meat

Prior to the widespread use of refrigeration in meat packing plants, wholesale and retail outlets, and the home, the meat packing industry was of more or less seasonal nature due to the lack of adequate means of preserving fresh meats during the warm months. Even with the benefits of mechanical refrigeration, however, the meat industry today is still not free of the spoilage problem caused by the activities of microorganisms; Tanner (1944) has stated that the industry depends largely upon strict control of these organisms.

Examination of the extensive works of Tanner and of Jensen (1954) reveals that many microorganisms may be involved in meat spoilage, yet the vast majority of investigators in the area of meat microbiology have been largely concerned with bacteria, and especially those bacteria which may be involved in synthesizing toxic materials or inciting human disease. While it is generally recognized that a number of fungi may grow on meat and some may be the cause of considerable spoilage, the opinion is rather prevalent that, unless fungus growth on meat is accompanied by the growth of putrefactive bacteria, no great amount of harm is done to the meat. Yesair (1928) isolated and studied fungi from meats and noted that molds are observed most frequently on ham, bacon, and dry or summer sausages; he also stated that fungi are found on the surface of pickling solutions as well as on equipment and on the walls and ceilings of packing plants. During his study Yesair isolated *Penicillium expansum, Aspergillus glaucus, A. clavatus, A. niger, Mucor racemosus, Monascus purpureus, Neurospora (Monilia) sitophila, Fusarium sp., Mortierella sp.,* and *Oidium lactis,* but stated that *P. expansum, A. glaucus,* and *M. racemosus* were found most frequently.

Before distribution to the consumer beef is usually subjected to a ripening and tendering period by aging it in coolers with controlled humidity and temperature. During this aging period molds (*Thamnidium, Rhizopus, Mucor*) usually appear on the surface but apparently do not harm the meat. There is considerable difference of opinion as to whether or not the desired qualities of beef are due to the growth of such molds.

Jensen states that a variety of molds may grow on bacon and lists *Aspergillus, Alternaria, Monilia, Oidium, Fusarium, Mucor, Rhizopus,*

Botrytis, and *Penicillium* as the fungus genera involved. Sometimes fungi may grow on the surface and form chromogenic substances which diffuse into the fat, causing pink or yellow-brown discolorations; yeasts and bacteria may also lead to discolorations of this type.

A number of species of fungi will grow on frozen meat, especially during prolonged storage or transportation periods such as those in-volved in the shipping of beef from Australia to England. Such fungus growth often leads to a condition known as "black spot," which gives the meat an unsightly appearance but which was shown many years ago to be harmless. Brooks and Kidd (1921) attribute black spot to the fungus *Cladosporium herbarum,* but several other investigators have implicated other fungi such as *Oidium carnis, Saccharomyces sp., Tham-nidium elegans, Mucor mucedo, Rhizopus nigricans,* and various species of *Penicillium* (Jensen, *loc. cit.*).

Vegetables

Like fruits, all vegetables may be rendered valueless as human food by a variety of microorganisms, but in general they are less sus-ceptible than fruits to rapid spoilage. This difference is due to the fact that such food materials contain less sugar and water and are generally composed of much firmer tissue than most fruits. As a result vegetables, especially root vegetables, can usually be stored for much longer periods of time.

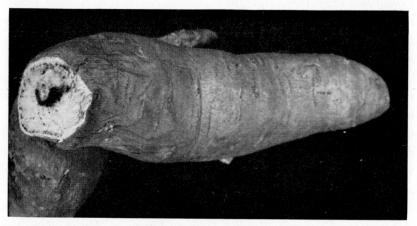

FIG. 168.   *Storage rot of sweet potato. Note growth of* Rhizopus nigri-cans *on broken end of root.*

The spoiling of sweet potatoes during storage has presented a very considerable problem to the food industry and has been the object of extensive research. The fact that sweet potatoes contain much greater amounts of sugar than most other vegetables makes them good substrates for the growth of mold fungi. Storage rots of sweet potatoes were studied by Harter and others (1918) and later by Lauritzen and Harter (1926). These latter investigators used *Rhizopus nigricans* and *R. tritici* in their experimental work and found that the invasion of stored sweet potatoes by these fungi occurs almost exclusively through fresh wounds (Fig. 168). They also found that the optimum conditions of humidity for infection range from 75 to 84 per cent, the percentage of infection decreasing rapidly as the humidity is raised or lowered. Lauritzen and Harter reported that a resistance to infection by *Rhizopus* developed in wounded sweet potatoes if they were held at a relative humidity of 89–97 per cent, and that this resistance was related to and associated with cork formation.

Although the home canner may occasionally encounter instances of fungus spoilage of vegetables, these organisms apparently do not create any serious problems in the vegetable canning industry. Processing temperatures used in the canning of vegetables are usually relatively high and holding times are commonly longer than those employed in the canning of fruit, so that sterilization is accomplished and fungi are rarely observed.

Miscellaneous Food Products

Of the many different types of oyster spoilage, one has been very aptly named "reddening of oysters." This type of spoilage was investigated by Hunter (1920), who found the etiologic agent to be a nonsporulating, pink-pigment-producing, yeastlike organism which he placed in the genus *Torula*. Hunter found this organism widely distributed in oyster houses and on utensils used therein; it was found only infrequently in oysters before they arrived at the oyster house, and occasionally in deep and surface water samples from the oyster beds. Since the oyster house and its equipment were the principal sources of contamination, a 0.04 per cent formaldehyde washing solution was recommended for occasional use in the house to prevent contamination of oysters.

We have seen that fungi of various types can grow on butter, so it is to be expected that spoilage of margarine by fungi has also been reported. Laxa (1930) found that a species of fungus caused black spots in margarine and named the causal organism *Margarinomyces bubaki.* He found that *M. bubaki* was somewhat resistent to sodium benzoate, but was not very heat resistant. The fungus was killed by boric acid, although the use of this as a preservative is prohibited in many countries.

Tanner (1944) reported that yeasts have caused much trouble in tomato products but that many of these incidents have not been reported in the literature. Yeasts have also been found to be a frequent cause of spoilage of carbonated beverages. In his study of the deterioration of such beverages, McKelvey (1926) found that yeasts were the most frequently encountered causative agents. Of the more than 1500 samples which he examined during a two-year period, about 85 per cent had spoiled as a result of the growth of yeasts. He also found that in order to kill spores of the yeasts he had isolated from carbonated beverages, he had to heat them for longer periods of time when they were placed in syrup of higher sugar concentration. For example, yeast spores were killed in two minutes at a temperature of 70C when placed in 24° Baume syrup, while five minutes were required for killing at this temperature when the spores were in 36° Baume syrup (almost a satuated sugar solution at room temperature). This same investigator reported that of 132 samples of sugar which he had obtained from 125 bottling plants located in 28 states, 47 per cent were found to contain yeasts; from this it would appear that many of the yeast contaminants in carbonated beverages may enter in the sugar used in making the beverages.

Batten and Bywaters (1918) found and reported an instance of spoilage of cocoa butter due to fungi. A large block of butter had black patches intermingled with streaks of brownish-yellow; *Penicillium glaucum* and a pink yeast were also isolated from the block, but these investigators stated that the spoilage was due mostly to a fungus believed to be *Aspergillus oryzae.*

According to Williams and Mrak (1949) yeast spoilage of salad dressing is not uncommon; however, these investigators reported an instance of spoilage of this type of food in which they not only identified the responsible organism but established the focal point of contamination. Considerable gassy spoilage developed in a starch-base salad dressing without any accompanying change in *p*H. Isolations made from spoiled jars yielded a pure culture of a yeast, which upon reinoculation into unspoiled dressing reproduced spoilage in a period of from three to five days. Upon examination the yeast was found to have the morphological and physiological characteristics of *Zygosaccharomyces globiformis*. Williams and Mrak were able to trace the contamination to a centrifugal pump which had not been disassembled for cleaning.

Commercial pickle packers often suffer severe losses through softening of salt-stock cucumbers during brining and storage (Fig. 169); this loss has been estimated by the Agricultural Research Service as amount-

Fig. 169. *Salt-stock pickles softened as a result of the action of fungus enzymes. (Courtesy Agricultural Research Service, U.S. Department of Agriculture.)*

ing to about $1 million annually. Cooperative research by a number of agencies has resulted in the isolation from cucumber brines of cellulolytic and pectinolytic enzymes which cause the softening. Further studies have shown that these two enzymes are synthesized by fungi which develop on the withering cucumber flower (Fig. 170) as the cucumber fruit develops. No practical, economical way for removing all of the flowers has as yet been developed, so other means are employed for disposing of the undesirable enzymes. Since enzyme concentration apparently reaches its peak 24 to 48 hours after vats are filled, it has been found that by draining off the original brine after 36 to 48 hours and replacing it with fresh brine, the enzyme concentration is markedly reduced and softening is effectively controlled.

Many similar and sometimes rather bizarre instances of food spoilage are known and have been reported in the literature. For further examples of fungus spoilage of food the reader should consult the work of Tanner (*loc. cit.*).

Fungi are not only responsible for the spoilage of food designed for

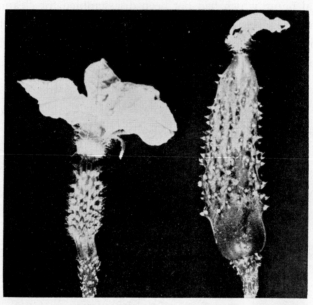

FIG. 170.   Left, *opened pistillate flower of cucumber;* right, *flower withering as the cucumber fruit develops. Fungi growing in the withering flower synthesize enzymes which diffuse into the salt solution in the pickling vats and result in pickle softening. (Courtesy Agricultural Research Service, U.S. Department of Agriculture.)*

human consumption, but may also spoil livestock feed. Both hay and stored grain will support the growth of a number of fungi if proper conditions of moisture and temperature exist. Grain with high moisture content stored in poorly ventilated bins or cribs will become moldy quite readily; such molding leads to actual grain losses as well as monetary losses resulting from the downgrading of moldy grain. Hay baled when the moisture content is too high will also become moldy, as will baled hay stored under moist conditions. Special precautions must be observed in the storage of molasses feeds, since such materials afford an especially good substrate for the growth of fungi.

Methods of Food Preservation

An account of the various methods used in the preservation of foods has already been given above in relation to the fungus spoilage problems encountered with various types of food products. A brief summation of these and other methods is presented in this section.

CHEMICAL PRESERVATIVES.   Prior to the establishment and rigid enforcement of the Pure Food and Drug Act, the addition of a variety of chemical preservatives to food was not uncommon. There are many chemical compounds that prevent or inhibit the growth of fungi, but some of these are also harmful to humans and their use in foods has accordingly been prohibited. Tanner states that the only chemical preservative allowed in the United States is sodium benzoate; however, chemical inhibitors of fungus growth such as sodium and calcium propionates are widely used to prevent mold growth in bread. Some of the antibiotics have been shown to be useful in preventing bacterial growth in certain foods, but such antibiotics have little or no effect in preventing fungus growth.

PRESERVATION BY DEHYDRATION.   This ancient method of food preservation has somewhat limited applications and has been superseded by better methods. Dehydration is effective because it decreases the water content to a level at which fungi grow very slowly or not at all, and it increases the sugar, acid, and salt concentrations to levels which also prevent fungal growth. It has a decided disadvantage in that with many foods the dried product loses most of the original taste, flavor, size and appearance of the fresh product.

CONCENTRATED SUGAR SOLUTIONS.   Fruits are frequently preserved in syrups of high sugar concentration, but in most instances relatively high temperatures must also be employed during processing to prevent spoilage. This type of preservation is obviously limited to foods in which large amounts of sugar are not objectionable, such as fruits.

CONCENTRATED SALT SOLUTIONS.   Preservation with concentrated salt solutions is also limited in use to certain foods that are compatible with salt. Yeast and filamentous fungi apparently vary with respect to their capacities to tolerate high salt concentrations. Wehmer (1897) isolated a yeast from herring brine which was inhibited by 15 per cent salt, but Speakman and others (1928) reported that solutions containing 10 per cent salt could be fermented by *Saccharomyces cerevisiae*. Tanner (*loc. cit.*) states that yeasts and filamentous fungi are inhibited by salt in concentrations of 20 to 30 per cent.

LOW TEMPERATURES.   Preservation of food through low temperatures has evolved from the running stream, to the spring house, to natural ice, to man-made ice, and finally to mechanical (gas or electric) refrigeration. In comparatively recent years the use of dry ice and quick-freezing of foods followed by storage in the frozen state has become widespread. Jensen (1954) states that "until some 75 years ago man depended largely upon the perishable food supplies produced within a few hudred miles of his home. The meat-packing business was carried on only during cold weather. Plant refrigeration changed the picture, and the development of the refrigerator car changed the entire perishable food industry." Of all of the methods of food preservation, the use of low temperatures offers the best known means of providing the consumer with a product that closely resembles the fresh product.

HIGH TEMPERATURES.   High temperatures as such are not used for food preservation but rather as a form of food processing prior to some other means of preservation. Thus for certain fruits a hot-water dip prior to dehydration has been recommended in order to destroy all or many of the surface microorganisms. Similarly, the practice of dipping fresh foods into hot water before quick-freezing greatly reduces the spore load. The use of high temperatures in canning processes has a twofold purpose: (1) it destroys most if not all of the microorganisms present in the food, and (2) it results in the production of a partial vacuum during the sealing and cooling of containers, thus creating conditions that mitigate against microbial growth. The importance of modern canning methods in the prolonged preservation of food cannot be overemphasized; under normal conditions canned food (including food packed in glass jars as well as in "tin" cans) may be kept indefinitely without risk of spoilage. An interesting series of papers concerned with the longevity of canned foods appeared in 1938 (Drummond and Lewis; Macara; Drummond and Macara; Wilson and Shipp; Lewis). For a report on the examination of some canned foods of historic interest, the reader should consult this series of papers.

H-ION CONCENTRATION. Acids reduce the amount of deterioration of food by microorganisms. The fact that a foodstuff is naturally acid in reaction may aid in its preservation. The incorporation of fatty acids in bread as mold inhibitors has already been discussed in connection with fungi and bread spoilage; in addition, the work of Levine and Fellers (1940) should be mentioned here. These investigators found that acetic acid inhibited various fungi and bacteria that are related to food spoilage. For example, they found that at pH 3.9 acetic acid was both inhibiting and lethal to *Saccharomyces cerevisiae* and lethal to *Aspergillus niger* at pH 3.9, but only inhibitory to this species at pH 4.1. Because of its lethal activity at comparatively high pH values, Levine and Fellers stated that the toxicity of acetic acid on various microorganisms was not entirely attributable to pH value but seems to be also a function of the undissociated acetic acid molecule.

PRESERVATION BY FERMENTATION. Some types of food products are prepared by fermenting other foods, primarily for the purpose of producing some desired flavor, odor, or consistency in the final product. The products of the fermentation, however, may themselves assist in the preservation of the final product. Thus, sauerkraut is prepared from cabbage by a process in which the sugar normally present in the cabbage is fermented by bacteria to lactic acid. The resulting high acid concentrations aid in inhibiting the subsequent growth of spoilage organisms. In a sense wine making is an example of preservation of certain fruit juices by alcoholic fermentation, although wine has a more utilitarian purpose.

PRESERVATION WITH CARBON DIOXIDE. Many types of perishable foods have been protected against microbial spoilage by storage in atmospheres of relatively high carbon dioxide content. Brown (1922) found that carbon dioxide had a retarding effect upon spore germination and growth of some of the common fruit-rotting organisms, and that the lower the storage temperature the more marked was the retardation. Tomkins (1932), working with fungi that grow on meat (*Thamnidium elegans, T. chaetocladioides, Sporotrichum carnis, Cladosporium herbarum, Mucor mucedo, Trichoderma sp.*), obtained similar results, but in addition pointed out that carbon dioxide has a greater retarding effect upon mycelial growth than upon spore germination. Moran (1937) has studied the effect of carbon dioxide upon egg storage, and Skovholt and others (1933) have shown that this gas will retard the development of molds on bread.

STERILIZATION BY ULTRAVIOLET RADIATION. Many exaggerated claims have been made regarding the effectiveness of ultraviolet radiation in killing spoilage organisms. The lethal effects of these rays on unprotected living cells, has long been established, but what may work under the special conditions of the laboratory may not be applicable under plant conditions; as Tanner has implied, the use of this method of sterilization does not necessarily mean that the millenium in food preservation has been reached. The Council of Physical Therapy of the American Medical Association (*J. Amer. Med. Assoc. 118:298–299;* 1942), after considering the possibility of accepting ultraviolet lamps for sterilizing purposes, concluded that there was insufficient evidence to warrant approval of this method of disinfecting solids. Although their report was not directly concerned with the food industry, it suggests that too much dependence should not be placed upon this method of sterilization.

Literature Cited

Baker, E. E., and Mrak, E. M. 1938. Yeasts associated with "sugaring" of dried prunes and figs. *J. Bact. 36:*317–318.

Barnett, H. L. 1955. *Illustrated genera of imperfect fungi.* Burgess, Minneapolis.

Batten, L., and Bywaters, H. W. 1918. Occurrence of mold in cocoa butter. *Soc. Chem. Ind. J. 37:*242–243.

Becquerel, P. 1910. Recherches expérimentales sur la latente des spores des Mucorinées des Ascomycètes. *Compt. Rend. Acad. Sci. 150:*1437–1439.

Brooks, F. T., and Kidd, M. 1921. Black spot of chilled and frozen meat. *Special Rept. No. 6,* Food Investigation Board, London.

Brown, W. 1922. On the germination and growth of fungi at various temperatures and in various concentrations of oxygen and carbon dioxide. *Ann. Bot. 36:*257–283.

Drummond, J. C., and Lewis, W. R. 1938. The examination of some tinned foods of historic interest. Part 1: Historical introduction. *Jour. Soc. Chem. Ind.* 57:808–814.

———, and Macara, T. 1938. Part 3: Chemical investigations. *Jour. Soc. Chem. Ind.* 57:828–833.

Esau, P., and Cruess, W. V. 1933. Yeasts causing "souring" of dried prunes and dates. *Fruit Prod. Jour.* 12:144–147.

Elliker, P. R. 1941. Factors influencing mold mycelia in cream. *Nat. Butter & Cheese Jour.* 32(7):8–9, 44, 46, 48–49.

Fabian, F. W. 1933. The influence of manufacturing operations upon the microbial content of grape juice. *Fruit Prod. Jour.* 12:141–142.

Harter, L. L., Weimer, J. L., and Adams, J. M. R. 1918. Sweet-potato storage-rots. *J. Agr. Res.* 15:337–368.

Henrici, A. T., 1947. *Molds, yeasts, and actinomycetes.* Wiley, New York. (2nd. ed. by Skinner, Emmons, and Tsuchiya).

Herter, W., and Fournet, A. 1919. Studien über die Schimmelpilze des Brotes. *Centralbl. f. Bakt. u. Parasiten.* 42:148–173.

Hunter, A. C. 1920. A pink yeast causing spoilage in oysters. *U.S.D.A. Bull.* 819.

Jensen, L. B. 1954. *Microbiology of meats.* Garrard Press, Champaign, Ill.

Kirby, G. W., Frey, C. N., and Atkin, L. 1935. The growth of bread molds as influenced by acidity. *Cereal Chem.* 12:244–255.

———, Atkin, L., and Frey, C. N. 1937. Further studies on the growth of bread mold as influenced by acidity. *Cereal Chem.* 14:865–878.

Lauritzen, J. L., and Harter, L. L. 1926. Relation of humidity to infection of sweet potatoes by *Rhizopus. J. Agr. Res.* 33:527–539.

Laxa, O. 1930. Margarinomyces Bubaki—ein Schädling der Margarine. *Centralbl. f. Bakt. u. Parasiten.* 81:392–396.

Levine, A. S., and Fellers, C. R. 1940. Action of acetic acid on food spoilage microorganisms. *J. Bact.* 39:499–514.

Lewis, W. R. 1938. The examination of some tinned foods of historic interest. Part 5: Investigation of the metal containers. *Jour. Soc. Chem. Ind.* 57:914–917.

Macara, T. 1937. Science and the conservation of food: some special problems. *Proc. Roy. Inst. Gt. Brit., April 16.* (in Chem. Abst. 31:5883).

———. 1938. The examination of some tinned foods of historic interest. Part 2: Special apparatus used for opening cans. *Jour. Soc. Chem. Ind.* 57:827–828.

Macy, H., Coulter, S. T., and Combs, W. B. 1932. Observations on the quantitative changes in the microflora during the manufacture and storage of butter. *Minn. Agr. Expt. Sta. Tech. Bull.* 82.

McCrae, A. 1923. Longevity of spores of *Aspergillus oryzae* and *Rhizopus nigricans. Science* 58:426.

McKelvey, C. E. 1926. Notes on yeasts in carbonated beverages. *J. Bact. 11:* 98–99.

Moran, T. 1937. Gas storage of eggs. *J. Soc. Chem. Ind. 56:*96T–101T.

O'Callaghan, M. A. 1901. Fishy-flavored butter, the cause and remedy. *Agr. Gaz. New South Wales 12(3)*:341–346. Sydney, N.S.W.; March, 1901.

Olliver, M., and Rendle, T. 1934. A new problem in fruit preservation. Studies on *Byssochlamys fulva* and its effect on the tissues of processed fruit. *J. Soc. Chem. Ind. 53:*T166–T172.

———, and Smith, G. 1933. *Byssochlamys fulva,* sp. nov. *J. Bot. 71:*196–197.

Owen, W. L. 1932. Ultraviolet rays prevent molding of bread. *Food Indus. 4:*208–210.

Prescott, S. C. 1920. Some bacteriological aspects of dehydration. *J. Bact. 5:* 109–125.

Raistrick, H., and Smith, G. 1933. Studies in the biochemistry of microorganisms. XXXV: The metabolic products of *Byssochlamys fulva* Olliver and Smith. *Biochem. Jour. 27:*1814–1819.

Reed, G. B. 1924. A bakery infection with *Monilia sitophila*. *Phytopath. 14:*346.

Rogers, L. A. 1909. Fishy flavor in butter. *U.S.D.A. Bur. An. Ind. Circ. 146.*

———, Dahlberg, A. O., and Evans, A. E. 1920. The cause and control of "buttons" in sweet condensed milk. *J. Dairy Sci. 3:*122–129.

Skovholt, O., and Bailey, C. H. 1933. The influence of carbon dioxide and humidity upon the development of molds on bread. *Cereal Chem. 10:*446–451.

Smith, A. P. 1885. Musty bread. *The Analyst 10:*181–183.

Speakman, H. B., Gee, A. H., and Luck, J. M. 1928. The influence of sodium chloride on the growth and metabolism of yeast. *J. Bact. 15:*319–340.

Tanner, F. W. 1944. *The microbiology of foods.* Garrard Press, Champaign, Ill.

Thom, C., and Ayers, S. H. 1916. Effects of pasteurization on mold spores. *J. Agr. Res. 6:*153–166.

———, and LeFevre, E. 1921. The flora of corn meal. *Abs. Bact. 5:*10–11.

———, and Shaw, R. H. 1915. Moldiness in butter. *J. Agr. Res. 3:*301–310.

Tomkins, R. G. 1932. The inhibition of the growth of meat-attacking fungi by carbon dioxide. *J. Soc. Chem. Ind. 51:*261T–264T.

———. 1936. The microbiology of fruit. *J. Soc. Chem. Ind. 55:*66T–70T.

Wehmer, C. 1897. Zur Bakteriologie und Chemie des Häringslake I. *Centralbl. f. Bakt., Parasiten., u. Infekt. 3:*209–222.

Williams, C. C., Cameron, E. J., and Williams, O. B. 1941. A facultatively anaerobic mold of unusual heat resistance. *Food Research 6:*69–73.

Williams, O. B., and Mrak, E. M. 1949. An interesting outbreak of yeast spoilage in salad dressing. *Fruit Prod. Jour. & Amer. Food Manu. 28(5)*:141, 153.

Wilson, G. S., and Shipp, H. L. 1938. Part 4: Bacteriological investigations. *Jour. Soc. Chem. Ind. 57:*834–836.

Yesair, J. 1928. The action of disinfectants on molds. Ph.D. dissertation, Univ. of Chicago (unpublished).

25 · *Medical Mycology—Fungi as Allergens—Poisonous Fungi*

Medical Mycology

FUNGI, as pointed out in Chapter 8, may be used medicinally in a variety of ways. A fungus metabolic product such as penicillin may be used in the treatment of infections, or a fungus may be an important agent in the synthesis of a valuable medicine (*l*-ephedrine; cortisone), or the entire fungus body (for example, yeast cells) may itself be used as a therapeutic agent. On the other hand, certain fungus species are known to be the causal agents of human and animal diseases.

For the most part, the common infectious diseases of man are caused by bacteria and viruses, while the majority of plant diseases are caused by fungi. But just as there are some diseases of plants known to be caused by bacteria and viruses, so also are there fungus diseases of man. These diseases, which may be generally termed *mycoses,* are less numerous than the various bacterial diseases of man but may well be far more widespread than is usually recognized by the layman.

Often regarded as "tropical" diseases, mycoses are also quite prevalent in temperate climates, as evidenced by an increasing number of reports. Ajello (1950) has pointed out the fallacy of regarding mycoses as primarily tropical diseases and has stated that only a few minor cutaneous mycoses exist in the tropics that are not found in the temperate regions of the United States. This author has estimated that there have been approximately one million cases of *coccidioidomycosis* in California alone. Such reports as those of Palmer (1946) and Beadenkopf and others (1949) have led to the estimation that at least 8 million persons in the Ohio and Mississippi valleys have been infected at one time or another with *Histoplasma capsulatum,* the causal agent of *histoplasmosis.* Fox and Shields (1949) have stated that over 50 per cent of all males in the United States have at some time in their lives been infected by fungi causing "Athlete's foot." From such figures it is apparent that mycoses are of fairly frequent occurrence and can no longer be considered inconsequential. Ajello (*loc. cit.*) has attributed the reported low incidence of human mycoses to the fact that the symptoms often simulate the clinical and pathological signs of certain non-mycotic diseases. Examples of incorrect diagnoses are reported by Froio and Bailey (1949) and by Smith (1940). The former workers write of a case of pulmonary cryptococcosis which was diagnosed as tuberculosis and lung tumor; Smith reported that cases of coccidioidomycosis have been incorrectly diagnosed as pneumonia, influenza, tuberculosis, measles, smallpox and occasionally even poliomyelitis, typhoid fever, and syphilis. Brasher and Furcolow (1955) state that there are probably a great many cases of histoplasmosis "masquerading" as, or combined with, tuberculosis in various tuberculosis sanatoria.

Historically, the first infectious agent of human disease to be described was a fungus, Schoelein demonstrating in 1839 that favus was a mycotic disease. Although medical mycology is thus older than the science of bacteriology, the field has had a relatively small number of workers, largely because medical mycology is in reality a kind of "merger" between two seemingly unrelated fields, medical pathology and mycology. In view of the importance to man of disease-producing fungi, it seems particularly unfortunate that collaboration between the pathologist and the mycologist has thus far been practically nonexistent. The mycologist usually knows that certain unusual types of fungi cause diseases in man and animals, but is often in doubt regarding their position in the system of fungus classification, and particularly with regard to their morphology and physiology in tissue. Without access to clinical material the average mycologist rarely has the opportunity to observe such pathogenic fungi and hence must largely disregard them. On the other hand the average physician is unfamiliar with the fungi as a group of living organisms and hence inadequately trained to do any considerable amount of work with them. The answer, of course, lies in increased collaboration between the doctor and the mycologist. Such collaboration might lead to more accurate and speedier diagnosis of the diseases caused by fungi, as well as to clarification of the taxonomy of fungi pathogenic to humans and animals.

Fatalities Caused by Mycoses

Henrici (1947) has pointed out that fatal fungus diseases in man, although less common than fatal bacterial infections, are nevertheless important numerically. Citing data from *Vital Statistics of the United States for 1942,* Henrici states that mycoses caused only 359 out of 1,385,187 deaths in that year—less than 0.3 per cent of the total number of deaths from all causes. However, these 359 deaths are more than half the number caused either by typhoid, tetanus, or poliomyelitis and polioencephalitis; more than the entire number of deaths from Rocky Mountain spotted fever and other typhuslike diseases, and nearly twice the total number of deaths from paratyphoid fever, undulant fever, smallpox, rabies, leprosy, yellow fever, and relapsing fever.

Naming of Mycoses

Human and animal diseases caused by fungi have been variously named. In some instances the name of the disease is based upon the affected part—*pulmonary mycosis* (fungus infection of the lungs) and *otomycosis* (fungus infection of the ear). Other mycoses bear a name similar to that of the causal agent: *blastomycosis,* which is caused by *Blastomyces dermatitidis,* and *coccidioidomycosis,* the causal agent of which is *Coccidioides immitis.* The names of the discoverers of certain mycoses are often reflected in the common names applied to them (Almeida's disease; Gilchrist's disease), as are the names of localities in which they are especially prevalent (San Joaquin Valley Fever; California disease; Chicago disease). A great number of popular names have been applied to the various *dermatophytoses* (fungus diseases involving superficial tissues): "Athlete's foot," "Hongkong foot," "Jungle rot," "Gym itch," "Ringworm," and the like.

Some Common Mycoses

Brief summaries of the details of some of the better-known mycoses are given below. For more comprehensive reviews and extensive bibliographies, the works of Jacobson (1932), Emmons (1940), and Conant and others (1954) should be consulted.

COCCIDIOIDOMYCOSIS.   This disease, initially termed coccidioidal granuloma, was first reported from South America by Wernicke (1892) and was discovered in the United States two years later by Rixford. The causal agent was first believed to be a protozoan, but was later correctly identified as a fungus by Ophüls and Moffitt (1900) and named *Coccidioides immitis.* As first described, coccidioidomycosis was a generalized disease with a very high fatality rate, reflected in the fact that, by 1936, 450 cases resulting in 224 deaths had been reported from the state of California alone. The earlier history of the disease is summarized by Rixford *et al* (1931).

The causal organism, *Coccidioides immitis,* exists in two phases—a "saprophytic phase" and a "parasitic phase" (Smith, 1943). In culture on solid media, the fungus grows as abundant septate hyphae (Fig. 171) which appear white and cottony but become pigmented with age. Old cultures contain an abundance of chlamydospores (intercalary spores formed directly from hyphal cells; also called arthrospores), which are presumably the infective spore form. Sporangia ("culture spherules") are rarely seen in culture. These spherules, which are really sporangia (Fig. 172), constitute the parasitic phase found in man and animals. When inhaled (or possibly after entry into wounds), the chlamydospores round up into spherules, the protoplasm within dividing into segments by the development of cleavage planes. These segments within the spherules then become endospores—a development comparable to the growth of sporangiospores within sporangia of the various species of Phycomycetes. Mature spherules range in diameter from 10 to 60 microns, but may occasionally be greater than 200 microns. The fungus spreads in the body when the spherule wall ruptures and the endospores are carried by blood or lymph to other regions.

Although Moore (1932) states that *C. immitis* forms asci, and places this species in his new family (Coccidioidaceae) in the Ascomycetes, this view is not generally accepted, and until a definite sexual cycle has been demonstrated for *C. immitis* it can be properly placed only in the Fungi Imperfecti. Baker and others (1943) suggest that this species may possibly belong in the Phycomycetes, but this suggestion is difficult

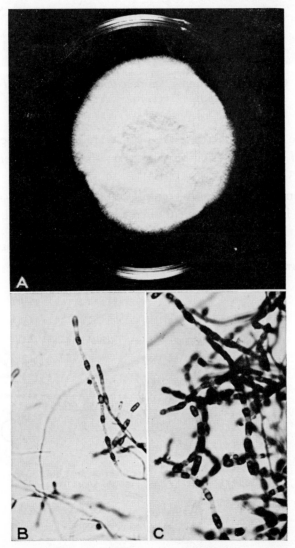

FIG. 171.   Coccidioides immitis, *the causal agent of coccidioidomycosis.* A, *Culture on Sabouraud's agar;* B, *Arthrospore formation in young culture;* C, *Arthrospore formation in old culture.* (*Courtesy N. F. Conant.*)

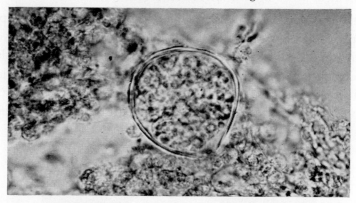

FIG. 172. Coccidioides immitis. *Sporangium (spherule) filled with endo-spores in sputum. (Courtesy N. F. Conant.)*

to reconcile with the fact that the hyphae are abundantly septate. The life cycle of *C. immitis* as outlined by Baker and his co-workers is shown in Fig. 173.

In the same general locality (central California) in which coccidioidal granuloma has been so prevalent, there also exists a nonfatal, influenza-

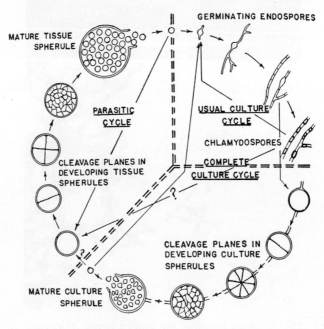

FIG. 173. *Life cycle of* Coccidioides immitis. *(From Baker, Mrak, and Smith, 1943.)*

like disease variously called valley fever, desert fever, desert rheumatism, and San Joaquin Valley fever. In 1937 Dickson called attention to the probability that *C. immitis* is the causal agent of both coccidioidal granuloma and valley fever, as is now generally believed. Thus, infection may result in the production of a rapidly progressive, usually fatal disease or a more benign, typically nonfatal disease. In its early stages valley fever bears a close resemblance to influenza, and in a small percentage of cases cutaneous lesions (*erythema nodosum* and *erythema multiforme*) occur; such lesions are often associated with arthritis, sore throat, and conjunctivitis. According to Stiles and Davis (1942), valley fever may be confused with pneumonia, tuberculosis, pleurisy, smallpox, measles, tularemia, syphilis, and typhoid, although rarely with poliomyelitis; mortality rate is negligible.

When infection of human beings with *C. immitis* produces coccidioidal granuloma (Fig. 174) there results a chronic, progressive, highly fatal disease in which the skin, lungs, lymph nodes, meninges, thoracic viscera, and other body tissues are affected. Kessel (1941) states that 70 per cent of the cases occurring in the Los Angeles County Hospital indicate that the initial lesion is in the lung. Coccidioidal granuloma may be mistaken for tuberculosis, but Stiles and Davis point out that the exclusion of acid-fast organisms and the recovery of *C. immitis* from sputum or body tissues should verify the diagnosis. These same investigators state that the disease appears to be acquired by inhaling spores, by skin infection, or (rarely) through the gastrointestinal tract. The principal means of infection seems to be through spore inhalation, since Smith

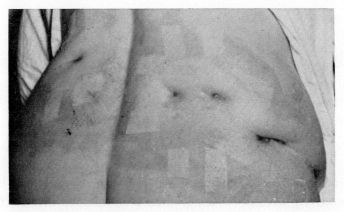

FIG. 174. *Coccidioidomycosis lesions.* (*Courtesy Samuel Saslaw.*)

(1943) notes that the peak of valley-fever incidence occurs during the dry or "dusty" season in the San Joaquin Valley.

Although the great majority of cases of coccidioidomycosis have been reported from central California, it is incorrect to refer to this mycosis as California disease, since Beck and others (1931) have reported cases of coccidioidal granuloma from Arizona, Colorado, Illinois, Kansas, Missouri, Nebraska, New Mexico, Pennsylvania, South Carolina, Texas, Washington, South America, and Italy; Miller (1936) reports the occurrence of the disease in Tennessee, Louisiana, Alaska, and Hawaii. The disease is obviously most prevalent in the arid Southwest, and Henrici (1947) is of the opinion that cases reported from other areas actually stem from infections acquired in the Southwest or are traceable to dusty materials which originated there. This is a definite possibility, since the incubation time is one to three weeks. Either the incidence of the disease is increasing in California or else the symptoms are becoming more generally recognized by physicians; Table 46 shows a steady rise over a 46-year period.

Table 46.—Incidence of coccidioidal granuloma in California, 1893–1939

Years	Number of Cases
1893–1899	4
1900–1904	7
1905–1909	9
1910–1914	17
1915–1919	23
1920–1924	50
1925–1929	123
1930–1934	163
1935–1939	264
Total	660

From Kessel (1941).

The immediate natural source of man's infection by *C. immitis* has not been positively established. It has often been assumed that the fungus grows in the soil during the wet season and that when the soil dries, spores may be carried on dust particles. Stewart and Meyer (1932) and others have isolated *C. immitis* from the soil, but many other investigators have attempted similar isolations without success. Giltner (1918) found that this organism may infect cattle, and Emmons (1943) has isolated it from a variety of wild rodents in Arizona. It has also been isolated from sheep and dogs. Emmons is of the opinion that wild rodents may constitute a natural reservoir of the disease and that the endemicity of coccidioidomycosis may be explained by the presence of susceptible species of rodents. This view is subject to question, since apparently there is no direct infection chain from man to man, animal to animal, or animal to man. Accordingly there is nothing to be gained from isolating known cases, and Smith (1943) states that elementary sanitation is an adequate safeguard.

Conant and others (1954) do not believe that animals serve as a primary reservoir in nature, but that man probably acquires the disease by coming into contact with soil contaminated with the fungus. More and more evidence is accumulating that the human pathogenic fungi are capable of growing as saprophytes in nature, as evidenced by the report of Lurie and Way (1957), who were able to isolate two dermatophytes (*Trichophyton mentagrophytes* and *Microsporon gypseum*) from the atmosphere of caves. Ajello (1955) reported that from 1892 to 1955, twenty-one species of pathogenic or potentially pathogenic fungus species have been isolated from nonliving sources (Table 47).

*Table 47.—Pathogenic or potentially pathogenic fungi
isolated from nonliving sources*

Absidia corymbifera	*Hormodendrum pedrosoi*
Absidia ramosa	*Microsporum gypseum*
Allescheria boydii	*Nocardia asteroides*
Aspergillus fumigatus	*Phialophora jeanselmei*
Candida albicans	*Phialophora verrucosa*
Candida guilliermondii	*Rhizopus arrhizus*
Candida krusei	*Rhizopus oryzae*
Coccidioides immitis	*Sporotrichum schenckii*
Cryptococcus neoformans	*Trichophyton mentagrophytes*
Epidermophyton floccosum	*Trichophyton rubrum*
Histoplasma capsulatum	

From Ajello (1955).

Since there is no known method of preventing infection by *C. immitis*, it has been recommended that major attention be directed toward arresting the initial infection. Iodide, thymol, sulfonamides and other chemotherapeutic agents have not effected consistent cures, and the best treatment seems to be rest. Excision and amputation have cured single lesions, but the lesions may recur. The best procedure is to care for the initial infection in the hope of arresting it and preventing dissemination. Recovery from an infection apparently confers immunity to reinfection from outside sources.

A skin test for detecting coccidioidomycosis has been devised which involves the intradermal injection of *coccidioidin,* a material prepared from cultures of *C. immitis.* If an individual has been sensitized by a past or present infection by *C. immitis,* an area of erythema and edema appears at the site of the injection. By means of the coccidioidin skin test it has been demonstrated that a high percentage of positive reactions occurs among the residents of an endemic area and that such reactions are rare or absent elsewhere. For example Kessel (*loc. cit.*) states that 90 per cent of 140 children on the Pima Indian Reservation near Phoenix, Arizona developed positive reactions to coccidioidin, but when the same coccidioidin was used in Philadelphia the subjects tested gave negative reactions. One objection to the use of the coccidioidin skin test is that apparently it does not distinguish individuals who have been infected with *C. immitis* from those who are currently infected. In addition to the coccidioidin skin test, complement fixation and precipitin tests are also used in the diagnosis of coccidioidomycosis.

Although the coccidioidal granuloma form of coccidioidomycosis is a serious disease with a very high incidence of fatality, it should be emphasized that the vast majority of individuals who become infected with *C. immitis* contract only the benign form of the disease.

CHROMOBLASTOMYCOSIS.   Although the first published accounts of this mycosis are those of Medlar (1915) and Lane (1915), who reported on a case that occurred in Boston, chromoblastomycosis had been studied four years earlier in Brazil by Pedrosa (Carrion, 1942). The name of the disease, which would indicate that a yeastlike organism is involved, was derived from the occurrence of dark-colored, spherical bodies in infected tissues which were earlier believed to divide by a budding process. Since its discovery over a hundred cases have been

FIG. 175.   *Sporulation types in chromoblastomycetous fungi. H-1 to H-3, the* Hormodendrum *type. A-1 to A-5, the pseudo-Acrotheca type. P-1 to P-4, the* Phialophora *type. T-1 to T-4, transitional types of sporulation. (Courtesy A. L. Carrion.)*

reported from all over the world, but apparently the disease is most prevalent in Puerto Rico and Brazil.

The organism isolated from the case observed by both Medlar and Lane was named *Phialophora verrucosa,* the generic name being so chosen because of the fact that in culture on artificial media, peculiar funnel- or cup-shaped conidiophores were formed. The species was placed in the family Dematiaceae of the Fungi Imperfecti. Other fungi isolated from chromoblastomycosis lesions have been variously named *Hormodendrum pedrosoi, H. compactum, H. langeroni,* and *Phialophora pedrosoi.* Carrion (*loc. cit.*) is of the opinion that the disease may be caused by different but closely related dematiaceous fungi, and recommends that *Fonsecaea pedrosoi* be accepted as the name for the causal fungi—a somewhat bizarre taxonomic approach if the fungi involved are of different species. In tissue the parasite is observed as spherical bodies measuring about 12 microns in diameter; these bodies are surrounded by a thick, dark membrane and often show internal septation. In culture on artificial media the fungus growth is filamentous and various types of spores are formed. Carrion has observed fungi isolated from a large number of patients suffering from chromoblastomycosis and reports that sporulation in culture may be of three distinct types: *Hormodendrum, Phialophora,* and *Acrotheca* (Fig. 175); however, he notes that only a few of these isolates sporulate by only one method, and that usually two or three types of sporulation occur in the same culture. In view of this observation and the demonstration by serological means that the fungi of chromoblastomycosis are closely related (Conant and Martin, 1937), the retention of several generic names seems unjustified, and perhaps Carrion's suggestion that one name be applied to all chromoblastomycetous fungi is the most acceptable answer at the moment to a perplexing taxonomic question.

Apparently chromoblastomycosis is contracted through some slight, perhaps unnoticed abrasion of the skin; in many of the cases reported the patients were farm laborers who worked barefooted. The disease usually starts as a small warty growth on an extremity (commonly the foot) and gradually spreads upwards through the development of "satellite" lesions. The course of the spread is slow, and in advanced cases some elephantiasis of the affected limb may occur. The lesions present a cauliflowerlike appearance (Fig. 176), and the infection appears to be localized, since no systemic cases of the disease have been reported. The lesions develop in the epidermis and the subcutaneous tissues, but there is very little disturbance of the deeper tissues.

Because of the high incidence of the disease among male farm laborers, it is believed that the causal organism is present in the soil. Conant (1937) compared eight species of *Cadophora* isolated from lumber and pulpwood with three strains of *Phialophora verrucosa* isolated from

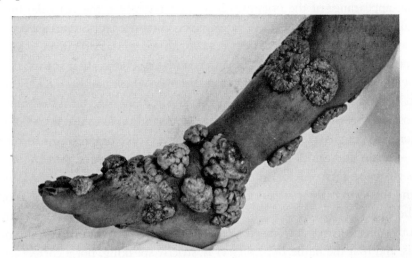

FIG. 176. *Cauliflowerlike lesions of chromoblastomycosis.* (*Courtesy A. L. Carrion.*)

chromoblastomycosis lesions and concluded that the name *Cadophora* should be placed in the synonomy of *Phialophora.* Martin (1938) demonstrated that *Cadophora americana,* isolated from wood pulp was closely related antigenically to pathogenic species of *Phialophora.* In view of these observations it seems probable that the causal organism of the disease may occur naturally as a saprophyte in soil or organic matter, especially since there are no known cases of contagious transmission of the disease. Gomes (1938) reported that he had isolated a blastomycetous fungus from a limb of a eucalyptus tree which in falling had caused a hand injury, the hand later becoming infected with chromoblastomycosis, but the evidence in support of this case is very meager.

No specific cure for chromoblastomycosis has been discovered, although iodides, various forms of copper, and other medicaments have been used with varying success. Carrion states that early infections have been eradicated by local surgery, but that in advanced cases amputation is the only effective treatment.

BLASTOMYCOSIS. This disease (also known as American blastomycosis or Gilchrist's disease) was first discovered by Gilchrist in 1894 and reported in 1896. In the year of Gilchrist's discovery, Buschke and Busse (*cf.* Martin and Smith, 1939) isolated a yeastlike fungus from a tibial abscess and named the condition *saccharomycosis*. Gilchrist, independently, named the disease *blastomycetic dermatitis,* since the appearance of the organism in section resembled the yeastlike fungus described by Busse. In a later paper Gilchrist and Stokes (1898) gave the name *Blastomyces dermatitidis* to the causal organism, which formed mycelia in culture. The latter workers believed that it probably belonged to the group of wild yeasts, some of which had been described as nonfermenting, mycelia-forming organisms. Since the term blastomycosis has been applied to diseases caused by two fungi—one a mycelium-forming fungus in culture and the other a yeastlike organism in culture—Martin and Smith suggest, that to avoid confusion, the term *blastomycosis* be reserved for infections caused by *Blastomyces dermatitidis* and the term *cryptococcosis* to infections caused by a yeastlike fungus of the genus *Cryptococcus (Torula)*. Emmons (1940) points out that various generic names have been applied to the causal agent of blastomycosis, and that the name *Blastomyces* is, strictly speaking, not a correct generic name for the fungus. Most investigators, however, seem to prefer the name *Blastomyces dermatitidis* as originally proposed by Gilchrist and Stokes.

According to Conant and Howell (1941) the causal organism of blastomycosis is seen in tissues as single-budding, thick-walled, yeastlike cells. On Sabouraud's glucose agar the organism grows as a septate mycelium with numerous spores which are sessile or borne on short pedicels on the hyphae; in old cultures, thick-walled, variously sculptured chlamydospores develop. When cultured on other types of media and incubated at 37 C the fungus grows as a yeastlike organism similar to forms observed in diseased tissue or pus. Moore (1938) and Dodge (1935) have reported that the organism forms asci, but this has not been confirmed by other workers. Macroscopic and microscopic appearances of the cultured fungus are shown in Fig. 177. In the diagnosis of this disease, both skin testing and complement fixation tests have been used.

The following brief account of the disease is taken very largely from the account of Martin and Smith (1939), who studied 347 case reports

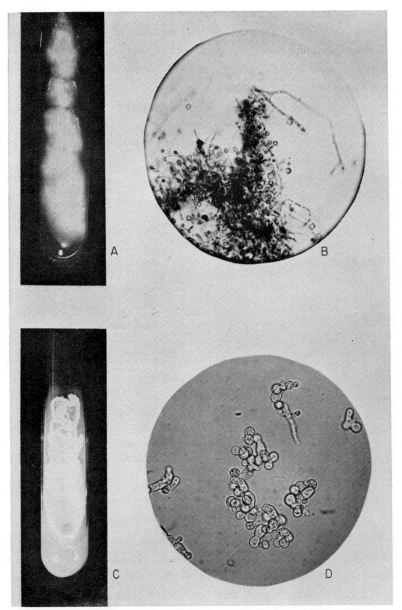

FIG. 177. *Macroscopic and microscopic appearance of* Blastomyces dermatitidis. A, *Culture of* B. dermatitidis *on dextrose agar after 14 days' growth at room temperature.* B, *Microscopic preparation from A, showing conidia and filamentous growth.* C, *Culture of* B. dermatitidis *on beef infusion dextrose agar containing laked blood after 7 days' growth at 37C.* D, *Microscopic preparation from C, showing budding cells.* (*Courtesy N. F. Conant and D. T. Smith.*)

of blastomycosis. For further details the reader should consult this paper, which in addition to a comprehensive account of the disease, also includes a bibliography of 249 pertinent references.

Blastomycosis is limited essentially to North America, with proved and presumptive cases having been found in 28 states. The infection has been referred to as "Chicago disease," but this is a misleading name, since only 20 per cent of the cases recorded up to 1939 have been from Illinois. The distribution of this disease in the United States, based on cases reported up to 1939, is shown in Fig. 178.

FIG. 178.   *Distribution of cases of blastomycosis which had been reported in the United States up to 1939. Solid squares indicate proved cases; solid circles, presumptive cases; open circles, inadequately described cases. (From Martin and Smith, 1939.)*

The disease may be either cutaneous or systemic. In the cutaneous form, skin lesions are usually single, while in generalized cases they are multiple and widely disseminated. Lesions of many of the internal organs may occur, but the lungs are the most frequently involved of the internal organs. In 50 per cent of the proved and presumptive cases, the first symptoms appeared in the respiratory tract, most frequently as cough, chest pains, and weakness. In 19 per cent of the cases, a skin lesion was noted first, and in 23 per cent the first symptom was a subcutaneous nodule or abscess (Fig. 179). Stober (1914) stated that the lungs are the principal atria of infection.

Since males are more frequently infected than females (ratio: 9 males to 1 female), and since more than 50 per cent of the cases reviewed by

Martin and Smith involved patients between the ages of 20 and 40 years, it seems very probable that the reservoir of the fungus is in nature. Human transmission has not been reported, although Evans (1903) reported contraction of the disease by a physician through puncturing of a finger during necropsy in a case of systemic blastomycosis.

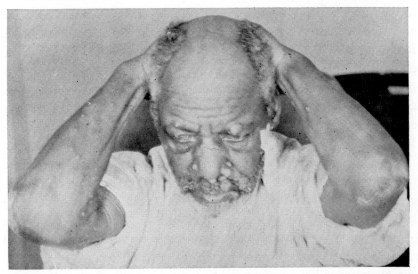

FIG. 179. *Blastomycosis. Patient with lesions on face and arms. (Courtesy Samuel Saslaw.)*

Systemic blastomycosis is highly fatal, the known mortality in 117 reported cases being 78 per cent. This percentage is based on the total reported cases although the records of some patients were not complete. Potassium iodide is helpful in the treatment of cutaneous blastomycosis, but if the patient is allergic to the fungus, desensitization by means of vaccine is recommended before the administration of iodide. Potassium iodide has also been used for treatment of the systemic form, but results have not been encouraging. The drug generally indicated today is 2-hydroxystilbamidine, which has been effective in the treatment of cutaneous blastomycosis and shows considerable promise in the treatment of the systemic form.

HISTOPLASMOSIS. This fungus disease, first discovered in 1905 and long regarded as a rare tropical malady, now seems to be appearing with increasing frequency in the United States. Darling (1906,

1909) first discovered the disease in the Canal Zone while attempting to verify the occurrence there of kala-azar, a disease native to India. Histoplasmosis, as described from three cases observed by Darling, was characterized by irregular fever, emaciation, leukopenia, anemia, and splenomegaly. In tissue the parasites were oviform or round, from one to four microns through their greatest diameter, and always intracellular in the lungs. Darling named the parasite *Histoplasma capsulatum* and apparently considered it a protozoan. His material was studied by da Rocha-Lima (1912), who concluded that the disease was similar to the epizootic lymphangitis of horses caused by a yeastlike organism, *Cryptococcus farcimosus.* According to Meleney (1925), Darling later concurred in this opinion. No further reports of the occurrence of this disease appeared until 1926, when Watson and Riley reported a case from Minnesota.

The causal organism of histoplasmosis was not obtained in culture until de Monbreun (1934) isolated it from a fatal case in a six-month-old infant studied by Dodd and Tompkins (1934). De Monbreun obtained both mycelia and a yeastlike form in culture and noted that the degree of moisture in the cultures, incubation temperature, and the nature of the culture medium determine the character of the growth of this fungus. He noted in his cultures what he termed yeastlike bodies. By means of intravenous injections of the yeastlike form he was able to induce in two monkeys a fatal disease possessing all of the important clinical and pathological features of histoplasmosis. In each case there was marked enlargement of the spleen, liver, and lymph nodes. Smears from these organs as well as bone marrow contained enormous numbers of intracellular parasites. A third monkey inoculated with the mycelial form failed to develop histoplasmosis.

De Monbreun stated that certain of the cultural characteristics of the organism were suggestive of the Endomycetales (an order of Ascomycetes), but held that the name *Histoplasma capsulatum* should be retained until it could be classified with certainty. Moore (1935), after studying both the fungus isolated by de Monbreun and another fungus isolated from a case reported by Hansmann and Schencken, refers to the two organisms as different species (*Podasia capsulata* and *P. pyriformis*). Moore cultured these organisms on various types of media and noted structures which he terms asci. His figures of these asci are not convincing, and at the present time it seems best to place the organism in the Fungi Imperfecti under the name originally proposed by Darling. In tissue this organism is yeastlike in appearance (Fig. 180). Conant (1941) made cultural studies of a strain of *H. capsulatum* isolated from an infant case of histoplasmosis and stated that the filamentous phase of the organism develops large tuberculate chlamydospores (Fig. 181), not asci as Moore reported. Conant is of the opinion that *H. cap-*

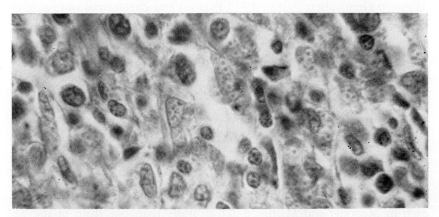

FIG. 180. Histoplasma capsulatum *in tissue, showing its yeastlike appearance. (Courtesy Samuel Saslaw.)*

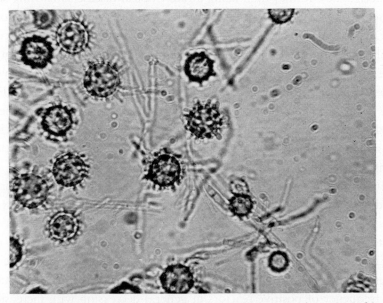

FIG. 181. Histoplasma capsulatum, *showing the large tuberculate chlamydospores which develop in cultures of this fungus. (Courtesy Samuel Saslaw.)*

sulatum should be placed in the family Moniliaceae of the Fungi Imperfecti.

Although twenty years elapsed between Darling's first report and the report of an additional case (Watson and Riley, 1926), the disease in recent years has begun to appear with increasing frequency in the United States. Thus Agress and Gray in 1939 reported the seventh case in the Western Hemisphere, but by 1945 Parsons and Zarafonetis were able to review reports of 71 cases, most of which had been fatal. Of the cases reviewed, 56 occurred in the United States; the remaining being distributed as follows: one case each in Austria, British Honduras, East Java, England, Mexico, the Phillipines, and Southern Rhodesia; two cases in Argentina; three cases each in Brazil and the Canal Zone. The distribution of cases in the United States by states was as follows: one case each in Florida, Iowa, Louisiana, Maryland, Minnesota, Mississippi, New York, North Carolina, Ohio, Oklahoma; two cases each in Alabama, California, Kentucky, Texas, Virginia, District of Columbia; three cases in Indiana; four cases in Illinois; seven cases in Tennessee; ten cases each in Missouri and Michigan. Thus, more than one third of the 71 cases reviewed by Parsons and Zarafonetis have occurred in four Midwestern states. Rather than being a rare tropical disease as Darling suggested, histoplasmosis must be considered a disease of temperate regions.

Conant and others (1954) state that probably less than 0.1 per cent of the primary infections with *H. capsulatum* develop into the progressive form of the disease. While the lungs may often become involved, apparently the initial lesion often occurs in or near the mouth (Fig. 182). In many instances recognized cases of histoplasmosis have been fatal. Treatment has been ineffective, although Meleney (1940) has recommended the use of organic salts—the trivalent organic preparations and pentavalent preparations of antimony. Use of a skin-testing antigen (histoplasmin) affords evidence that the disease may occur in a mild and usually unrecognized form, since apparently healthy individuals have been strong reactors to histoplasmin. Palmer (1946) has reported the results of tests in which 8,141 student nurses were tested for reaction to histoplasmin and states than an area of high prevalence of positive reactors exists in the eastern central part of the United States, the frequency of positive reactors in general decreasing with increasing distance from this area. On the basis of results obtained from 6,000 skin tests, Beadenkopf and others (1949) report that the presence of histo-plasmin sensitivity was highest in the Lower Mississippi Basin of the United States.

The natural reservoir of *H. capsulatum* is as yet not known with cer-tainty, but the organism has been isolated from the soil and has also

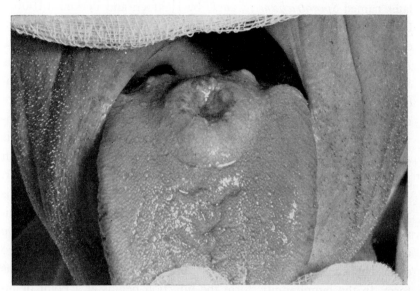

FIG. 182.   *Crater-like ulcer on the tongue caused by* Histoplasma capsula-tum. (*From Prior, Saslaw, and Cole, 1954.*)

been recovered from dogs, rats, and mice (Emmons and others, 1947). The portal of entry of the organism into the human body, while still un-known, appears to be either the mouth (since a large number of patients with histoplasmosis have ulcerated lesions of the mouth, pharynx, and gastrointestinal tract) or the respiratory tract (since the lungs are fre-quently involved, and a persistent cough has been a symptom in a num-ber of reported cases). According to Parsons and Zarafonetis (*loc. cit.*) the skin might also be the portal of entry in a small number of cases.

As first described, histoplasmosis appeared to be a rare and highly fa-tal disease of the tropics, but is now generally regarded as a common and typically nonfatal disease of temperate regions. In a small percentage of individuals infected with *Histoplasma capsulatum* the disease may be-come progressive and result in fatality, but in the vast majority of cases it appears only in benign—perhaps even unnoticed—form.

SPOROTRICHOSIS. This disease was first described in the United States by Schenck (1898), who noted that the cultural characteristics of the causal organism were similar to those of many fungi and yeasts. He submitted the organism to Erwin F. Smith, who expressed the opinion that it fitted best into the genus *Sporotrichum;* this fungus was later named *Sporotrichum schencki* by Hektoen and Perkins (1900). De Beurmann and Ramond (de Beurmann, 1912) described the disease from France in 1903 and named the causal organism *S. beurmanni.* A species of *Sporotrichum* causes a disease of horses and is referred to as *S. equi.* Emmons (1940) has noted that several critical studies have indicated that these three names as well as others are synonymous. Since the reports of Schenck in this country, and the report of the French investigators, sporotrichosis has been reported from many countries and is apparently world-wide in distribution, although it seems to occur with greater frequency in the Middle West, rural France, and Madagascar.

Various clinical types of the disease have been described. Curtis (1938) lists four types: (1) localized lymphangitic type, (2) disseminated, subcutaneous, gummatous type, (3) disseminated, ulcerative type, and (4) systemic type. Benham and Kesten (1932) list only two clinical types, the lymphangitic form and the disseminated gummatous form. In the lymphangitic form the infection begins at a point of injury where a chronic, slowly ulcerating granuloma develops, known as a sporotrichic chancre. The next stage is marked by the appearance of a chain of gummalike nodules in or beneath the skin, apparently following the course of the lymphatics draining the primary lesion (Fig. 183).

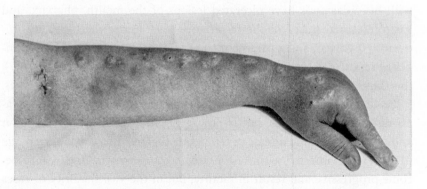

FIG. 183.   *Sporotrichosis, showing the upward progress of lesions. (Courtesy Rhoda W. Benham.)*

In the disseminated gummatous form, the subcutaneous lesions appear successively in scattered regions and seem to result from a hematic distribution of the infection from some undetected portal of entry. In addition to these two more characteristic forms, various other types of sporotrichosis have been described. These include isolated ulcerations and subcutaneous abscesses, granulomas in the bones, joints, muscles, liver, kidneys, and testicles, and lesions of the mouth, pharynx, nose, and conjunctiva.

Resemblance of sporotrichosis to common forms of tuberculosis, syphilis, and other infections may often lead to diagnostic errors. Foerster (1924) states that because of such errors many sporotrichosis sufferers undoubtedly go through long, futile periods of therapeutic mismanagement, citing as one illustration the case mentioned by Gougerot in which a patient, after undergoing four unsuccessful operations for osteomyelitis during three years of hospitalization, was finally cured after only six weeks of treatment with potassium iodide. The same author tells of patients, later found to have sporotrichosis, who were variously subjected to double amputation of the thighs, an arm amputation, and a nephrectomy following misdiagnoses of pyelonephritis, and also cites a case of suspected glanders in which extensive cauterization resulting in disfigurement was followed by a recurrence of sporotrichosis.

Direct transmission of sporotrichosis from a previous human case has never been proved, although contagion from diseased animals has been suspected. Meyer (1915) reported that he acquired sporotrichosis by handling equine strains of *Sporotrichum*. He pointed out that while equine sporotrichosis is very common in Pennsylvania, and is often treated, undoubtedly necessitating close contact with infectious material, the absence of sporotrichosis among farmers and veterinarians of that region indicates that human sporotrichotic infections via this channel of contact are quite rare. De Beurmann (*loc. cit.*) reported that one patient became infected as the result of a rat bite, but such instances are uncommon, and the majority of evidence indicates that infection results almost entirely from contact with vegetable materials.

De Beurmann has stated that all objects soiled with vegetable debris may become inoculated with *Sporotrichum* and that infection may result from the eating of uncooked vegetables, berries or fruit. Pathogenic species of *Sporotrichum* grow on a variety of substrates: bark, soil, thorns, cereal grains and the like. In Transvaal Province, Union of South Africa, the extremely rapid decay of mine timbers has been a serious problem urgently requiring the development of various methods of timber preservation. Findlay (1949) reports that the preservative treatment apparently not only inhibited the growth of wood-decaying fungi but also prevented the growth of *Sporotrichum,* which was growing saprophytically on the timbers; the corollary result was that sporotrichosis among mine workers was likewise controlled.

Further substantiation of the view that this pathogen grows on plant materials is supplied by the work of Foerster (1926), who recorded 18 cases of sporotrichosis; of these, 14 patients were employees of a tree nursery and at least ten acquired the infection as a result of sustaining injuries from barberry thorns. This investigator stated that of the 148 United States cases reported by 1926, 130 occurred in the Mississippi River basin. Foerster regarded sporotrichosis as an occupational hazard among individuals engaged in farming and horticulture, and considered barberry as an important source of infection. Benham and Kesten (1932) inoculated carnation buds with *S. schencki* with resultant occurrence of a bud rot. The organism was reisolated from these buds and was found to have retained its virulence for infecting animals. These investigators interpret such results as an indication that *S. schencki* may live

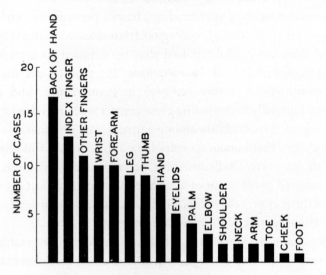

FIG. 184.   *Distribution of initial sporotrichosis lesions. (Based on data of Foerster, 1924.)*

parasitically on plants. This view, however, is open to question, since the organism may have been living saprophytically on bud tissues mechanically killed by the inoculation procedure.

That a wound is the usual portal of entry of the causal organism seems obvious, especially since the primary lesions occur in places most commonly subject to slight wounds. Furthermore, there is a rather high frequency of infection among individuals engaged in some occupation in which the hands and arms are likely to sustain some injury. Foerster (1924) has listed the site of the primary lesion in 109 cases of sporotrichosis; Fig. 184 diagrammatically illustrates the distribution as listed by this investigator.

There seems to be rather general agreement that potassium iodide, usually administered orally as a saturated solution, is practically a specific against sporotrichosis. For individuals intolerant to this compound, Curtis (*loc. cit.*) recommends Lugol's solution, tincture of iodine, or sodium iodide administered orally, intravenously, or by rectum. Autogenous vaccines have been used, as well as potassium iodide administered in conjunction with belladonna or arsenicals. Surgical intervention is not recommended.

CANDIDIASIS.   Strictly speaking, candidiasis (also called moniliasis) is not a single or specific disease but rather a group name for a great number of clinical types of infections caused by species of the genus *Candida* ("*Monilia*"). But even the use of the generic name *Monilia* in this connection is in error, since the pathogenic yeastlike fungi referred to as *Monilia* by the earlier medical mycologists is in no sense applicable to the genus *Monilia* as ordinarily used by the mycologist. Diddens and Lodder (1939) urged that the generic name *Candida* be substituted for *Monilia* with reference to those pathogenic yeastlike fungi commonly referred to under the latter generic name, and Emmons (1940) stated that the name *Candida* was coming into wider acceptance in this usage.

Several medically important species of *Candida* have been named, the most common one apparently being *C. albicans* (Fig. 185). As with other pathogenic species of this genus, the yeast form predominates, although mycelium may also be formed. Because of their rudimentary structure the recognition of species of *Candida* on morphological grounds is quite difficult. Henrici (1945) recognizes six species of medical importance (based upon the work of Martin and others and of Langeron and Guerra): *C. krusei, C. parakrusei, C. tropicalis, C. pseudotropicalis, C. guilliermondi,* and *C. albicans.*

Candidiasis primarily attacks the mucous membranes, but infections may also involve the skin, as well as the bronchi and lungs (Fig. 186). The various clinical types of candidiasis have been listed by Hopkins (1932) as follows: *erosio interdigitalis, paronychia, perlèche, intertrigo*

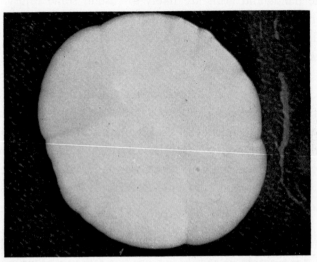

FIG. 185.   *Colony of* Candida albicans *from a petri plate culture (enlarged about 4 diameters). Note the yeastlike appearance of the colony.*

and diabetic vulvitis, lesions of the toes, thrush, vaginal thrush, dermatitis, and infections of the gastrointestinal tract.

Erosio interdigitalis is an infection of the hand which involves the web and extends a short distance onto the sides of the fingers. The infected area consists of a rounded patch of white, macerated epidermis. Usually there are red fissures in the centers of the lesions, and sometimes the entire area desquamates, exposing a moist red base.

Paronychia is an infection of the skin at the base of the nail, commonly referred to as a "whitlow" or "felon," which has the following characteristics: a cushionlike thickening of the paronychial tissue, and occasional discharge of thin pus; the lateral borders of the nails become slowly eroded, and there is a gradual thickening and discoloration of the nail plates.

The disease known as perlèche is found most frequently among children but may also occur in adults. The clinical symptoms are the presence of open fissures or cracks at the corners of the mouth. Frank (1932) and others apparently believe that *C. albicans* is of etiologic importance in perlèche, but Sebrell and Butler (1938) have presented evidence indicating that riboflavin deficiency may be the important factor in this disease.

Both the vulva and groins may be involved in infections of the type

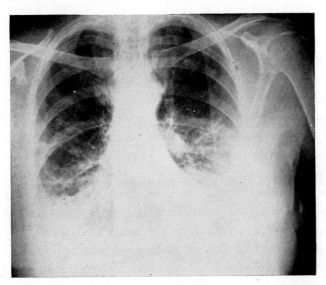

FIG. 186. *Chest roentgenogram of patient with "monilial pneumonia" with pleural effusion. (Courtesy Samuel Saslaw.)*

known as intertrigo and diabetic vulvitis; indications are that such infections may be more common among diabetics.

Most fungus infections of the feet are caused by the dermatophytes which are discussed later; however, *C. albicans* has also been isolated from interdigital lesions of the toes, but apparently has been found in only a few instances.

According to Henrici (*loc. cit.*), thrush is one of the most common mycoses of man. In this type of infection, soft whitish patches appear on the mucous membranes of the mouth, gums, tonsils, and occasionally the tongue.

Vaginal thrush (yeast vaginitis) is an infection of the lower genital tract which seemingly occurs most often in pregnant women. During pregnancy there is an increase in glycogen content of the vaginal mucosa, regarded as a favorable condition for the growth of *C. albicans* in the vagina. Waters and Cartwright (1939) isolated vaginal microorganisms during pregnancies and found fungi present in 54 out of 500 cases (10.8 per cent). In a study of 402 women in the third trimester of pregnancy, Woodruff and Hesseltine (1938) found the incidence of fungi in the vaginal tract to be 28 per cent. These latter investigators state that a baby born of a mother harboring fungi in the vagina is 35 times more likely to develop oral thrush than one born of an uninfected mother. Bland and others (1937) produced vaginal thrush experimentally in both pregnant and nonpregnant women and demonstrated that pregnancy is a predisposing factor. According to Davis and Pearl (1938) it is almost impossible to eradicate this condition during pregnancy, yet following parturition the infection disappears without treatment.

In addition to infections of the mucous membranes, *C. albicans* may also cause eczematous infections of the smooth skin. Ordinarily such infections occur on moist skin or skin folds. Diagnoses of cutaneous candidiasis have been attempted, using extracts of *C. albicans,* but the work of Lewis and others (1937) indicates that such extracts have limited diagnostic value. Of 42 patients suffering from cutaneous candidiasis, 43 per cent reacted *negatively* to subcutaneous doses of extract; conversely, of 192 patients clinically and microscopically free of all types of fungus infections, 46 per cent reacted *positively* to identical subcutaneous doses.

In 1917 Ashford described *Monilia psilosis* (*C. albicans*) which he had isolated as the etiological factor from more than 100 cases of sprue, a gastrointestinal disease of the tropics. In the same year Anderson (1917) reported the results of a study of intestinal fungi and described an organism similar to that isolated by Ashford. Apparently it is now generally believed that *C. albicans* is of no significance in the causation of sprue.

Although thrush was formerly a serious disease often resulting in fatality, infections by *C. albicans* are no longer regarded as particularly serious. Except in severe, generalized cases, therapy with potassium iodide, gentian violet, potassium permanganate, alkaline washes, or chrysarobin is successful (Emmons, 1940). More recently the antibiotic *mycostatin* has been used successfully in the treatment of *Candida* infections of mouth, throat, and gastrointestinal tract. Since mycostatin is an antifungal agent, it is sometimes administered in connection with antibacterial agents in order to control *C. albicans,* which might possibly develop more extensively in the gastrointestinal tract after competitive bacteria have been eliminated.

CRYPTOCOCCOSIS. This disease, which has also called torulosis, torula meningitis, yeast meningitis, and European blastomycosis, results from the invasion of human or animal tissues by a yeastlike fungus that forms no mycelium, reproduces only by budding, and does not ferment sugars. The causal organism has been variously called *Cryptococcus neoformans, C. hominis,* and *Torula histolytica.* Todd and Herrmann (1936) studied two strains of *T. histolytica* isolated from spinal fluids of patients suffering from the disease and saw structures which they interpreted as asci. Since each ascus contained but a single spore, these investigators suggested that this organism properly belongs in the yeast genus *Debaryomyces* and accordingly named it *Debaryomyces hominis.* Henrici (1945) states that the correct name is probably *Cryptococcus neoformans,* while Emmons is of the opinion that the name should be *Debaryomyces neoformans.* In view of this lack of agreement, the generic name *Cryptococcus* is used in the present work because of its similarity to the name commonly applied to the disease.

Cryptococcosis is usually a generalized infection in Europe, whereas in the United States it is commonly a disease of the central nervous system (Henrici, *loc. cit.*). For this reason pathologists formerly believed that two different organisms were involved. The work of Benham (1934) indicates that the American and European forms of the disease are caused by identical or very closely related organisms. No explanation has been advanced as to why the clinical aspects of the disease in the United States typically differ from those in Europe. Because the disease in this country usually involves the central nervous system, only this aspect of cryptococcus will be considered here. The discussion is taken primarily from the work of Freeman (1931).

Cryptococcal infection of the central nervous system in many instances produces a specific lesion only in the meninges, although sometimes there may be a general infection. Ordinarily the onset of the disease is marked by headache and stiffness of the neck. These early symptoms become increasingly more intense and are later associated with vomiting, dimness of vision or actual blindness, paresis or hemiplegic paralysis, and occasionally convulsions. The disease finally terminates in progressive stupor, coma, and respiratory failure. Post-mortem confirmation of the disease is based upon the finding of yeastlike bodies in the spinal fluid. The organism is usually very easily cultured.

The lungs are most frequently involved in pathogen invasion of other body tissues. In a few reported generalized infections, the kidneys, spleen, lymph nodes, bone marrow, liver, suprarenal, thyroid, and skin have also been affected. Freeman states that the portal of entry is probably the respiratory tract, never the skin.

The prognosis of *Cryptococcus* infection of the central nervous system is extremely poor, as treatment is altogether ineffective. Infection of other parts of the body is apparently much less serious, and there have been reports of a number of recovered cases.

ASPERGILLOSIS.   This disease, generally caused by strains of *Aspergillus fumigatus* (Fig. 187), is common among birds, being often referred to as "brooder pneumonia" among chicken breeders. According to Fox (1923) the disease is found in practically all groups of birds. This author states that *A. fumigatus* and *A. glaucus* can cause inflammation of the avian air sac and tubercles in the viscera. It is generally believed that the disease is contracted by birds through eating moldy grain

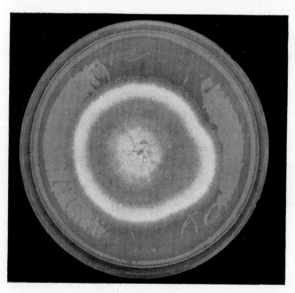

FIG. 187.   *Petri plate culture of* Aspergillus fumigatus, *the causal agent of aspergillosis.*

or by roosting in damp quarters in contact with moldy straw or similar material.

There is some difference of opinion concerning the incidence of aspergillosis in man. Henrici (1939) states that *A. fumigatus* causes infections in domestic mammals and in domestic and wild fowl, but that in man or in undomesticated mammals such infections are so rare that they are of little practical importance. Schneider (1930) suggested that in all likelihood some cases of aspergillosis are undetected as such, since clinical symptoms and X-ray findings are identical with those of chronic pulmonary tuberculosis. He further points out that tuberculin tests are of no diagnostic value, since aspergillosis gives the same local reaction as tuberculosis. Lapham (1926) called attention to our ignorance of the frequency of aspergillosis both as a primary and secondary disease; he is of the opinion that aspergillosis in humans occurs far more frequently than is generally believed. In view of the reports of Schneider and Lapham it might be well to re-examine certain tuberculosis diagnoses in order to determine if aspergillosis might not be, in part at least, responsible for the supposed tubercular condition. According to Schneider, iodide salts seem to be a specific for aspergillosis.

A. fumigatus as well as other species of *Aspergillus,* including the much-used and very common *A. niger,* may sometimes cause ear infections in man. In many instances only the outer ear is invaded, and the result is a plugging of the canal with mycelium which leads to impaired hearing. In some cases, however, the walls of the canal may be involved, the eardrum penetrated, and the middle ear invaded.

DERMATOPHYTOSIS.　The dermatophytoses are not only the most common of all fungus diseases, but also account for most observed diseases of the skin. All are more or less superficial infections, since they involve only the keratinized layers of the epidermis and such epidermal appendages as hair, nails, hooves, horn, and feathers. Dermatophytosis is actually a disease caused by any one of a number of fungi known as dermatophytes (Emmons, 1940). These fungi all share the same physiological characteristic—the capacity to utilize keratin, the highly insoluble scleroprotein present in cornified animal tissues. Although dermatophytes have frequently been proved capable of invading the skin and other keratinized tissues, there is little or no evidence that they are able to parasitize other types of tissue. Yet there is considerable evidence that dermatophyte spores may be carried in the blood stream, and Gregory (1935) has tabulated fourteen separate instances where investigators have isolated dermatophytes from aseptically drawn blood samples obtained from patients with various dermatophytoses.

That dermatophytes may live saprophytically has long been known. Sabouraud (1910) developed two principal media for the cultivation of dermatophytes and found that these fungi would also grow on cereals and decayed wood. Bonar and Dreyer (1932) were unable to culture the dermatophyte *Trichophyton interdigitale*—one of the several names applied to fungi that cause Athlete's foot—on clean, sound wood, but found that this fungus would grow readily on floors covered with a coating of slime or algal growth. Davidson and Gregory (1933, 1934) have suggested that under moist conditions dermatophytes might remain viable in the saprophytic phase on infected tissues shed from an animal infected with the fungus. These investigators note that dermatophytes are slow-growing fungi and probably could not colonize dead vegetable material as readily as faster-growing saprophytes. It would appear then that either vegetable or animal debris might serve as substrata for the saprophytic phase of the dermatophytes.

When growing parasitically, the dermatophytes are seen only as hyphae and small spores, but in culture on artificial media they form a number of structures—conidia, macroconidia, and helically coiled hyphae—that are unknown outside of the laboratory. These structures are referred to by medical mycologists as *aleuriospores, fuseaux,* and *spirals* respectively. Dermatophytes are generally believed to be members of the lower Ascomycetes (Emmons, *loc. cit.*), but since ascus formation has never been proved it would seem best to classify these organisms in the Fungi Imperfecti until such time as the details of their life cycles have been clarified.

Various systems for classifying these superficial parasites have been proposed. Sabouraud described 45 species in 1910; by 1958 nearly 200 had been reported as agents of human disease. Sabouraud's original classification distributed the various species of dermatophytes in four genera—*Achorion, Epidermophyton, Microsporon,* and *Trichophyton.* Though various revisions have been proposed, most workers seem to regard Sabouraud's system of classification as workable. For a review of the various attempts at systematic studies, the report of Gregory (1935) should be consulted.

Superficial fungus infections of various types are worldwide in their distribution. Emmons states that dermatophytosis of the foot is probably as prevalent in temperate climates as in the tropics, but that other types of dermatophytoses are more commonly seen in warmer climates. This investigator warns that attempts to determine the geographic distribution of the various species of dermatophytes are difficult in some instances because of lack of agreement on the correct names and taxonomic limits

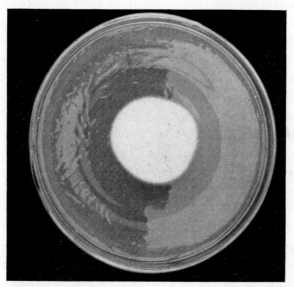

FIG. 188.   *Petri plate culture of* Trichophyton mentagrophytes, *one of the dermatophytes which causes Athlete's Foot.*

of species. He does state that dermatophytosis of the foot in the north and central United States may be caused by either *Epidermophyton floccosum, Trichophyton purpureum,* or *T. mentagrophytes* (Fig. 188), but that it is usually caused by the latter. In the southern United States and in many warm countries, however, *T. purpureum* is more commonly the cause of this type of dermatophytosis. Fox and Shields (1949) state that in the eastern and midwestern states scalp ringworm is caused by one species of *Microsporon,* whereas this type of fungus disease is caused by another species of the same genus in the southern states.

In their recent review of the most common skin diseases, Fox and Shields consider the most important dermatophytoses to be (1) tinea circinata (corpis), (2) dermatophytosis of the foot, (3) tinea cruris, (4) tinea capitis, and (5) onychomycosis. The following discussion of these dermatophytoses is taken from their review article. For further details the original paper should be consulted.

TINEA CIRCINATA. This type of ringworm is characterized by one or more scaling patches which are usually dry, slightly erythematous, and may be pea-sized or larger. The borders of the patches are usually slightly raised above the level of the surrounding skin and are studded with small vesicles. The majority of cases of tinea circinata are caused by *Microsporon lanosum,* but species of *Trichophyton* may also be responsible. The disease may be transmitted from man to man, from animals to man, and from man to animals (Bonar and Dreyer, 1932). It is transmitted by means of spores formed on the skin either by direct contact or by means of such objects as combs, towels, or brushes. Treatment of most dermatophytoses involves the use of a fungicide in combination with some keratolytic agent which will facilitate penetration by the fungicide. Tinea circinata usually yields to medication with 5 to 10 per cent ammoniated mercury ointment, undecylenic or propionic acid ointment, or 2 to 5 per cent salicylic acid in alcohol.

DERMATOPHYTOSIS OF THE FOOT. This is the most common of all of the fungus infections, about 50 to 70 per cent of the male population of the United States being infected at one time or another. The causal organism is usually *Trichophyton mentagrophytes* (also called *T. interdigitale* and *T. pedis*) in the northern states and *T. purpureum* in the southern states, but other species may be involved (Emmons, *loc. cit.*). The primary infection usually consists of vesicles with patches of macerated epidermis, and fissures between and under the toes; any of the interdigital webs may be affected. In some cases of such dermatophytosis, secondary nonparasitic lesions may occur on other parts of the feet or hands. Such lesions are reputedly not caused by the fungus itself but by a fungus metabolic product (trichophytin), which is produced in the primary lesion; such reactions which occur in tissues not invaded by the fungus are often referred to as "id reactions." Verification of the presence of a fungus in a foot infection can be made by microscopic examination of material removed from the tops of vesicles. Such material is first cleared with 10 per cent sodium hydroxide solution or lactophenol and then examined microscopically for the presence of fine hyphae. Cultures may be obtained by plating out bits of such infected material on agar.

Davidson and Gregory (*loc. cit.*) state that the fungus may be demonstrated by placing infected hairs or scales in a moist chamber; according to these workers, the dermatophytes will grow out of such material.

For the treatment of acute infections of this type, the feet should be washed with soap and water, followed by wet dressings or soaks of aluminum-acetate solution or a dilute potassium permanganate solution, and in turn by application of mercurochrome or 2 to 5 per cent ammoniated mercury ointment at night and a drying lotion or powder during the day. After the acute phase of the infection has subsided, frequent application of undecylenic and propionic acid ointments or half-strength benzoic and salicylic acid ointments should be made for a period of several weeks to prevent recurrence. Reinfection from shoes is probably of very frequent occurrence; to avoid this, shoes should be sterilized by placing them in a closed box containing an open jar or bottle of formaldehyde for a period of about twenty-four hours. Reinfection from clothing is possible in some instances, Bonar and Dreyer (*loc. cit.*) stating that the standard power-laundry practice employed for woolen and colored cotton fabrics is of doubtful effectiveness in killing dermatophytes, although with white cotton fabrics there is a much better margin of safety. The same investigators showed that the application of standard dry-cleaning solvents to dermatophytes growing in fabrics or imbedded in skin scales has a negligible killing action even with exposure of one or two hours. The widespread practice of placing wading troughs containing sodium hypochlorite solution in shower rooms and swimming-pool dressing rooms seems of questionable value in view of the findings of Bonar and Dreyer that a one per cent solution of sodium hypochlorite requires one hour or longer to kill *T. interdigitale* borne in skin scales.

TINEA CRURIS. This dermatophytosis, popularly referred to as jock-strap itch, dhobie itch, or gym itch, occurs mostly in men on the inner and upper thigh surfaces. Tinea cruris begins as a small erythematous scaling or vesicular area which spreads with partial clearing in the center. Lesions are characterized by their irregular borders which have many small vesicles. The most important species involved in tinea cruris is *Epidermophyton floccosum* (*E. inguinale; E. cruris*), although *Trichophyton purpureum* may also sometimes be the causal agent of this infection. In some cases palm-sized or larger lesions may develop.

An acute exudative dermatitis may develop from tinea cruris if considerable care is not exercised in its treatment. Undecylenic and propionic acid ointments are less likely to irritate and are useful in the acute stage. In chronic infections the use of coal-tar ointment and a variety of other materials has been recommended.

TINEA CAPITIS. This infectious disease (ringworm of the scalp) occurs principally among school children. In recent years there have been a number of widespread epidemics of tinea capitis in many eastern and midwestern cities, wherein the majority of the infections were due to *Microsporon audouini*. In the southern states *Microsporon lanosum* (*M. canis; M. felineum*) is usually the causal agent. The first symptom of the infection is the sudden appearance of small, slightly inflamed lesions (5 to 10 mm in diameter) on the scalp. The area of these lesions then increases in size, and scaling and breaking of hairs into "stumps" rapidly develop. As an infectious disease, ringworm of the scalp causes extreme discomfort, and if not diligently treated it may persist for a year or longer.

Treatment of tinea capitis involves close clipping of the hair or shaving the entire head, followed by shampoo with soap and water once or twice daily, with the subsequent removal of all crusts and loose hairs, manual epilation of all hairs in the lesions, and application of proper medicines. A variety of ointments have been proposed, 5 to 10 per cent ammoniated mercury ointment being most generally prescribed. Because of the infectious nature of this disease, epilated hairs and scales should be burned immediately to prevent the spores they may carry from spreading the disease. Identification of a scalp disturbance as a fungus infection may sometimes be made by viewing hairs from the infected areas in ultraviolet light, since Margarot and Devèze (1925) observed that hairs from microsporon ringworm or favus fluoresced with long-wave ultraviolet light. Observations of this type may also be used to follow the efficacy of treatment of scalp ringworm.

Favus, another disease of the scalp, is usually caused by *Trichophyton schoenleini*. The disease once occurred mainly among the "unwashed" poor of backward countries; although it still exists in some world areas, favus is rarely if ever found in the more culturally advanced regions. It is primarily of historic importance, since the fungus which causes favus was the first described infectious agent of human disease.

ONYCHOMYCOSIS. This disease (fungus infection of the nails) is caused principally by species of *Trichophyton* (*T. gypseum* and *T. purpureum*). The nails first become brittle, lusterless, grooved, pitted, and thickened. The end result, destruction of the nail, is a slow process that may take many years. The infection does not respond readily to local medication and is typically resistant to radiation. A single infected nail may occasionally be cured by careful paring, daily filing, and application of benzoic and salicylic acid ointment. The best therapeutic measure where several nails are involved is surgical evulsion of the individual nails. This is followed by daily treatment with ammoniated mercury ointment and later by gentle daily filing with an emery board and the application of benzoic and salicylic acid ointment. Infection of new nails will recur in some cases and a second or third removal may be required.

OTHER MYCOSES. Several other fungus diseases of man have been described, such as mucoromycosis, penicillosis, and rhinosporidiosis. On the basis of present information, however, these diseases do not seem especially significant and hence need not be discussed here.

Recent Developments in Medical Mycology

A somewhat surprising development has recently been reported by Emmons and others (1957), who isolated *Basidiobolus ranarum* from subcutaneous lesions of two patients and *Cercospora apii* from subcutaneous lesions of a third patient (Fig. 189). Of especial interest is the isolation of *C. apii,* since this organism is usually considered to be a plant-pathogenic fungus (see Chapter 20). The *C. apii* infection, for which no cure was effected, was of many years' duration, the fungus being easily observed as brown hyphae in skin sections. Emmons was able to produce leaf spots experimentally on lettuce, potato, and tomato with the strain of *C. apii* isolated from human lesions. Such a report as this suggests that perhaps fungi which are ordinarily not pathogenic to humans may become so if they come into contact with the proper individual under the proper set of conditions.

In a later paper Chupp (1957) disagreed with the species identification made by Emmons and his colleagues and denied that the causal agent was *Cercospora apii.* As of the present writing (1958) the difference of opinion regarding the proper classification of this fungus has apparently not been resolved; so that the question of whether a plant pathogen such as *C. apii* can also be pathogenic to humans must still be regarded as unanswered.

A development that may have considerable impact on the future treatment of mycotic diseases is the search for antibiotics which are antifungal

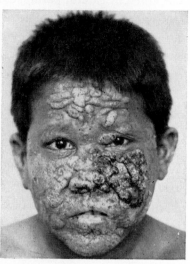

FIG. 189.   *Patient with subcutaneous lesions from which* Cercospora apii *was isolated. (From Emmons and others, 1957.)*

rather than antibacterial in their action. Several promising agents of this type have already been discovered, and it is indeed possible that human pathogenic fungi may one day be controlled through the use of metabolic products of other fungi.

Fungi as Allergens

It has long been known that air-borne pollen grains of many different types of plants are allergenic to sensitized persons and cause the distressing symptoms we call "hay fever." Many types of fungus spores are also air-borne in great numbers and have been definitely established to be capable of causing similar allergenic symptoms.

Feinberg (1946) states that patients with fungus allergy can usually be recognized clinically by (1) aggravation of their symptoms during the warmer months, (2) lack of coincidence between the "symptoms season" and the pollen seasons, and (3) a history of aggravation under conditions in which the patient would be likely to come into contact with fungus spores. According to Feinberg the fungi mainly responsible for allergies are members of the family Dematiaceae (Fungi Imperfecti), particularly species of *Alternaria* and *Hormodendrum*. The central part of the United States, between the Rockies and the Alleghenies, is apparently the major source of such fungi. That other fungi besides species of these two genera may also be allergenic is indicated by the data in Table 48.

Table 48.—*Percentage of skin reactions to various fungi in 261 fungus-sensitive patients*

Fungus	Reactions (%)	*Fungus*	Reactions (%)
Alternaria	91	*Penicillium*	30
Helminthosporium	60	*Trichophyton*	29
Yeast	56	*Mucor*	28
Smut	54	Mushroom	25
Phoma	52	*Fusarium*	25
Ergot	52	*Rhizopus*	24
Hormodendrum	47	*Botrytis*	21
Monilia	42	*Monilia nigra*	20
Cephalosporium or *Trichoderma*	37	Slime fungi	12
Chaetomium	36	Puff ball	6
Aspergillus	34	*Aspergillus niger*	6

From Feinberg (1946).

The treatment of patients who are allergic to fungi is quite similar to that used in pollen-allergy treatment, whereby the patient is gradually desensitized by the administration of properly prepared extracts of the allergenic agent.

Mushroom Poisoning

Authorities may differ regarding the number of species of poisonous fungi, but there is ample evidence that the poisonous species are definitely in the minority, being vastly outnumbered by the nonpoison-

FIG. 190.   Amanita brunnescens, *an American species of* Amanita, *which is closely related to the highly poisonous European* Amanita phalloides. (*Courtesy A. H. Smith.*)

ous ones. However, such statistics make little impression on an individual who has been made violently ill by eating a poisonous mushroom, and less on his relatives if he fails to survive the experience.

Most investigators agree that the most poisonous of all species of mushrooms are members of the genus *Amanita* (Fig. 190), and that of these species, *A. phalloides* and closely related species such as *A. verna* and *A. virosa* are the deadliest. Bessey (1950) illustrates their extreme toxicity by stating that as little as 1 cc of such fungi will cause severe illness or even death. Henrici (1945) sets the mortality rate following ingestion of these fungi at 50 to 70 per cent, and Ramsbottom (1945) reports that it has been put as high as 90 per cent. According to some specialists the true *A. phalloides* does not occur in the United States, although related species are found here. Several toxic principles have been reported as occurring in *A. phalloides,* but death due to eating the cooked mushroom apparently is caused by amanitatoxin, a heat-resistant compound. VanderVeer and Farley (1935) state that nearly all of the severe cases of mushroom poisoning in this country result from the eating of one of the species of *Amanita*. These workers divide cases of mushroom poisoning into two types: (1) rapid type, occurring from 1 to 3 hours after ingestion of fungi of the *A. muscaria* group; mortality is low and patients respond to proper treatment, (2) delayed type, occurring 6 to 15 hours after ingestion of fungi of the *A. phalloides* group;

mortality is at least 50 per cent. Hotson (1934) described eight cases of poisoning due to the ingestion of *A. pantherina,* a member of the *A. muscaria* group. Of these eight cases, only one resulted in fatality—a patient with a weak heart.

Ford (1911) divided the poisonous fungi into three groups, based on the characteristics of the poison contained in these fungi, but in a later paper (1923) classified mycetismus (mushroom poisoning) into five categories as follows:

1. MYCETISMUS GASTROINTESTINALIS. The symptoms (nausea, vomiting, and diarrhea) may vary greatly in severity but terminate rapidly and usually spontaneously, and health is restored in a day or two. There are practically no fatalities. Fungi principally responsible for this type of poisoning are *Russula emetica, Boletus satanas, B. miniato-olivacius, Lactarius torminosus, Entoloma lividum,* and *Lepiota morgani.*

2. MYCETISMUS CHOLERIFORMIS. Gastrointestinal symptoms predominate at the outset and appear 10 to 15 hours after ingestion. The symptoms are violent cramps accompanied by vomiting and purging. Loss of strength and weight is rapid, and patients may die in two to five days. The lesions of this type of mycetismus are localized in the liver, kidney, and heart muscle and are degenerative in character. *Amanita phalloides* and related species are the responsible fungi. Ford states that little can be accomplished in treatment beyond the relief of intense suffering and the administration of remedies to relieve kidney complications; however, Limousin and Petit (VanderVeer and Farley, *loc. cit.*) found that cats succumbed when fed *A. phalloides* but that rabbits did not, and hence they inferred that substances secreted by the rabbit's stomach may counteract the effects of the poison. When cats were fed lethal dosages of *A. phalloides* accompanied by fresh rabbit stomach and fresh rabbit brain they survived. On the basis of these findings, Limousin and Petit fed fresh uncooked rabbit brain and stomach minced together to patients poisoned with *A. phalloides* and considered the patients to be definitely improved by such therapy.

3. MYCETISMUS NERVOUS. Violent gastrointestinal symptoms appear early, often only two or three hours after ingestion of the fungi.

Such symptoms are accompanied by contracted pupils, profuse perspiration and salivation, convulsive movement of muscles, and often convulsions of almost the entire body. The patients then develop delirium, have hallucinations, and die in coma. In this type of mycetismus are placed all cases of poisoning from fungi containing muscarin, which acts on the nerve terminals. This type of poisoning can be satisfactorily treated by atropin, a good antidote, which should be administered early and in large doses. Fungi principally involved in this mycetismus are *Amanita muscaria* (Fig. 191), *A. pantherina, Clitocybe illudens,* and various species of *Inocybe.*

FIG. 191.   Amanita muscaria, *the fly agaric, a poisonous mushroom.* (*Courtesy A. H. Smith.*)

4. MYCETISMUS SANGUINAREUS.   This type of mycetismus results from eating fungi containing substances that act directly on the red blood corpuscles. Ford states that the only mushroom producing hemolytic intoxication is *Helvella esculenta* (*Gyromitra esculenta;* False morel) which contains a heat-resistant hemolytic poison, helvellic acid; however, Smith (1949) also lists *H. infula* as being poisonous. Helvellic acid is water soluble; hence parboiling fungi containing this acid (and discarding the water) renders them safe for consumption.

5. MYCETISMUS CEREBRALIS. Four or five hours after the fungi have been ingested, patients show peculiar cerebral symptoms. They are greatly exhilarated, laugh on slight provocation, show disturbances of vision, and develop a staggering gait. The symptoms eventually disappear and the patients are usually restored to health in 24 to 48 hours. Fungi chiefly responsible for this type of poisoning are *Panaeolus paplionaceus* and *P. campanulatus*.

In his *Mushrooms in Their Natural Habitats,* Smith (1949) lists 20 poisonous species of mushrooms. The names of these poisonous forms, as well as their distribution in the United States, are listed in Table 49.

In spite of oft-repeated warnings against the indiscriminate eating of wild mushrooms, people continue to get mushroom poisoning by eat-

Table 49.—Poisonous mushrooms and their distribution

Species	Northeastern and Central States	Rocky Mountain States	Pacific Coast States
Amanita cothurnata	•		
" *muscaria*	•	•	•
" *pantherina*			•
" *spreta*	•		
" *verna*	•		
Cantherellus floccosus			•
Clitocybe illudens	•		
Hebloma crustuliniforme		•	•
Helvella esculenta	•	•	•
" *infula*	•	•	•
Hygrophorus conicus	•	•	
Inocybe sp.			•
Lactarius trivialis	•	•	
" *vellereus*	•		
Lepiota clypeolaria			•
Naematoloma fasciculare	•	•	•
Panaeolus campanulatus		•	•
Russula foetans	•	•	•
Stropharia coronilla	•	•	
Tricholoma vaccinum		•	

* Not all species are poisonous.
Based on the listing of Smith (1949).

ing forms wrongly presumed to be innocuous. Warnings against this practice (Chapter 5) cannot be overemphasized. The use of one of the better mushroom manuals coupled with careful observation will prevent the collector from making a fatal mistake.

Study of poisonous fungi may lead to important contributions in the field of medicine. For many years in remote areas of the world specifically proscribed mushrooms have been eaten in connection with religious and orgiastic ceremonies. For example, certain Siberian tribes in the Kamchatka peninsula have for many years eaten the common poisonous mushroom *Amanita muscaria* orgiastically. This mushroom is prized very highly by the tribesmen because of its intensely stimulatory effects. The druglike stimulant is not decomposed in the stomach but apparently is excreted unchanged in the urine; several writers (e.g., Taylor, 1949) have commented on the common practice of renewing the stimulation by drinking the urine of someone who has already eaten the mushroom. Apparently *A. muscaria* was also eaten orgiastically in early times in Scandinavian countries, since scholars now believe that the act of going "berserk" (*Berserksgang*) came from eating this fungus (Fabing, 1957), which seems to have led to intoxication, hallucinations, and often superhuman feats of strength. Another mushroom-eating practice has received wide publicity: the eating of a sacred fungus, *teonancatl*, first by the Aztecs and later by other Indians. This latter practice has been studied by Wasson and Wasson (1957), who have eaten mushrooms used by the Mexican Indians and reported the following as after-effects: visual hallucinations in colors, an ecstatic state, a loss of time-and-space perception, and a feeling of inward peace lasting six hours or longer. The mushrooms used by the Mexican Indians are species of the genera *Psilocybe, Conocybe,* and *Stropharia,* but at least their hallucinatory effect is similar to that of *Amanita muscaria,* and hence they may be referred to as *hallucinogenic* fungi.

Since studies of brain structure have as yet provided no explanation of the peculiar type of insanity known as schizophrenia, an answer might well be sought through comparative biochemical studies. For example, Fabing has suggested the possibility that schizophrenia is associated with abnormal indole synthesis in the bodies of afflicted individuals. In view of the known hallucinogenic powers of certain fungi and also in the light of the isolation of *bufotine* (an hallucinogenic indole compound) from *Amanita muscaria,* this suggestion warrants careful consideration as a step toward solving the mystery of schizophrenia.

Literature Cited

Agress, H., and Gray, S. H. 1939. Histoplasmosis and reticuloendothelial hyperplasia. *Amer. Jour. Dis. Children* 57:573–589.

Ajello, L. 1950. The need for diagnostic services in the public health laboratory. *The Pub. Health Lab.* 8:88–91.

———. 1955. Soil as the natural reservoir for human pathogenic fungi. In *Therapy of fungus diseases.* Little, Brown, Boston.

Anderson, H. W. 1917. Yeastlike fungi of the human intestinal tract. *Jour. Infect. Dis.* 21:341–385.

Ashford, B. K. 1917. The etiology of sprue. *Am. Jour. Med. Sci.* 154:157–176.

Baker, E. E., Mrak, E. M., and Smith, C. E. 1943. The morphology, taxonomy, and distribution of *Coccidioides immitis* Rixford and Gilchrist, 1896. *Farlowia* 1:199–244.

Beadenkopf, W. G., Loosli, C. G., Lack, H., Rice, F. A., and Slattery, R. V. 1949. Tuberculin, coccidioidin, and histoplasmin sensitivity in relation to pulmonary calcifications. *Pub. Health Rept.* 64:17–32.

Beck, M. D., Traum, J., and Harrington, E. S. 1931. Coccidioidal granuloma. *Jour. Am. Vet. Med. Assoc.* 78:490–499.

Benham, R. W. 1934. The fungi of blastomycosis and coccidioidal granuloma. *Arch. Derm. & Syphil.* 30:385–400.

———, and Kesten, B. 1932. Sporotrichosis: its transmission to plants and animals. *Jour. Infect. Dis.* 50:437–458.

Bessey, E. A. 1950. Morphology and taxonomy of fungi. Blakiston, Philadelphia.

Bland, P. B., Rakoff, A. E., and Pincus, I. J. 1937. Experimental vaginal and cutaneous moniliasis. *Arch. Derm. & Syphil.* 36:760–780.

Bonar, L., and Dreyer, A. D. 1932. Studies on ringworm funguses with reference to public health problems. *Am. Jour. Pub. Health* 22:909–926.

Brasher, C. A., and Furcolow, M. L. 1955. Problems in treatment of chronic histoplasmosis as experienced in over twenty cases. In *Therapy of fungus diseases,* Little, Brown, Boston.

Carrion, A. L. 1942. Chromoblastomycosis. *Mycologia* 34:424–441.

Chupp, C. 1957. The possible infection of the human body with *Cercospora apii. Mycologia* 49:773–774.

Conant, N. F. 1937. The occurrence of a human pathogenic fungus as a saprophyte in nature. *Mycologia* 29:597–598.

———. 1941. A cultural study of the life cycle of *Histoplasma capsulatum*

Darling 1906. *Jour. Bact. 41:*563–579.

———, and Howell, A. 1941. Etiological agents of North and South American blastomycosis. *Proc. Exptl. Biol. & Med. 46:*426–428.

———, and Martin, D. S. 1937. The morphologic and serologic relationships of the various fungi causing dermatitis verrucosa (chromoblastomycosis). *Am. J. Trop. Med. 17:*553–577.

Conant, N. F., Smith, D. T., Baker, R. D., Callaway, J. L., and Martin, D. S. 1954. Manual of clinical mycology. Saunder, Philadelphia.

Curtis, G. H. 1938. Disseminated, subcutaneous, gummatous, ulcerative sporotrichosis (*S. schencki—beurmanni*). *Cleveland Clinic Quarterly 5:*57–67.

Darling, S. T. 1906. A protozoan general infection in producing pseudotubercles in the lungs and focal necroses in the liver, spleen and lymphnodes. *Jour. Am. Med. Assoc. 46:*1283–1285.

———. 1909. The morphology of the parasite (*Histoplasma capsulatum*) and the lesions of histoplasmosis, a fatal disease of tropical America. *Jour. Exptl. Med. 11:*515–531.

da Rocha-Lima, H. 1912. Beitrag zur Kenntnis der Blastomykosen. Lymphangitis epizootica und Histoplasmosis. *Centralbl. f. Bakt., Paras., u. Infekt.* (*Abt. 1*) 67:233–249.

Davidson, A. M., and Gregory, P. H. 1933. Development of fuseaux, aleuriospores, and spirals on detached hairs infected by ringworm fungi. *Nature 131:*836.

———. 1934. *In situ* cultures of dermatophytes. *Canad. Jour. Res. 10:*373–393.

Davis, M. E., and Pearl, S. A. 1938. Biology of the human vagina in pregnancy. *Am. Jour. Obst. & Gynec. 35:*77–97.

de Beurmann, L. 1912. On sporotrichosis. (Translated by R. W. MacKenna.) *Brit. Med. Jour. 2:*289–296.

de Monbreun, W. A. 1934. The cultivation and cultural characteristics of Darling's *Histoplasma capsulatum. Am. Jour. Trop. Med. 14:*93–125.

Dickson, E. C. 1937. "Valley fever" of the San Joaquin valley and fungus Coccidioides. *California and Western Med. 47:*151–155.

Diddens, H. A., and Lodder, J. 1939. An appeal for unification of the generic taxonomy in the Mycotoruloideae. *Mycopathologia 2:*1–6.

Dodd, K., and Tompkins, E. H. 1934. A case of histoplasmosis of Darling in an infant. *Am. Jour. Trop. Med. 14:*127–137.

Dodge, C. W. 1935. *Medical mycology.* Mosby, St. Louis.

Emmons, C. W. 1940. Medical mycology. *Bot. Rev. 6:*474–514.

———. 1943. Coccidioidomycosis in wild rodents. A method of determining the extent of endemic areas. *Pub. Health Rept. 58:*1–5.

———, Bell, J. A., and Olson, B. J. 1947. Naturally occurring histoplasmosis in *Mus musculus* and *Rattus norvegicus. Pub. Health Rept. 62:*1642–1646.

———, Lie-Kian Joe, Njo-Injo, Tjoei Eng, Pohan, A., Kertopati, S., and Van der

Meulen, A. 1957. *Basidiobolus* and *Cercospora* from human infections. *Mycologia 49:1–10.*

Evans, N. 1903. A clinical report of a case of blastomycosis of the skin from accidental inoculation. *Jour. Am. Med. Assoc. 40:1772–1775.*

Fabing, H. D. 1957. Toads, mushrooms, and schizophrenia. *Harper's 214* (1284):50–55.

Feinberg, S. M. 1946. *Allergy in practice.* Year Book, Chicago.

Findlay, W. P. K. 1949. Decay of timber by fungi. *Endeavour 8:112–119.*

Foerster, H. R. 1924. Sporotrichosis. *Am. Jour. Med. Sci. 167:54–76.*

———. 1926. Sporotrichosis, an occupational dermatosis. *Jour. Am. Med. Assoc. 87:1605–1609.*

Ford, W. W. 1911. The distribution of haemolysins agglutinins and poisons in fungi, especially the Amanitas, the Entolomas, the Lactarius and the Inocybes. *Jour. Pharmacol. & Exper. Therap. 2:285–318.*

———. 1923. A new classification of mycetismus (mushroom poisoning). *Trans. Assoc. Am. Physicians 38:225–229.*

Fox, E. C., and Shields, T. L. 1949. *Résumé of skin diseases most commonly* seen in general practice. *Jour. Am. Med. Assoc. 140:763–768.*

Fox, H. 1923. *Disease in captive wild mammals and birds.* Lippincott, Philadelphia.

Frank, L. J. 1932. Perlèche in adults. Report of four cases apparently due to *Monilia* with experimental observations. *Arch. Derm. & Syphil. 26:451–455.*

Freeman, W. 1931. Torula infection of the central nervous system. *Jour. f. Psych. u. Neurol. 43:236–345.*

Froio, C. F., and Bailey, C. P. 1949. Pulmonary cryptococcosis. Report of a case with surgical care. *Dis. Chest. 16:354–359.*

Gilchrist, T. C. 1896. A case of blastomycetic dermatitis in man. *Johns Hopkins Hosp. Repts. 1:269–283.*

——— and Stokes, W. R. 1898. A case of pseudo-lupus vulgaris caused by a *Blastomyces. Jour. Exper. Med. 3:53–78.*

Giltner, L. T. 1918. Occurrence of coccidioidal granuloma (oidiomycosis) in cattle. *Jour. Agr. Res. 14:533–541.*

Gomes, J. M. 1938. Chromoblastomycosis caused by a fungus of the genus *Hormodendron. Arch. Derm. & Syphil. 38:12–18.*

Gregory, P. H. The dermatophytes. *Biol. Rev. 10:208–233.*

Hektoen, L., and Perkins, C. F. 1900. Refractory subcutaneous abscesses caused by Sporothrix Schencki a new pathogenic fungus. *Jour. Exper. Med. 5:77–89.*

Henrici, A. T. 1939. An endotoxin from *Aspergillus fumigatus. Jour. Immunol. 36:319–338.*

———. 1947. *Molds, yeasts and actinomycetes.* Wiley, New York.

Hopkins, J. G. 1932. Moniliasis and moniliids. *Arch. Derm. & Syphil. 25:* 599–615.

Hotson, J. W. 1934. Mushroom poisoning at Seattle. *Mycologia 26:194–195.*

Jacobson, H. P. 1932. *Fungus diseases: a clinico-mycological text.* Thomas, Springfield, Ill.

Kessel, J. F. 1941. Recent observations on Coccidioides infection. *Am. Jour. Trop. Med. 21:447–453.*

Lane, C. G. 1915. A cutaneous disease caused by a new fungus (*Phialophora verrucosa*). *Jour. Cutaneous Dis. 33:840–846.*

Lapham, M. E. 1926. Aspergillosis of the lungs and its association with tuberculosis. *Jour. Am. Med. Assoc. 87:1031–1033.*

Lewis, G. M., Hopper, M. E., and Montgomery, R. M. 1937. Infections of the skin due to *Monilia albicans.* I: Diagnostic value of intradermal testing with a commercial extract of *Monilia albicans. N.Y. State Jour. Med. 37:878–881.*

Lurie, H. I., and Way, M. 1957. The isolation of dermatophytes from the atmosphere of caves. *Mycologia 49:178–180.*

Margarot, J., and Devèze, P. 1925. Aspect de quelques dermatoses en lumière ultra-paraviolette. Note préliminaire. *Bull. Soc. des Sci. Med. et Biol. de Montpellier 6:375–378.*

Martin, D. S. 1938. The antigenic similarity of a fungus *Cadophora americana* isolated from wood pulp to *Phialophora verrucosa* isolated from patients with dermatitis verrucosa (chromoblastomycosis). *Am. Jour. Trop. Med. 18:421–426.*

————, and Smith, D. T. 1939. Blastomycosis (American blastomycosis, Gilchrist's disease). *Am. Rev. Tuberc. 39:275–304.*

Medlar, E. M. 1915. A cutaneous infection caused by a new fungus, *Phialophora verrucosa,* with a study of the fungus. *Jour. Med. Res. 32:507–521.*

Meleney, H. E. 1925. The histopathology of kala-azar in the hamster, monkey, and man. *Am. Jour. Path. 1:147–168.*

————. 1940. Histoplasmosis (reticulo-endothelial cytomycosis): a review. *Am. Jour. Trop. Med. 20:603–616.*

Meyer, K. F. 1915. The relation of animal to human sporotrichosis. Studies on American sporotrichosis III. *Jour. Am. Med. Assoc. 65:579–585.*

Miller, H. E. 1936. Coccidioidal granuloma, weekly bulletin. *Calif. State Dept. Public Health, Jan. 11.* (cf. Stiles and Davis, 1942).

Moore, M. 1932. Coccidioidal granuloma: a classification of the causative agent, *Coccidioides immitis. Ann. Mo. Bot. Gard. 19:397–428.*

————. 1935. A morphological and physiological study of two species of *Posadasia. P. capsulata* (Darling) Moore and *P. pyriformis* Moore. *Ann. Mo. Bot. Gard. 22:335–360.*

————. 1938. Blastomycosis, coccidioidal granuloma and paracoccidioidal granuloma. *Arch. Derm. & Syphil. 38:163–190.*

Ophüls, W., and Moffitt, H. C. 1900. A new pathogenic mold. (Formerly described as a protozoan: Coccidioides Immitis Pyogenes). *Phila. Med. Jour. 5:1471–1472.*

Palmer, C. E. 1946. Geographic differences in sensitivity to histoplasmin among student nurses. *Pub. Health Rept. 61:475–487.*

Parsons, R. J., and Zarafonetis, C. J. D. 1945. Histoplasmosis in man. *Arch. Internal Med. 75:*1–23.

Prior, J. A., Saslaw, S., and Cole, C. R. 1954. Experiences with histoplasmosis. *Ann. Internal Med. 40:*221–244.

Ramsbottom, J. 1945. Fungi and modern affairs. *Smithsonian Institution Rept. for 1945,* 313–326.

Riley, W. A. and Watson, C. J. 1926. Histoplasmosis of Darling with report of a case originating in Minnesota. *Am. Jour. Trop. Med. 6:*271–282.

Rixford, E., Dickson, E. C., and Beck, M. D. 1931. Coccidioidal granuloma. *California Dept. Pub. Health,* Spec. Bull. No. 57.

Sabouraud, R. 1910. *Maladies du cuir chevelu. III: Les maladies cryptogamiques. Les Teignes.* Masson, Paris.

Schenck, B. R. 1898. On refractory subcutaneous abscesses caused by a fungus possibly related to the Sporotricha. *Bull. Johns Hopkins Hosp. 9:*288–290.

Schneider, L. V. 1930. Primary aspergillosis of the lungs. *Am. Rev. Tuberc. 22:*267.

Schoenlein, J. L. 1839. Zur Pathogenie der Impetigines. *Arch. fur Anat. und Physiol. von J. Mueller.*

Sebrell, W. H., and Butler, R. E. 1938. Riboflavin deficiency in man. *Pub. Health Rept. 53:*2282–2284.

Smith, A. H. 1949. *Mushrooms in their natural habitats.* Vol. I. Sawyer's, Inc., Portland, Oregon.

Smith, C. E. 1940. Epidemiology of acute coccidioidomycosis with erythema nodosum ("San Joaquin" or "Valley Fever"). *Am. Jour. Pub. Health 30:* 600–611.

———. 1943. Coccidioidomycosis. *Med. Clinics N. Amer.,* May, 1943, 790–807.

Stewart, R. A., and Meyer, K. F. 1932. Isolation of *Coccidioides immitis* (Stiles) from the soil. *Proc. Soc. Exper. Biol. & Med. 29:*937–938.

Stiles, G. W., and Davis, C. L. 1942. Coccidioidal granuloma (Coccidioidomycosis). Its incidence in man and animals and its diagnosis in animals. *Jour. Am. Med. Assoc. 119:*765–769.

Stober, A. M. 1914. Systemic blastomycosis. A report of its pathological, bacteriological and clinical features. *Arch. Internal Med. 13:*509–556.

Taylor, N. 1949. *Flight from reality.* Duell, Sloan & Pearce, New York.

Todd, R. L., and Herrmann, W. W. 1936. The life cycle of the organism causing yeast meningitis. *Jour. Bact. 32:*89–103.

VanderVeer, J. B., and Farley, D. L. 1935. Mushroom poisoning (mycetismus). *Arch. Internal Med. 55:*773–791.

Wasson, R. G., and Wasson, V. P. 1957. *Mushrooms, Russia and History.* 2 vols. Pantheon Books, New York.

Waters, E. G., and Cartwright, E. W. 1939. The significance of vulvovaginitis in pregnancy. *Jour. Am. Med. Assoc. 113:*30–31.

Watson, C. J., and Riley, W. A. 1926. A case of Darling's histoplasmosis originating in Minnesota. *Arch. Path. & Lab. Med. 1:*662–667.

Wernicke, R. 1892. Ueber einen Protozoenbefund bei Mycosis fungoides (?). *Centralbl. Bakt. und Parasitenk. 12:*859–861.

Woodruff, M. D., and Hesseltine, H. C. 1938. Relationship of oral thrush to vaginal mycosis and the incidence of each. *Am. Jour. Obst. & Gynec. 36:* 467–471.

INDEX

Index

abnormal growth, fungi and, 297–299
Absidia, 299
acervulus, 22
acetaldehyde, 184, 220–221, 255, 273, 275, 302
acetic acid, 176, 221–222; in controlling bread mold, 429–430
acetone, synthesis of, 307
acetone-butyl-alcohol fermentation, 73
Achorion, 474
acid: formation, by fungi, 304–306; hydrolysis, in alcohol production, 182, 188
Acrasiae, 8
Acrostalagmus, 412
Acrotheca, 453, 454
ACTH (adrenocortocotropic hormone), 159
Actinomycetales, 2
actinomycetes, 40, 155, 299
adenosine triphosphate, 184
adhesives, fungal attack on, 392–393
aeciospores, 363
aeration: in industrial fermentations, 77; in yeast production, 130
Aerobacter aerogenes, 78
aethalia, 8
afforestation projects, fungi and, 68
agar: cultures, 25; slants, 84
agaric, 139
Agaricaceae, 50
Agaricus bisporus, 96, 101, 105
Agaricus campestris, 96
Agricultural Research Service, 435
alcohol: 176–178; as beverage, 186, 260–261; commercial production of, 186–196; fungal activity and, 302; as gasoline substitute, 196; industrial, 186, 263; livestock feed and, 134; production from grain mashes, 90; synthesis, mechanism of, 182–186; by yeasts, 182–183; tolerance, of yeast, 191
alcoholic fermentation: 73, 77, 90, 176–199, 266; batch and continuous processes, 192; bread making and, 125; distillation in, 195; glycerol production and, 273; itaconic acid and, 239; organisms employed in, 178–181; raw materials and yield calculations, 181–183; recovery of dried grain and solubles, 195–196; sequence of reactions in, 185; temperature in, 190; yeasting in, 193–195
Alcoholics Anonymous, 177
alcohol industry: early beginnings of, 177–178; enzymes in, 260–261
alcoholism, 177
alcohol production: fermentation in, 188–193; fungi in, 176–177; raw material used, 91–92
aldehydes
condensation products of, 250
synthesis of, by fungi, 302
aldolization, in citric acid synthesis, 218–219
aleuriospores, 474
Aleurodiscus, 17
algal fungi, 10
alizarin brown, 202
allergens, fungi as, 480–481
allylarsonic acid, 333
Almeida's disease, 445
Alnus icana, 55
Alternaria, 22, 412, 421–422, 481
Amanita: 482–483; *muscaria,* 483–486
amberlites, 214
American Medical Association, 440
American Type Culture Collection, 82
amidase, 266

fication of, 23; insect-parasitic, 10; isolation and laboratory cultivation of, 24–26; "jelly" or "trembling," 17–18; largest natural class of, 13; in medicine, 138–172; morphology of, 5–6; mutants in, 82, 243–245; number of, 23–24; parasitic, 4, 10, 14–15, 18, 292–293; pathogenic, *see* disease; medical mycology; plant disease; plant-parasitic, 4; poisonous, 94, 483–486; position of in plant kingdom, 2–3; saprophytic, 17–18; steroid-transforming, 161–162; synthesis activities of, 136, 166–170, 296–299, 302–303; "weed" types, in mushroom culture, 100

fungicides, 366, 390, 401–403

Fungi Imperfecti, 2, 7, 21–23, 59, 102, 162, 343, 454, 461, 481; in food spoilage, 418; mycorhizal formation in, 50; in paper decay, 413; plant diseases caused by, 361; spores and spore-bearing structures of, 22; in timber decay, 411

Fungi Which Cause Plant Disease, 346

fungus activity, 31–46; beneficial, 31–334; harmful, 339–486; miscellaneous, 289–310

fungus biochemistry, 5, 72

fungus cultures, storage of, 84
  see also cultures

fungus diseases of man, *see* medical mycology; mycoses

fungus enzymes, *see* enzymes

fungus fermentations, *see* fermentations

fungus metabolism, theory of, 308–309

fungus pigments, 303–304

fungus roots, 48, 50; *see also* mycorhiza

Fusarium, 299, 395, 413, 421, 431; *moniliforme,* 297

fuseaux, 474

Gaff, Fleischman and Co., 126

gallic acid, 72; synthesis of, 200–205

gallnuts, 202

gallocyanin, 202

gallotannin, 202–203

gametangia, 12, 351

gametes, 8, 13

gangrenous ergotism, 141

gasoline, alcohol as substitute for, 196

Gastrodia elata, 64

gastrointestinal tract, fungal infection of, 470–471

Genera of Fungi, The, 23

gentisyl alcohol, 302

Geotrichum, 134, 423

Gibberella: fujikuroi, 297; *saubinetti, zeae,* 365; 85, 89

gibberellic acid, 297

gibberellin, 297–299

gigantic acid, 146

Gilchrist's disease, 445, 456

gin, 178, 186

glass, nonshatterable, 236

Gliocladium catenulatum, 165

gliotoxin, 146

gluconic acid, 72, 218; fermentation reaction, 80; synthesis of, 225–234

glucose: 41–42, 181, 184, 219, 226, 260, 269, 291; in alcohol fermentation, 194; itaconic acid from, 243; in kojic acid synthesis, 253; in power alcohol production, 198

glucose-aerodehydrogenase, 227, 269

glucose concentration, fat formation and, 282–284

glucose-oxidase, 269

glucuronic acid, 218

glyceraldehyde phosphate, 184

glycerol: 291, 306, 308; fermentation reaction, 91, 274–277; properties and uses of, 272–274

glycerophosphatase, 266

glycolic acid, 221

Gorgonzola cheese, 119, 121–123

grain, fermentation: in commercial alcohol production, 186–187, 264; as livestock feed, 135–136

gramicidin, 147

grapes: botrytized, 294–296; downy mildew of, 344, 350–354

Graphium, 358

green plants, 1

growth, abnormal, 297–299

growth-substance assays, 334

gum, objects made from, 289–291

gym itch, 477

Gymnospermae, 2

Gymnosporangium juniperi-virginianae, 362

WILLIAM D. GRAY

The author received his B.A. from DePauw University in 1933, and his Ph.D. from the University of Pennsylvania in 1938. He was an instructor of botany at Swarthmore College and Miami University, and later became director of research for Joseph E. Seagram and Sons, Inc. From 1944 to 1946 Professor Gray was associate chief, and then chief, of the U. S. Quartermaster Biological Laboratory in Jeffersonville, Indiana. From there he went to Iowa State College, where he spent one year as associate professor of botany and plant pathology. He went to The Ohio State University in 1947 and has been there since that time as professor of botany and plant pathology.

Professor Gray's twenty years of teaching experience have been primarily in the areas of fungus physiology and industrial mycology. Author of over thirty research papers, he has been particularly concerned with research in Myxomycete physiology, yeast physiology, tropical deterioration, and biosynthetic potentialities of fungi. He has received numerous awards and fellowships, including a recent award of a Fulbright lectureship at the University College of Rhodesia and Nyasaland.

T